# COMPREHENSIVE
# INORGANIC CHEMISTRY

# COMPREHENSIVE INORGANIC CHEMISTRY

*VOLUME I*

PRINCIPLES OF ATOMIC AND MOLECULAR STRUCTURE
THEORETICAL AND APPLIED NUCLEAR CHEMISTRY
THE ACTINIDE SERIES

*VOLUME II*

COPPER, SILVER, AND GOLD

*VOLUME III*

THE HALOGENS

*VOLUME IV*

ZINC, CADMIUM, AND MERCURY
SCANDIUM, YTTRIUM, AND THE LANTHANIDE SERIES

*VOLUME V*

NITROGEN; PHOSPHORUS, ARSENIC, ANTIMONY,
AND BISMUTH; NONAQUEOUS CHEMISTRY

*VOLUME VI*

THE ALKALI METALS—HYDROGEN AND ITS ISOTOPES

*VOLUME VII*

THE ELEMENTS AND COMPOUNDS OF GROUP IVA

*FORTHCOMING VOLUMES*

OXYGEN—SULFUR, SELENIUM, AND TELLURIUM—THE
INERT GASES

THE TRANSITION ELEMENTS OF GROUPS IV, V, VI, AND VII—
COORDINATION COMPOUNDS—CATALYSIS

IRON, COBALT, AND NICKEL—THE PLATINUM METALS

BERYLLIUM, MAGNESIUM, AND THE ALKALINE EARTH
METALS—BORON—ALUMINUM, GALLIUM, INDIUM, AND
THALLIUM

# COMPREHENSIVE
# INORGANIC CHEMISTRY

---

### M. CANNON SNEED
*Professor Emeritus of Chemistry, School of Chemistry*
*University of Minnesota*

### ROBERT C. BRASTED
*Professor of Chemistry, School of Chemistry*
*University of Minnesota*

---

### VOLUME SEVEN

THE ELEMENTS AND COMPOUNDS OF GROUP IVA
*HAROLD P. KLUG AND ROBERT C. BRASTED*

## D. VAN NOSTRAND COMPANY, INC.
### PRINCETON, NEW JERSEY

TORONTO                    LONDON

#### NEW YORK

### D. VAN NOSTRAND COMPANY, INC.
120 Alexander St., Princeton, New Jersey (*Principal office*)
257 Fourth Avenue, New York 10, New York

### D. VAN NOSTRAND COMPANY, LTD.
358, Kensington High Street, London, W.14, England

### D. VAN NOSTRAND COMPANY (Canada), LTD.
25 Hollinger Road, Toronto 16, Canada

Published simultaneously in Canada by
D. VAN NOSTRAND COMPANY (Canada), LTD.

Library of Congress Catalogue Card No. 53–8775

*First Printing, June 1958*
*Second (Prepublication) Printing, June 1958*

PRINTED IN THE UNITED STATES OF AMERICA

# PREFACE

Comprehensive Inorganic Chemistry is an eleven-volume reference work on the chemical elements and their inorganic compounds. It is comprehensive in the extensiveness of the fields covered rather than in the fullness of their treatment; hence, the volumes are offered individually as a *vade mecum* for the advanced worker—whether industrial or academic—not as an encyclopedic work. Their purpose, therefore, is to serve as a ready reference to those engaged in chemical manufacture and development and to those in advanced studies in chemistry in institutions of higher learning. To meet the requirements of these groups, emphasis has been placed largely on chemical properties and relationships and their interpretation in terms of theoretical concepts of atomic and molecular structure, the deductions from the periodic system, and the basic ideas relating to electrolytes. As a consequence, chapters on the elements are supplemented by special topics, as coordination compounds, catalysis, and reactions in nonaqueous solutions.

The various volumes of Comprehensive Inorganic Chemistry have certain usefulness in courses, especially advanced courses in colleges and universities. Nevertheless, the organization and manner of presentation of these books are not primarily pedagogic. Each chapter is essentially an independent unit, not based upon another coming before or after it. Terms are used with or without definition and statements are made with or without previous background for their understanding, for readers are assumed to be equipped with such knowledge of mathematics, physics, and chemistry to understand what is written. Indeed, the level at which the subject is presented is not too high for the average senior in chemistry or the recent graduate in this field. Notwithstanding the independence of the separate topics, there is a general unity in the treatment brought about by adhering very closely to the relationships in the periodic system and to the interpretations derived from atomic and molecular investigations.

Another feature is the presentation in tabular form of the chief physical constants of the elements. Chemical properties and the uses of the elements and their compounds are severally stressed for the most part according to their relative importance. Many inorganic compounds are not mentioned at all, and for a description of these substances the

v

literature may be consulted. From this source also may be obtained fuller treatment of the history, occurrence, physical properties, and methods of production of the elements. Selected references are given as footnotes where they are easily available when one wishes to consult the original literature. Throughout, the nomenclature used is that recommended by the committee of the International Union of Chemistry.

Many contributing authors have not only made these volumes possible, but have also added much to their usefulness and value. Such success as may come to this endeavor will in no small measure be the result of the efforts of these chemists. Acknowledgment is made to these contributors at chapter headings.

M. C. SNEED
ROBERT C. BRASTED

*Minneapolis, Minn.*

# CONTENTS

PART I

# THE ELEMENTS OF GROUP IV*A*: CARBON, SILICON, GERMANIUM, TIN, AND LEAD

# INTRODUCTION

The chemistry of the first member of Group IV$A$, carbon, is herein discussed largely in terms of its simple binary compounds. No emphasis is placed upon organic compounds. The ternary compounds, as the metal carbonates, are treated in other volumes of this series in conjunction with the various metals. The same may be said for the chemistry of the silicates. The carbides and silicides are discussed in Part II of this volume.

**General Characteristics and Family Relationships.** Physical properties and certain of the thermodynamic relationships of the Group IV$A$ elements are enumerated in Tables I.1, I.2, and I.3. It is evident that there is an increase in metallic nature with increase in atomic number and weight from such properties as the heats of vaporization, sublimation, melting point, boiling point, etc. The trend in this group is as marked

TABLE I.1. SOME PHYSICAL PROPERTIES OF THE GROUP IV$A$ ELEMENTS

| Property | Carbon | Silicon | Germanium | Tin | Lead |
|---|---|---|---|---|---|
| Atomic number | 6 | 14 | 32 | 50 | 82 |
| Atomic weight | 12.011[a] | 28.06 | 72.60 | 118.70 | 207.72 |
| Density, g/cc, 20°C | 3.51 (diamond) | 2.33 | 5.36 | 7.29 (white) 5.75 (gray) | 11.34 |
| Valence orbitals | $2s^2\,2p^2$ | $3s^2\,3p^2$ | $4s^2\,4p^2$ | $5s^2\,5p^2$ | $6s^2\,6p^2$ |
| Atomic volume, cc/g atom | 3.42 (diamond) | 12.04 | 13.2 | 16.3 | 18.2 |
| Ionic diam., M$^{+4}$, A (from chlorides) | 0.30 | 0.82 | 0.53 | 0.71 | 0.84 |
| Melting point, °C | 3570 (?) | 1414 | 958.5 $(937.2\pm0.5°)$[b] | 231.8 | 327.4 |
| Boiling point, °C | 3470 (sub.) | 2355 | 2700 | 2275 | 1750 |
| Heat of fusion, kcal/g | — | — | — | 1.69 $\pm$0.01[c] | 5.9 |
| Heat of vaporization, cal/g | — | — | — | 720 | 206 |
| Coefficient of linear thermal expansion, cm/°C $\times10^6$ | 1.18 (40°C) (diamond) 5.40 (40°C) (gas) 7.86 (40°C) (graphite) | 7.63 (40°C) | — | 22.57 | 27.08 |
| Thermal conductivity, cal/sec/cm/sq cm/°C | 0.01 | — | — | 0.1528 (0°C) | 0.083 (0°C) |
| Hardness, Mohs scale | 10.00 | 7.0 | 6.0–6.5 | 1.5–1.8 | 1.5 |
| Electrical resistivity, ohm-cm, 20°C | 3500 (0°C) 2700 (500°C) 800 (0°C), graphite | — | $8.9\times10^{-2}$ | $1.14\times10^{-5}$ | $2.19\times10^{-5}$ |
| Ionization potential, ev | | | | | |
| First electron | 11.264 | 8.149 | 8.09 | 7.30 | 7.38 |
| Second electron | | | 15.86 | 14.5 | 14.96 |
| Electronegativity[d] | 2.60 | 1.90 | 2.00 | 1.93 | 2.45 |

[a] E. Wichers, *J. Am. Chem. Soc.* **76**, 2033 (1954).

[b] E. S. Greiner and P. Breidt, *J. Metals, AIME Trans.* **203**, 187 (1955).

[c] W. Olsen *et al.*, *2. Metalkunde* **46**, 555 (1955).

[d] A. L. Allred, Ph.D. Thesis, Harvard University, 1956. Determined from nuclear magnetic resonance studies on M(IV) organic derivitives.

TABLE I.2. SOME AQUEOUS ELECTRODE POTENTIALS OF GROUP IV$A$
METALS AND THEIR IONS*

| System | $E_0$, 25°C |
|---|---|
| $C + 4H^+ \rightleftharpoons CH_4(g) - 4e^-$ | +0.13† |
| $C_2H_4(g) \rightleftharpoons C_2H_2(g) + 2H^+ + 2e^-$ | +0.73 |
| $HCN(aq) \rightleftharpoons \frac{1}{2}(CN)_2 + H^+ + e^-$ | −0.37 |
| $CN^- + 2OH^- \rightleftharpoons CNO^- + H_2O + 2e^-$ | +0.97 (basic) |
| $CO(NH_2)_2 + H_2O \rightleftharpoons CO_2 + 6H^+ + 6e^-$ | −0.1 |
| $\frac{1}{2}(CN_2) + H_2O \rightleftharpoons HCNO + H^+ + e^-$ | −0.33 |
| $Si + 4H^+ \rightleftharpoons SiH_4(g) - 4e^-$ | −0.102† |
| $Si + 4H_2O \rightleftharpoons SiH_4(g) + 4OH^- - 4e^-$ | +0.73 (basic) |
| $2H_2O + Si \rightleftharpoons SiO_2 + 4H^+ + 4e^-$ | +0.86 |
| $3H_2O + Si \rightleftharpoons H_2SiO_3 + 4H^+ + 4e^-$ | +0.84 |
| $6F^- + Si \rightleftharpoons SiF_6^- + 4e^-$ | +1.2 |
| $6OH^- + Si \rightleftharpoons SiO_3^- + 3H_2O + 4e^-$ | +1.7 (basic) |
| $Ge + 2H_2O \rightleftharpoons GeO_2 + 4H^+ + 4e^-$ | +0.15 |
| $Ge + 3H_2O \rightleftharpoons H_2GeO_3(aq) + 4H^+ + 4e^-$ | +0.131 |
| $Ge + 5OH^- \rightleftharpoons HGeO_3^- + 2H_2O + 4e^-$ | +1.0 (basic) |
| $2H_2O + Ge^{++} \rightleftharpoons GeO_2 + 4H^+ + 2e^-$ | ~+0.3 |
| $Ge \rightleftharpoons Ge^{++} + 2e^-$ | ~0.0 |
| $Sn \rightleftharpoons Sn^{++} + 2e^-$ | +0.136 |
| $Sn + 3OH^- \rightleftharpoons HSnO_2^- + H_2O + 2e^-$ | +0.91 (basic) |
| $Sn + S^- \rightleftharpoons SnS + 2e^-$ | +0.94 |
| $Sn^{++} \rightleftharpoons Sn^{+4} + 2e^-$ | −0.15 |
| $Sn + 6F^- \rightleftharpoons SnF_6^- + 4e^-$ | +0.25 |
| $H_2O + 3OH^- + HSnO_2^- \rightleftharpoons Sn(OH)_6^- + 2e^-$ | +0.93 (basic) |
| $Pb \rightleftharpoons Pb^{++} + 2e^-$ | +0.126 |
| $Pb + 3OH^- \rightleftharpoons HPbO_2^- + H_2O + 2e^-$ | +0.54 (basic) |
| $Pb + 2Cl^- \rightleftharpoons PbCl_2 + 2e^-$ | +0.268 |
| $Pb + 2Br^- \rightleftharpoons PbBr_2 + 2e^-$ | +0.280 |
| $Pb + 2I^- \rightleftharpoons PbI_2 + 2e^-$ | +0.365 |
| $Pb + S^- \rightleftharpoons PbS + 2e^-$ | +0.98 |
| $Pb + SO_4^- \rightleftharpoons PbSO_4 + 2e^-$ | +0.3563 |
| $Pb + CO_3^- \rightleftharpoons PbCO_3 + 2e^-$ | +0.506 |
| $PbSO_4 + 2H_2O \rightleftharpoons PbO_2 + SO_4^- + 4H^+ + 2e^-$ | −1.685 |
| $Pb + 2H_2O \rightleftharpoons PbO_2 + 4H^+ + 4e^-$ | −1.455 |
| $2OH^- + PbO \rightleftharpoons PbO_2 + H_2O + 2e^-$ | −0.248 (basic) |
| $Pb^{++} \rightleftharpoons Pb^{+4} + 2e^-$ | ~−1.7 |
| $2OH^-(8.4N) + PbO_2 \rightleftharpoons PbO_3^- + H_2O + 2e^-$ | 0.208 (basic) |

* W. M. Latimer, *The Oxidation States of the Elements and Their Potentials in Aqueous Solutions*, 2nd Edition, Prentice-Hall, Inc., New York, 1952.
† Very high activation energy for M–M bonds precludes $MH_4$ formation.

as that in Group V$A$. The first member of the family, as expected, exhibits somewhat anomalous properties.

The $ns^2$, $np^2$ orbital configuration for each of the members suggests the common oxidation states of +2, +4, and −4. Tin has a stronger tendency to form stable compounds in the +4 state than does lead. The −4 state may be assumed for carbon, although the covalency of the compounds of carbon is extremely marked. Only the very electropositive metals form carbides in which an ionic $-4$ state may be assumed. It is doubtful that succeeding members of the group exhibit a negative state. Even in the case of the so-called ionic carbides there is a high degree of covalency. Compounds of carbon and fluorine would be expected to be largely ionic, however the C–F bond is at the most 50% ionic. Compounds in which silicon is in the $+2$ state are known, but the strong tendency to reach a formal $+4$ state is evident in the ease with which such $C^{+2}$ compounds are oxidized. The metallic transition in the family is evident in the stable $+2$ states of tin and lead.

As noted in Tables I.1 and I.2, the gaseous and aqueous potentials reflect the increased ease in attaining the $+2$ state from the metal as the value of $Z$ increases.

Carbon is thermodynamically stable to hydrolysis

$$2C + 2H_2O \rightleftharpoons CO_2 + CH_4 \quad \Delta F^0 = 6.73 \text{ kcal}$$

whereas silicon is not

$$2Si + 2H_2O \rightleftharpoons SiO_2 + SiH_4 \quad \Delta F^0 = -88.4 \text{ kcal}$$

An anomalous situation exists for carbon when an attempt is made to account for the tetracovalency of the element in virtually all of its compounds based upon the $2s^2\,2p^2$ outer electrons. A covalency of two would be expected. In order that hybridization may take place in the formation of four covalent bonds, one of the $2s$ electrons must become unpaired and be promoted to the third or $2p_z$ orbital. The resulting structure is, then,

TABLE I.3. SOME THERMODYNAMIC PROPERTIES OF GROUP IV$A$ ELEMENTS

| Property | Carbon | Silicon | Germanium | Tin | Lead |
|---|---|---|---|---|---|
| Heat of formation, kcal/mole, 0°K | 170.39 (g) <br> 0.5766 (diamond) <br> 0.00 (graphite) | 87 (g) | 78 (g) | — | 45.6 (g) |
| 298.16°K | 171.698 (g) <br> 0.4532 (diamond) <br> 0.000 (graphite) | 88.04 (g) | 78.44 (g) | 72 (g) <br> 0.6 (gray) <br> 0.00 (white) | 46.34 (g) |
| Free energy, kcal/mole, 298.16°K | 160.845 (g) <br> 0.6850 (diamond) <br> 0.000 (graphite) | 77.41 | 69.50 | 64.0 (g) <br> 1.1 (gray) <br> 0.000 (white) | 38.47 (g) |
| Equilibrium constant of formation, $\log_{10} K_f$, 298.16°K | −117.8971 (g) <br> −0.50210 (diamond) <br> 0.000 (graphite) | −56.740 (g) | −50.943 (g) | −47.6 (g) <br> −0.806 (gray) <br> 0.000 (white) | −28.198 (g) |
| Entropy, cal/deg mole | 37.7611 (g) <br> 0.5829 (diamond) <br> 1.3609 (graphite) | 40.120 (g) <br> 4.47 (c) | 40.106 (g) <br> 10.14 (c) | 40.245 (g) <br> 10.7 (gray) <br> 12.3 (white) | 41.890 (g) <br> 15.51 (c) |
| Heat capacity, cal/deg mole | 4.9803 (g) <br> 1.449 (diamond) <br> 2.066 (graphite) | 5.318 (g) <br> 4.75 (c) | 7.346 (g) <br> 6.24 (c) | 5.081 (g) <br> 6.16 (gray) <br> 6.30 (white) | 4.968 (g) <br> 6.41 (c) |

$2s^1$, $2p_x^1\,2p_y^1\,2p_z^1$.  Energetically this promotion is compensated for by the two additional covalent bonds that may now be formed.  Structural studies of carbon compounds indicate that the four bonds are oriented from the central atom toward the apices of a regular tetrahedron.  The usually nondirectional or spherically shaped $s$ orbital has thus become fixed at 109.5° and the three $p$ orbital electron clouds, normally at 90° to one another, are expanded to 109.5°.  The resulting hybrid is $sp^3$.

The binary compounds of carbon (oxides, halides, carbides, etc.) are formed with a stoichiometry based more upon covalent rules than on any formal oxidation number.  This situation is particularly evident in such oxides of carbon as $CO$, $CO_2$, $C_2O_3$, and $C_5O_2$.  Oxides of lead likewise form in apparently anomalous oxidation states of the metal, as $Pb_2O_3$ and $Pb_3O_4$.  A lack of stoichiometry is exhibited in these oxides.  Tin oxides are more regular in their behavior.

Advantage is taken of the four covalency of silicon and germanium in the formation of the $p$-$n$ junction transistor systems.  Thus, one of the four Si–Si bonds may be replaced by a Si–B bond to yield an electron deficient or $p$ (positive) junction.  Likewise a Si–Si bond may be converted to a Si–As or Si–Sb bond with an excess electron or $n$ (negative) junction.  By incorporating very minute quantities of these "alloy" elements with silicon of very high purity, electrodes for the production of electrical current or conversion of solar to electrical energy may be produced.  Very small energies are needed to move electrons from the $n$ to the $p$ junctions.

The intermediate position of the Group IV$A$ elements in the periodic table would infer amphoterism.  Such is the case since even the most metallic members of the family exhibit this property.  A contrast may be made between lead and its neighboring element bismuth in the fifth group.  Lead in both the $+2$ and $+4$ states is alkali soluble whereas bismuth in the $+3$ state is almost alkali insoluble.  As expected, the higher oxidation states of tin and lead exhibit a greater degree of acidic behavior than do the lower.

The radio and stable isotopes of the Group IV$A$ elements are listed in Table I.4.

TABLE I.4. ISOTOPES* OF CARBON, SILICON, GERMANIUM, TIN, AND LEAD

| Isotope | Class† | Type of Decay | Half-life | Energy of Radiation in Mev | Method of Production and Genetic Relationships |
|---|---|---|---|---|---|
| $^{10}_{6}$C | A | $\beta^+$ | 19.1 s | 2.2 abs | B-$p$-$n$; $^{10}$B-$p$-$n$; C-$\gamma$-$2n$ |
| $^{11}$C | A | $\beta^+$ | 20.4 m | 0.99 spect | Be-$\alpha$-$2n$; Be-$^3$He-$n$; B-$d$-$n$; B-$p$-$\gamma$; C-$\gamma$-$n$; C-$n$-$2n$; C-$d$-$dn$; C-$p$-$pn$; C-$^3$He-$\alpha$; C-$\alpha$-$\alpha n$; N-$p$-$\alpha$; N-$n$-$p3n$; N-$\gamma$-$p2n$; N-$\pi^-$-$3n$; O-$\gamma$-$\alpha n$; O-$n$-$\alpha 2n$; O-$\pi$-$p4n$; spall Cu |
| $^{12}$C; % abundance = 98.892 | | | | | |
| $^{13}$C; % abundance = 1.108 | | | | | |
| $^{14}$C | A | $\beta^-$ | 5568 y | 0.155 spect | C-$d$-$p$; C-$n$-$\gamma$; N-$n$-$p$; O-$n$-$\alpha$ |
| $^{15}$C | C | $\beta^-$ | 2.4 s | 8.8 abs | $^{14}$C-$d$-$p$; not found by $^{14}$C-$n$-$\gamma$ |
| $^{28}_{14}$Si; % abundance = 92.27 | | | | | |
| $^{29}$Si; % abundance = 4.68 | | | | | |
| $^{30}$Si; % abundance = 3.05 | | | | | |
| $^{31}$Si | A | $\beta^-$ | 2.62 h | 1.471 spect | Si-$d$-$p$; Si-$n$-$\gamma$; Si-$^3$He-$2p$; P-$n$-$p$; S-$n$-$\alpha$; spall Fe |
| $^{32}$Si | B | $\beta^-$ | ~100 y | Soft $\beta^-$ | spall Cl, parent $^{32}$P |
| $^{66}_{32}$Ge | A | $\beta^+$(?) | ~150 m | | spall Cu, spall Ge, As; parent $^{66}$Ga |
| $^{67}$Ge | A | $\beta^+$ | 21 m | | spall Cu, spall Ge, As; parent $^{67}$Ga |
| $^{68}$Ge | A | EC | 250 d | | spall Cu, spall As; Zn-$\alpha$-$2n$; parent $^{68}$Ga |
| $^{69}$Ge | A | EC ~ 67%, $\beta^+$ ~ 33% spec | 39.6 h | 1.215 (88%), 0.60 (10%), 0.22 (2%) | Zn-$\alpha$-$n$; Ga-$d$-$2n$; Ca-$p$-$n$; Ge-$n$-$2n$; Ge-$\gamma$-$n$; spall As |
| $^{70}$Ge; % abundance = 20.55 | | | | | |
| $^{71}$Ge | A | EC, no $\beta^+$ | 11.4 d | | Ga-$d$-$2n$; Ga-$p$-$n$; Ge-$d$-$p$; Ge-$n$-$\gamma$; Ge-$n$-$\gamma$; $^{70}$Ge-$n$-$\gamma$; spall As; daughter $^{71}$As |

TABLE I.4—*Continued*

| Isotope | Class† | Type of Decay | Half-life | Energy of Radiation in Mev | Method of Production and Genetic Relationships |
|---|---|---|---|---|---|
| $^{72m}$Ge | A | IT | $2 \times 10^{-7}$ s | | daughter $^{72}$Ga; daughter $^{72}$As |
| $^{72}$Ge; % abundance = 27.37 | | | | | |
| $^{73}$Ge; % abundance = 7.67 | | | | | |
| $^{74}$Ge; % abundance = 36.74 | | | | | |
| $^{75m}$Ge | A | IT | 42 s | conv: 0.14 abs | $^{74}$Ge-$n$-$\gamma$; Ge-$n$-$\gamma$; As-$n$-$p$ |
| $^{75}$Ge | A | $\beta^-$ | 82 m | 1.137 (85%, not coinc. with $\gamma$) 0.614 (15%) spect | $^{74}$Ge-$n$-$\gamma$; Ge-$n$-$\gamma$; Ge-$d$-$p$; Ge-$n$-$2n$; Ge-$\gamma$-$n$; As-$n$-$p$; Se-$n$-$\alpha$ |
| $^{76}$Ge; % abundance = 7.67 | | | | | |
| $^{76m}$Ge | E | IT | ~0.35 s | | Ge-$n$-$\gamma$ |
| $^{77m}$Ge | A | $\beta^- \sim 50\%$; IT $\sim 50\%$ | 59 s | | Ge-$n$-$\gamma$; parent $^{77}$As; $^{76}$Ge-$n$-$\gamma$ |
| $^{77}$Ge | A | $\beta^-$ | 12 h | 2.196 (42%, coinc. with $\gamma$), 1.379 (35%), 0.71 (23%) spect | $^{76}$Ge-$n$-$\gamma$; Ge-$n$-$\gamma$; Ge-$d$-$p$; Se-$n$-$\alpha$; fission Th, U; parent $^{77}$As |
| $^{78}$Ge | D | $\beta^-$ | 2.1 h | ~0.9 abs | fission U, parent $^{78}$As |
| $^{108}_{50}$Sn | B | EC | 4.0 h | | $^{106}$Cd-$\alpha$-$2n$; Cd-$\alpha$-$2n$; parent $^{108}$In; spall Sb |
| $^{111}$Sn | B | EC $\sim 71\%$, $\beta^+ \sim 29\%$ | 35.0 m | 1.51 spect | Cd-$\alpha$-$3n$; $^{108}$Cd-$\alpha$-$n$ |
| $^{112}$Sn; % abundance = 0.95 | | | | | |
| $^{113}$Sn | A | EC, no $\beta^+$ | 112 d | | Cd-$\alpha$-$n$; In-$p$-$n$; In-$d$-$2n$; Sn-$d$-$p$; Sn-$\gamma$-$n$; Sn-$n$-$\gamma$; $^{112}$Sn-$n$-$\gamma$; spall Sb; parent $^{113m}$In |
| $^{114}$Sn; % abundance = 0.65 | | | | | |
| $^{115}$Sn; % abundance = 0.34 | | | | | |
| $^{116}$Sn; % abundance = 14.24 | | | | | |
| $^{117m}$Sn | A | IT | 14.0 d | | $^{114}$Cd-$\alpha$-$n$; Cd-$\alpha$-$n$; $^{116}$Sn-$n$-$\gamma$; $^{116}$Sn-$d$-$p$; $^{117}$Sn-$n$-$n$; spall Sb |

TABLE I.4—*Continued.*

| Isotope | Class† | Type of Decay | Half-life | Energy of Radiation in Mev | Method of Production and Genetic Relationships |
|---|---|---|---|---|---|
| $^{117}$Sn; % abundance = 7.57 | | | | | |
| $^{118}$Sn; % abundance = 24.01 | | | | | |
| $^{119m}$Sn | A | IT | ~250 d | | $^{118}$Sn-$n$-$\gamma$ |
| $^{119}$Sn; % abundance = 8.58 | | | | | |
| $^{120}$Sn; % abundance = 32.97 | | | | | |
| $^{121m}$Sn | E | $\beta^-$ | >400 d | 0.42 spect | $^{120}$Sn-$n$-$\gamma$ |
| $^{121}$Sn | A | $\beta^-$ | 27.5 h | 0.383 spect | Sn-$d$-$p$; Sn-$n$-$\gamma$; $^{120}$Sn-$d$-$p$; $^{120}$Sn-$n$-$\gamma$; $^{122}$Sn-$n$-$2n$; Sb-$d$-$\alpha$; spall-fission Th |
| $^{122}$Sn; % abundance = 4.71 | | | | | |
| $^{123}$Sn | A | $\beta^-$ | 39.5 m | 1.26 spect | Sn-$d$-$p$; Sn-$n$-$\gamma$; Sn-$n$-$2n$; Sn-$\gamma$-$n$; $^{124}$Sn-$d$-$t$; $^{122}$Sn-$n$-$\gamma$; $^{124}$Sn-$n$-$2n$ |
| $^{123}$Sn | A | $\beta^-$ | 136 d | 1.42 spect | $^{122}$Sn-$n$-$\gamma$; $^{122}$Sn-$d$-$p$; $^{124}$Sn-$n$-$2n$; $^{124}$Sn-$d$-$t$; Sb-$n$-$p$; spall-fission Th, U; fission $^{233}$U, $^{235}$U |
| $^{124}$Sn; % abundance = 5.98 | | | >2×10$^{17}$ y | | |
| $^{125}$Sn | A | $\beta^-$ | 9.5 m | 2.04, 1.17, 0.51 (?) spect | Sn-$d$-$p$; Sn-$n$-$\gamma$; $^{124}$Sn-$n$-$\gamma$ |
| $^{125}$Sn | A | $\beta^-$ | 9.4 d | 2.37 (~95%), 0.40 (~5%) spect | Sn-$n$-$\gamma$; Sn-$d$-$p$; $^{124}$Sn-$n$-$\gamma$; $^{124}$Sn-$d$-$p$; spall-fission Th, U; fission $^{233}$U, U, parent $^{125}$Sb; not parent $^{125}$Sb |
| $^{126}$Sn | B | $\beta^-$ | ~50 m | | fission $^{235}$U, parent $^{126}$Sb; fission $^{235}$U, parent $^{127}$Sb |
| $^{127}$Sn | A | $\beta^-$ | 1.5 h | | fission $^{235}$U, parent $^{127}$Sb |
| $^{198}_{82}$Pb | B | EC | 25 m | | Tl-$p$-$6n$; parent $^{198}$Tl, daughter $^{198}$Bi |
| $^{199}$Pb | B | EC | ~80 m | | daughter $^{199}$Bi, parent $^{199}$Tl |

TABLE I.4—*Continued*.

| Isotope | Class† | Type of Decay | Half-life | Energy of Radiation in Mev | Method of Production and Genetic Relationships |
|---|---|---|---|---|---|
| $^{200}Pb$ | A | EC | 18 h | | daughter $^{200}Bi$, parent $^{200}Tl$ |
| $^{201m}Pb$ | D | IT | 50 s | | Tl-$p$-3$n$ |
| $^{201}Pb$ | B | EC | 8 h | | Tl-$d$-4$n$; daughter $^{201}Bi$, parent $^{201}Tl$ |
| $^{202m}Pb$ | E | IT | 5.6 s | | Tl-$p$-2$n$ |
| $^{202}Pb$; % abundance = <4×10⁻⁴ | | | >500 y | | Tl-$d$ |
| $^{203}Pb$ | B | EC | 52 h | | Tl-$d$-2$n$; Tl-$p$-$n$; Pb-$n$-2$n$; $^{204}Pb$-$n$-2$n$; Pb-$\gamma$-$n$ |
| $^{204m_2}Pb$ | B | IT | 68 m | | Tl-$d$-$n$; Tl-$d$-3$n$; Pb-$n$-$n$; Pb-$\gamma$-2$n$; daughter $^{204}Bi$; parent $^{204m_1}Pb$ |
| $^{204m_1}Pb$ | B | IT | $3 \times 10^{-7}$ s | | daughter $^{204m_2}Pb$; daughter $^{204}Bi$ |
| $^{204}Pb$; % abundance = 1.48 | | | | | |
| $^{206}Pb$; % abundance = 23.6 | | | | | |
| $^{207m}Pb$ | A | IT | 0.84 s | | $^{207}Pb$-$n$-$n$; Pb-$n$-$n$; daughter $^{207}Bi$; not daughter $^{211}Po$ |
| $^{207}Pb$; % abundance = 22.62 | | | | | |
| $^{208}Pb$; % abundance = 52.3 | | | | | |
| $^{209}Pb$ | A | $\beta^-$ | 3.22 h | | Pb-$d$-$p$; Pb-$n$-$\gamma$; Bi-$d$-2$p$; Bi-$n$-$p$; daughter $^{213}Po$, daughter $^{209}Tl$ |
| $^{210}Pb$ | A | $\beta^-$ | 22 y | 0.018 ion-ch | natural source, daughter $^{210}Tl$(RaC″), daughter $^{214}Po$(RaC′), parent $^{210}Bi$(RaE) |
| $^{211}Pb$ | A | $\beta^-$ | 36.1 m | | natural source, daughter $^{215}Po$(AcA), parent $^{211}Bi$(AcC) |

TABLE I.4—*Continued.*

| Isotope | Class† | Type of Decay | Half-life | Energy of Radiation in Mev | Method of Production and Genetic Relationships |
|---------|--------|---------------|-----------|---------------------------|-----------------------------------------------|
| $^{212}$Pb | A | $\beta^-$ | 10.6 h | 0.355, 0.589 spect, $\beta$-$\gamma$ coinc. | natural source, daughter $^{216}$Po(ThA), parent $^{212}$Bi(ThC) |
| $^{214}$Pb | A | $\beta^-$ | 26.8 | 0.65 spect | natural source, daughter $^{218}$Po(RaA), parent $^{214}$Bi(RaC) |

\* From J. M. Hollander, I. Perlman, and G. T. Seaborg, *Revs. Mod. Phys.* **25**(2), 469–651 (1953).

† The degree of certainty of each isotopic assignment is indicated by a letter, according to the following code:

A = Element and mass number certain.

B = Element certain and mass number probable.

C = Element probable and mass number certain or probable.

D = Element certain and mass number not well established.

E = Element probable and mass number not well established or unknown.

# CHAPTER 1

## CARBON

**Forms of Carbon.** Carbon in its elemental or allotropic and in its manufactured or fabricated forms, quite apart from its use as a fuel, plays an important part in our daily lives and our chemical industries. The pure mineralized form of carbon as the diamond is the hardest material known. Its gem uses are self-evident; its industrial applications are less appreciated. An allotropic form of carbon—namely, graphite—is one of the softest of materials, being widely appreciated as a lubricant. Its resistance to chemical attack is greater than any other known material, making it in its manufactured forms an essential in the electrolytic industries.

The commercial forms of carbon may be divided into those which are mined, including the diamond and graphite; the black coloring materials, including carbon black produced by the restricted combustion of natural gas, furnace black by the decomposition of the same raw material, acetylene black by the decomposition of acetylene in turn made from calcium carbide, and lampblack manufactured by the restricted combustion of oils, fats, and resins. Another group comprises the adsorbents or materials which are important as a result of their surface forces. These include the decolorizing carbons made by destructive distillation of a wide variety of organized vegetable substances, bone black from the destructive distillation of bones, the gas-adsorbent carbons or activated materials manufactured by the carefully controlled destructive distillation of dense nuts, shells, wood, and the like, with after-treatment to cleanse their surfaces, as well as a number of related materials specifically applied as their name indicates, including medicinal carbons and metal-adsorbent materials. Another group are the manufactured or fabricated materials whose starting points are commonly petroleum coke, coal, and the like, which are treated to purify them, after which they are ground, mixed with binding material, formed, and baked to give electrodes, electrical machinery brushes, arc-light and illuminating carbons, resistors, electronic tube components, refractories, and materials of construction in a wide variety of shapes, such as towers, pumps, packings, and "lumber," for our severely corrosive chemical industries. When the baking is pro-

Note. The authors are indebted to Dr. C. L. Mantell for selected portions of the material on carbon.

longed in an electric furnace, these articles may be partially or completely converted into graphite having the same range of applications and reaching commerce in hundreds of forms.

The diamond is visibly highly crystalline; the graphites, the carbon blacks, and the lampblacks are composed of the same elemental atoms, yet they differ markedly in their properties and utility. A major reason

FIG. 1.1 Diamond, graphite, and carbon black are composed of the same elemental atoms, yet they differ greatly in their properties. These differences are due to differences in the arrangement of the carbon atoms. (Courtesy *Godfrey L. Cabot, Inc.*)

for the divergencies is found in the differences in the spatial arrangement of the carbon atoms in relation to each other and those adjoining them. In graphite it is believed the carbon atoms lie at the corners of regular hexagons and that all atomic layers or planes are parallel to each other. In carbon black the hexagon atomic arrangement is somewhat definite in one plane, but the arrangement of these to other planes is helter-skelter and random. Upon graphitizing carbon black, the semicrystalline or

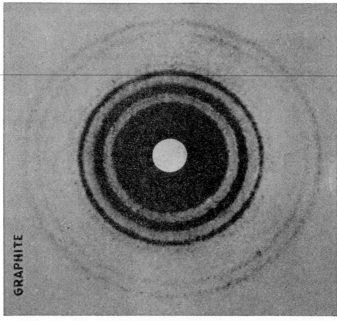

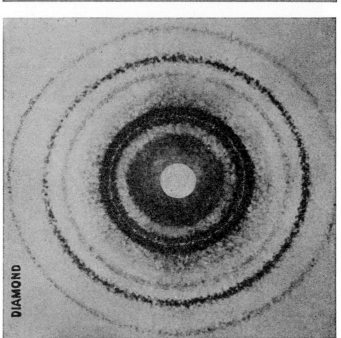

FIG. 1.2. The sharp, well-defined powder-pattern of diamond indicates a very high degree of crystallinity. The somewhat "peppered" or grainy appearance is due to the fact that the sample of diamond dust was quite coarse. (Courtesy *Godfrey L. Cabot, Inc.*)

FIG. 1.3. The number and the sharpness of the rings in the graphite pattern indicate a large number of perfectly developed crystal planes. X-ray diffraction patterns are as distinctive as a set of fingerprints. (Courtesy *Godfrey L. Cabot, Inc.*)

mesomorphic form is obtained, in that the planes or platelets are fairly definite in two dimensions but random in the third.

Figure 1.1 shows the three elemental forms. Carbon black differs also from the other two as the result of substances adsorbed on its enormous surface. A carbon pellet no bigger than the head of a pin may contain as many as a thousand billion discrete particles.

Figure 1.2 shows the sharp, well-defined and oriented powder pattern of the diamond. With coarse powders such as used for this sample, the pattern is "grainy." Figure 1.3 is the X-ray pattern of graphite in which there is a large number of rings which are quite sharp. Figure 1.4 is the X-ray pattern of carbon black with a small number of rings, these in turn being poorly defined. When the X-ray diffraction pattern of carbon black held at a high temperature as shown in Fig. 1.5 is examined, the rings are more numerous than in carbon black and their sharpness approaches that of graphite, indicating along with the loss of many of the physical properties of carbon black that the material has been partially converted to graphite.

The relationship of carbon black (the product of a flame), highly heated carbon black or partially graphitized material, and the diamond is shown in Fig. 1.6 which is a composite of 120 degree segments of their X-ray diffraction patterns. The increase in sharpness of the rings in the change from carbon black to graphite, with the intermediate form of graphitized carbon black, can be readily seen.

1. *Diamonds.* Diamonds are the hardest and most imperishable of minerals. The hardness of the diamond makes it indispensable for many abrasive purposes. Numerous efforts have been made to produce diamonds artificially but thus far without commercial success.

Physically the diamond has been the subject of much study. Its base, carbon, is chemically identical with graphite or charcoal, into which it can be resolved by the action of heat or electricity.

Some of the important physical properties of the diamond are related to its structure. A diamond crystal is cubic, with each carbon atom surrounded by four others located at the corners of a regular tetrahedron. Each pair of atoms is linked by a pair of electrons in an arrangement like that found in molecules of organic compounds. Thus, since all the electrons are used in bond formation, there are no mobile electrons in the system. Therefore the crystal is a nonconductor of electricity. Furthermore, its structure makes cleavage very difficult, and this accounts for the extreme hardness of the diamond. However, a diamond has a series of cleavage planes parallel to its octahedral faces. Advantage is taken of these planes in shaping rough diamonds, and the edges formed by

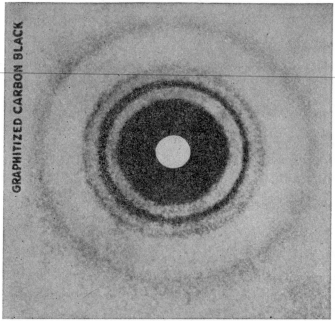

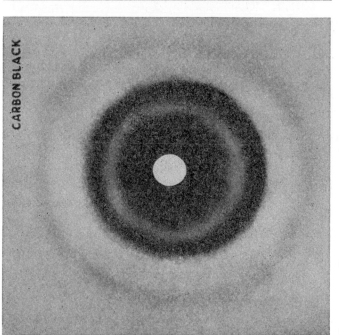

FIG. 1.4.    The diffuse rings in the carbon-black pattern indicate a much lower degree of crystallinity than is evident in graphite.    Although carbon black has some features of the graphite structure, it can in no way be considered as identical with graphite.    (Courtesy *Godfrey L. Cabot, Inc.*)

FIG. 1.5.    As carbon black is held at high temperatures its diffraction pattern reveals the presence of new rings indicative of a more highly developed graphite structure. At the same time the valuable physical properties of carbon black diminish.    (Courtesy *Godfrey L. Cabot, Inc.*)

splitting them are used for cutting glass. The high melting point, probably the highest of all the elements, is also related to the structure.

There are three well-defined varieties of diamonds, all finding industrial applications. They are the crystallized or gem variety; bort, also known as bortz, boort, boart, or bowr, a round form with radiate or confused crystalline structure; and carbonado, also known as black diamond carbon or carbonate, an impure aggregate of small diamond crystals

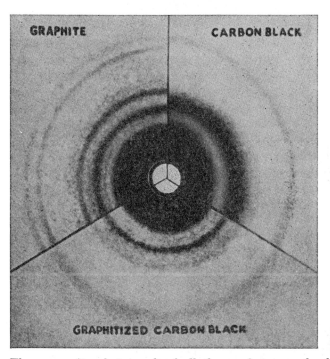

FIG. 1.6. The composite photograph of all three substances clearly reveals the fact that the differences in structure are differences in degree only. At high temperatures carbon black is converted to graphite. (Courtesy *Godfrey L. Cabot, Inc.*)

which forms a rock, granular in texture, compact, and without cleavage. The definitions of gem and carbonado are followed by the trade, but the term bort is extended to all impure diamonds and even to fragments and powder of gem diamonds which, because of impurities or small size, are valueless as gems. A special variety of bort is known as ballas. It is round in form, light in color, and consists of crystals radiating from a common center. It is used as a test stone for determining the hardness of diamonds.  Ballas is relatively rare, probably only a dozen or so of the bigger sizes being found per month on the average.

Fluctuations in the prices of gem and industrial diamonds are independent of each other.  The value of carbonado is determined by the size and quality of the stone, the value per carat of a half-carat stone being about one half that of the carat stone and about one third that of a three-carat stone.  The price of the material should increase, as the demand is increasing and no new carbonado areas are being found.

*Carbonado* is found in important quantities only in the states of Bahia and Minas Gerais, Brazil.  Carbonado is opaque.  It may be of black, dark green, brown, red, or gray color, generally, however, with a lustrous black surface.  The stones range in size from a quarter of a carat to several hundred carats each.

*Bort* occurs in the Brazilian and British Guiana alluvial deposits and in the South African pipe and alluvial mines.  The best grades are the Brazilian ballas, equal in value to the better grade of carbonado.  They are very hard, globular stones found in small quantities, the yearly production being only a few hundred carats.

Dies for wire drawing constitute one of the major uses for industrial diamonds for the preparation of wires of very small sizes, and particularly for those tantalum, tungsten, and osmium filaments for incandescent lamps.  A second major use is rock drilling in mining and petroleum, while a third is for machine tools.

2. *Graphite*.[1]  The nature and identity of *natural graphite* as elemental carbon were not established until the latter part of the eighteenth century, when Scheele, igniting it in a current of oxygen, demonstrated its carbon content.

In physical properties graphite is quite unlike the diamond: it conducts electricity and has a lower density, 2.25.  It burns with difficulty and melts under a few atmospheres of pressure at about $3527\,°C$.  At ordinary pressures the solid passes directly from this state to a vapor at a temperature of about $3500\,°C$.

The softness, ready cleavage, and conduction of the electric current are all in agreement with the structure of graphite.  Carbon atoms are arranged in coplanar, hexagonal groups of six in the crystals (Fig. 1.8).  Three electrons of each carbon atom are shared with three other carbon atoms to form connected hexagons in a single plane; the fourth electron of each atom probably serves as a bond between planes.  The black, flaky, unctuous character of graphite shows this binding is weak.  Fur-

[1] See also Part II, Chap. 8, This Volume.

thermore, the electrical conductivity of the substance is evidence for the somewhat mobile character of one or more electrons of each of the atoms. The crystals have tabular form and are six sided, the faces commonly striated. They are seldom very distinct because of the softness of the material. Graphite is softer than talc, which is 1 on the Mohs hardness scale, on which the diamond is 10.

The streak of graphite is black and lustrous. The mineral is easily sectile, flexible, but not elastic. Because of its softness it marks other substances readily and is greasy to the touch. It is a good conductor of heat and electricity. The flakes have a perfect basal cleavage and are opaque even in the thinnest scales. Graphite is highly resistant to weathering influences and to attack by most chemical reagents.

Fig. 1.7. Structure of the diamond.

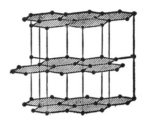

Fig. 1.8. Structure of graphite.

The natural graphites are divided into three classes, according to the character of the mineral: disseminated flake, amorphous or black lead, and crystalline or plumbago.

*Flake graphite* is a scaly or lamellar form commonly found in metamorphic rocks, such as crystalline limestones, gneisses, and schists. In such cases, each flake is a separate individual and has crystallized as such in the rock.

*Amorphous graphite* is commonly found in the form of minute particles distributed more or less uniformly in feebly metamorphic rocks, such as slates or shales, or in beds consisting almost entirely of graphite. The latter usually represent metamorphosed coal seams, carrying as high as 80 to 85% graphitic carbon; while the former, being altered carbonaceous sediments, generally range from 25 to 60%. The graphite content of such amorphous deposits depends upon the amount of carbon originally present in the sediments.

*Graphite* or *plumbago crucibles*, made of a mixture of clay and graphite, are largely used in the melting of metals. The graphite contributes toward the refractoriness and heat conductivity of the mass, prevents oxidation, and produces a smooth surface for pouring. The function of the clay is that of a bonding material, which makes possible the forming of the crucible and the cementing of the graphite flakes. At the same time it covers them and prevents their oxidation.

*Artificial graphite* is at present prepared in large quantities. The method which is most used is that patented by Acheson, who in 1896 perfected the first successful commercial process. Graphite is obtained by passing an alternating current through a mass of petroleum coke or granular anthracite mixed with pitch and a little sand and iron oxide. The latter substances act as catalysts in the transformation of carbon into graphite. Apparently the silicon and iron form carbides which then decompose into these elements and graphite. Carbides are again formed, and so the process is repeated until all the carbon is converted into graphite.

The charge of anthracite or petroleum coke, ground to about the size of grains of rice, is placed between carbon electrodes. Since the material is a poor conductor when cold, a core of carbon rods is provided to carry the current until sufficient heat is evolved to start the reaction. As the temperature rises, the conductivity increases. A furnace 30 ft long and 20 in. by 14 in. in cross section consumes about 800 kilowatts. In the passage of the current through the charge, innumerable arcs form, and the temperature of the incandescent mass rises to a maximum of about 4100°F. Heating is continued for 12 to 24 hours, while about four days are required for cooling, taking out the sides and top of the furnace, and reloading. Thus the usual cycle is five days.

Graphite in the form of electrodes is used in the electrochemical industries, such as the manufacture of chlorine. Powdered graphite, free from grit, is mixed with clay and water to make a paste. This is squirted into threads and used in the manufacture of lead pencils. As a stove polish graphite protects the iron from rusting. Because graphite is made up of slippery scales it is used as a lubricant. Finely divided graphite is suspended in oil or water, and the suspensions are stabilized with tannin. These permanent suspensions of *deflocculated* graphite are known as *oildag* and *aquadag*, respectively. They are used in the entire field of mechanical lubrication.

3. *Carbon black.* Carbon black (also known as gas black, natural gas black, ebony black, jet black, hydrocarbon black, satin gloss black, and silicate of carbon) is the material resulting from the incomplete combustion of a gas, deposited by actual contact of a flame on a metallic surface.[2] It was first manufactured from artificial gas. The product is very glossy, has an intense color, and makes a high-priced printing ink. Carbon black of slightly lower grade made from cheaper natural gas is the commercial product on the market today. It is a fluffy, velvety black material of very great fineness.

Carbon black is produced by one of the following methods: (1) formation by direct contact of a flame upon a depositing surface, usually of metal; (2) production by heating carbonaceous vapors or gases to a decomposition temperature by external heating with or without air in the forming chamber. The latter method is generally termed cracking or thermal decomposition. It produces a soft black not unlike lampblack, sometimes grayish and semigraphitic.

Electrical conductivity, $\sigma$, studies on vacuo-heat-treated carbon black (1000°C), graphitized-black, and untreated black indicate that the bulk density is a controlling factor. Various samples of the carbon black show a range of $\sigma$ of 1 to $10^{-3}$ mho cm$^{-1}$ at bulk density of 0.5. Individual samples of graphitized black show a greater range of $\sigma$ than do other types of black. Values[3] of $\sigma$ for the three types of black noted above are 3.2, 0.74, and 2.25 $\times$ $10^{-2}$ mho cm$^{-1}$ at bulk densities of 0.5.

Given in the order of importance, the uses of carbon black are in the manufacture of rubber, printing ink, paints and enamels, lacquers, stove polishes, other products such as phonograph records, carbon paper, crayons, typewriter ribbons, black and gray paper, tarpaulins, black leather, bookbinders' board, marking and stenciling inks, rubber goods, artificial stone and black tile, insulating materials, electric arc carbons, buffing powders, and to a very small extent in case hardening. From 200 to 300 million lb per year are used in rubber, 20 to 25 million in printing inks, approximately 10 million lb in paints, about 4 million lb in stove polishes, and somewhat more than 10 million lb for other miscellaneous uses, not including more than a hundred million pounds annually exported.

For certain purposes, such as phonograph records, medical hard rubber, all soft rubber goods like footwear, tubing, and heavy truck tires, certain kinds of printer's ink and black paint, it is possible to substitute

[2] U. S. 2,704,242, Mar. 15, 1955; D. M. Strasser, *Petroleum Refiner* **33**(12), 177 (1954); W. C. Ekholm, U. S. 2,705,189, Mar. 29, 1955.

[3] Y. Sasaki, *Tokai Technol. J.* 15(2) 5 (1954); B. S. Gol'perin, *Zhur. Tekh. Fiz.* **23**, 1001 (1953).

lampblack for carbon black. For most purposes, however, these two products are quite dissimilar in their physical properties and to date have proved unsuitable for substitution.

4. *Lampblack.* Lampblack, generally speaking, is the smoke from an unobstructed hydrocarbon flame, the solid particles being deposited in chambers as the smoke is conducted through flues from the furnace. Various oils, fats, and resins have been used for centuries to make lampblack, the resins to a greater extent than other materials. They were generally heated in an iron pan over a small fire, ignited, and the smoke led into tents lined with sheepskin. The sides of the tent were beaten at frequent intervals to knock down the deposit of soot.

In Continental Europe where natural gas is not available, lampblack is employed for many of the purposes which, in America, are entirely met by carbon black. Lampblack is of a very soft, flocculent nature, whereas carbon black is hard and brilliant. The "tinting strength" of carbon black is many times that of lampblack.

Lampblack has been used for printer's ink since the invention of the printing press. After the advent of carbon black in 1864, lampblack was employed less and less for ink making. Today it is little used except to impart certain properties to an ink already containing carbon black. Lampblack is used in the manufacture of inks, lead pencils, electrical machinery brushes, paints, metal polishes, stove polishes, phonograph records, carbon paper, crayons, and black-colored materials as a filler.

5. *Acetylene black.* Acetylene black is produced from acetylene gas by thermatomic cracking, with hydrogen gas as a by-product, as well as by methods similar to that employed for natural gas. The attainment of a uniform product is very much an industrial art. Large quantities of specially prepared acetylene black are used in the manufacture of the batteries as a constituent of the depolarizer (cathodic) mix. The internal resistance of the cell is reduced by mixing $MnO_2$ with carbon black in the "dry cell."

6. *Bone black.* Bone black or bone char is the carbonaceous residue obtained as a result of destructive distillation of bones in the absence of air. Only fresh, hard bones free from extraneous matters can be used. Whale, fish bones, and the skeletons of marine animals are unsuitable as they produce a soft char. Bones exposed to atmospheric action or buried in the ground, due to their decomposition, give chars deficient in carbon.

The principal constituent of bones is tricalcium phosphate. Besides this compound, bones contain magnesium phosphate, calcium carbonate, some alkaline salts, and fatty and cartilaginous matter intimately associated with the mineral contents.

Examined under a suitable magnifying power, each grain of char will be seen to consist of a series of cavities connected by a great number of minute tubes and channels. The framework of this cellular structure consists essentially of the phosphates and carbonates of calcium. The framework is entirely coated or lined by a deposit of carbon in a state of very fine subdivision. The actual surface of bone char is enormous.

Bone char exercises a selective adsorption for different substances—that is, when it has become completely saturated with respect to certain coloring matters or to certain salts, it can yet continue to take up and hold other coloring matter and other salts in adsorption.

7. *Vegetable decolorizing carbon.* Charcoal made by burning wood in a closed vessel has a low power of removing coloring matter from solutions. This property was known as early as the fifteenth century. The function of wood charcoal as a decolorizing agent seems to have been forgotten until it was rediscovered in 1785 by Lowitz who used it in the production of tartaric acid crystals. Lippmann states that in 1794 an English refinery employed wood charcoal in the clarification of raw sugar. Guillon is said to have utilized wood charcoal in sugar manufacture in 1805. Since that time many processes for the manufacture of decolorizing carbons have been patented. Almost any vegetable substance can be converted into a decolorizing char.

When bone char came into use in the sugar industry at the beginning of the nineteenth century, vegetable carbons and charcoal were forgotten. They showed relatively slight decolorizing power when compared to bone char. Early in the twentieth century a number of chars were subjected to activating processes which increased their decolorizing power. Active carbon was manufactured primarily for color removal in early industrial applications. However, since 1926 the use of active carbon has been extended into water purification for the elimination of tastes and odors.

Most of the vegetable decolorizers appear as black glistening powders. All are soft chars. Their market form and characteristics vary widely, some of them being neutral, some acid, and some alkaline.

The commercial activated carbons possess markedly enhanced characteristics as compared to charcoal or bone black. They may be divided on the basis of their particle size, physical structure, hardness, mechanical strength, and adsorption characteristics into those employed for the removal of odors and tastes from water and designated as water-treatment carbon; those used for the removal of colors primarily from solutions of inorganic and organic compounds, termed decolorizing carbons; those finding application in reclaiming of dry-cleaning fluids and the decolorization of vegetable oils and organic liquids, called oil-treatment carbons;

those specifically manufactured for reuse in sugar refining, referred to as sugar carbons; a group conditioned by manufacturing treatment to take up metal ions on their surface, and while more efficient, compete with locally made charcoal—these are metal-adsorbent carbons; others which are highly purified and originate from special raw materials as adsorbents for toxins, viruses and the like—the medicinal carbons; and the hard, granular, shock-resistant, highly activated carbons employed in gas masks to take up toxic gases as well as the gas-adsorbent carbons used for solvent recovery, deodorization of gases, and abatement of stenches.   In general, the water, decolorizing, oil-treatment, medicinal, and metal-adsorbent materials are used once, retreated or revivified and reused, often in cyclic procedures.   No one type of carbon can be universally used or is effective for all purposes.

**Gaseous Sorption on Carbon.**   The sorption of gases (halogens, rare gases, etc.) has been extensively studied on several of the carbon forms. Carbon black adsorbs both iodine and bromine from the vapor as well as aqueous and nonaqueous solutions.   This adsorption property has been utilized in the determination of the specific surface of the carbon black. A hysteresis effect is observed and is ascribed to activated physical adsorption and not to chemisorption.[4]   Active charcoal with 0.17% ash absorbs iodine according to the equation

$$t = \beta \ln (a_0/a) - \gamma[1 - (a/a_0)]$$

where $t$ is the time needed for the absorbed iodine to decrease from a value $a_0$ to $a$, and $\beta$ and $\gamma$ are constants.[5]   Alternately the absorption may be described as

$$t = \rho \ln (a_0 - a_1)/(a - a_1)$$

The term $\rho$ is a constant and $a_1$ is the amount of iodine that cannot be washed out of the active charcoal by such an eluant as KI solution.   In general, the rate of desorption is greater with a decrease in the carbon grain size (3 to 0.6 mm).   The rate increases with increase in KI solution concentration.   The time of activation of the charcoal is also an important factor.   The ratio $a_1/a_2$ (where $a_2$ represents the amount absorbed at saturation) increases with a longer period of activation (heating).

Channel black absorbs butane and 1-butene by a physical adsorption process.   The coverage is greater for carbon black than for a siliceous material such as "Cab-O-Sil."   Presorption of oxygen will cause the polymerization of 1-butene.   Graphitized carbon black absorbs krypton

[4] J. W. Watson and D. Parkinson, *Ind. Eng. Chem.* **47**, 1053 (1955).
[5] M. V. Tovbin and A. D. Grinberg, *Zhur. Fiz. Khim.* **28**, 1755 (1954).

according to a fashion permitting a straight-line plot of log $p/p_0$ vs $1/\theta^3$. The term $p/p_0$ is a relative vapor pressure and $\theta$ is the coverage. A study of the argon absorption indicates that this plot extrapolates through the origin. Argon and xenon are of a necessity compatible.[6] The adsorption isotherm of krypton on graphitized carbon black (P-33, heat treated at 2700°C) shows a pronounced stepwise character. Less highly graphitized carbon black (as Spheron, also heat treated at 2700°C) shows a less pronounced stepwise absorption. Heat data and the isotherms point to a highly homogeneous surface for the P-33 graphitized black.[7]

While in America the activated carbon of the gas-adsorbent type most widely used is that made from coconut shells and fruit pits, on the Continent gas-adsorbent carbons made from raw materials, such as sawdust, peat, etc., are employed. One is made from peat, employing phosphoric acid as the activating material.

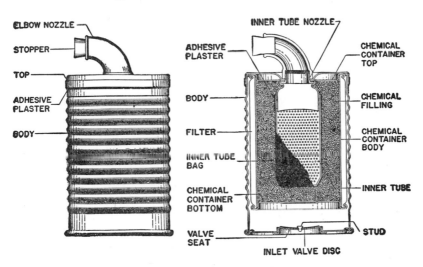

Fig. 1.9. Gas mask canister.

Silica gel and activated alumina are commonly thought of as being specific for the adsorption of water in driers, dehumidifiers, and the like, while activated carbon is specific for the adsorption of organic vapors. It therefore finds application in the recovery of solvents, the abatement of stenches, deodorization as in air conditioning, the recovery of gasoline

[6] M. H. Polley, *Can. J. Chem.* **33**, 314 (1955); J. H. Singleton and G. D. Halsey, Jr., *ibid.* **33**, 184 (1955).

[7] P. H. Amberg *et al.*, *ibid.* **33**, 304 (1955).

from natural gas, and the purification of industrial gases used in beverages, such as carbon dioxide.

Activated carbon is the basic adsorbent in gas masks designed for both peacetime and wartime use. Many of the harmful gases and vapors encountered in industry and in chemical warfare are eliminated by adsorption (Fig. 1.9). Solid particles are not adsorbed by the charcoal in masks but must be removed by a filter. Substances such as soda lime (a mixture of sodium hydroxide and calcium oxide) and potassium permanganate are included in the canister to remove or render harmless by chemical action those noxious materials not adsorbed.

**Metal Adsorbent Chars.** Alkaline activated chars which can be used for removing metals, such as gold and silver, from their solutions are structurally identical[8] with ordinary decolorizing carbons and can easily be converted into them by acid treatment. This change is not mere neutralization, for the original properties cannot be restored by alkaline washing.

It is interesting to note that bone black or decolorizing chars will remove a blue dyestuff from solution but will not remove the ionic blue color from copper sulfate. This latter job, however, can be done by a metal-adsorbent char.

**Carbon in Chemical Construction.** The search for more resistant materials of construction for chemical engineering equipment has brought forth many fabricated forms of amorphous carbon and graphite as blocks, rings, adsorption chamber parts, electrostatic precipitator tubes, linings for paper digesters, condenser tubes, heat interchangers, porous carbons for filters, as well as aerator plates. These materials show unusual resistance to chemical attack and corrosive influences. They have shown exceptional performance in connection with acid manufacture, paper making, the electrochemical industries, petroleum oil refining and by-products, as well as parts of machinery operating in chemical plants under severe conditions.

Manufactured carbon shapes show high compressive strengths and good physical properties. Carbon has high electrical conductivity and an extremely low coefficient of thermal expansion. It shows almost universal resistance to chemical action, having found particular application in connection with the highly corrosive fumes of sulfuric, hydrofluoric, and phosphoric acids. Carbon is susceptible to attack by oxygen at temperatures exceeding 315.6°C and by carbon dioxide and water vapor at comparatively high temperatures. Because of the fact that commer-

[8] R. H. McKee and P. M. Horton, *Chem. & Met. Eng.* **32**, 13–61, 56–59, 164–167 (1925).

cial forms are made up of ground material held together by a binder, the whole mass afterwards being formed or pressed and baked to carbonize or coke this binder, it can be readily appreciated that the particles of carbonized binder form the weakest portion of the shape as far as chemical attack is concerned. Carbon is not immune to destruction by oxidizing agents, such as nitric acid, failure occurring because of oxidation of the binding material. Of the entire group of common reagents, only active oxygen, oxygen at temperatures above 329°C, and strong nitric and chromic acids attack carbon.

1. *Electrodes.* Sir Humphry Davy in 1800 was probably the first to employ carbon electrodes in connection with the electric arc. His electrodes were made of charcoal and were simply points or rods cut out of carbonized wood. As a result, they were neither dense nor homogeneous.

Carbon electrodes were first successfully manufactured on a commerical scale of 1876 by Carré, a Frenchman. At that time most of the work was in the direction of arc light carbons. The development of our present gigantic electric furnace electrodes has taken place during the past few decades.

In 1878 Brush was making electrodes in the United States on a commercial scale from petroleum coke, then a waste product of petroleum refining that the oil companies burned under their stills.

Electrode production divides itself into five divisions: (1) the selection of the raw materials, (2) calcination of these materials, (3) grinding, mixing with a binder, and shaping, (4) baking the green shape, and (5) finishing, machining, and testing the final electrode.

Almost all carbonaceous matters have at one time or another been used as starting substances, but today only two are used: anthracite coal, mostly for large electrodes for electric furnaces, and petroleum coke for reduction electrodes (e.g., for aluminum). Petroleum coke is the final residue of the intermittent distillation of petroleum. It is a hard, brittle substance of shiny, oily appearance, very high fixed carbon, and low in ash. It is one of the purest forms of carbon available in large quantities. Formerly it was a waste by-product; today, due to the electrode industry, the refiners regard it as a valuable commercial material. Only selected low ash coals, of low volatile content, are used as raw materials.

The materials are freed of their volatile matter by heating to a white heat. The calciners employed are either developments of the industry and its close connections with electrothermic and electrolytic processes, or are adaptations from gas manufacture. The electrical types are commonly vertical, heating to the required temperature by the resistance of the charge to the electric current.

The pulverization of the calcined cokes to a fine powder is done almost entirely in machines of the impact pulverizer or tube mill type.

The dust is proportioned from the storage bin with the proper percentage of binder, and delivered to the mixing machines. The binders are coal tar or pitch. Mixers are of various types, the one most commonly used consisting essentially of a steam-heated drum mounted on its side. Mixing is accomplished by the rotation of the central shaft with arms attached. The forward tilt of the arms, which during rotation carry the mix forward, finally discharges it through the door at the end of the drum.

The material is shaped by compressing the hot plastic mass from the mixers either in molding presses, in steel molds so formed as to give the desired dimensions, or in slug presses where the mass is pressed together preparatory to the plug presses, through the orifices of which it is extruded in the shape desired. All shaping presses are operated hydraulically.

The shaped or "green" electrodes, of high electrical resistance and low tensile strength, are converted to a condition where their properties vary little with temperature, of low resistance and high tensile strength, by the process of baking in which the temperature is raised to approximately 1100°C. This temperature is high enough to carbonize the binder and, after carbonization, free it from almost all volatile matter.

After baking, the cooled electrodes are removed from the furnace and cleaned of all adhering packing material. They are tested for ash, resistivity, apparent density, volatile matter, and tensile strength. The composite flowsheet shown in Fig. 1.10 is self-explanatory. The manufacture of graphite electrodes is a branch of this industry.

The essential role of the carbon electrode in industry is attested by the fact that it enters into the manufacture of the following substances: electrical steel, ferro-alloys, calcium carbide, silicon carbide and related abrasives, aluminum, calcium, and magnesium metals, phosphorus and phosphoric acid, electrical resistance wire, titanium and zirconium, carbon disulfide, tungsten, cyanamid, sodium, caustic, chlorine, and the electric furnace alloys and products.

2. *Carbon brushes.* Carbon brushes for electrical machinery are closely related to electrodes in their manufacture. The processes are much the same, but due to the desirability of producing a low-resistance brush, only pure substances with as low an ash content as possible are used. A greater variety of raw materials may be used for brushes than for electrodes, due to the different characteristics and the wide range of products.

3. *Arc light carbons.* Arc light carbons are practically electrodes manufactured on a small scale. The raw materials are the same with the

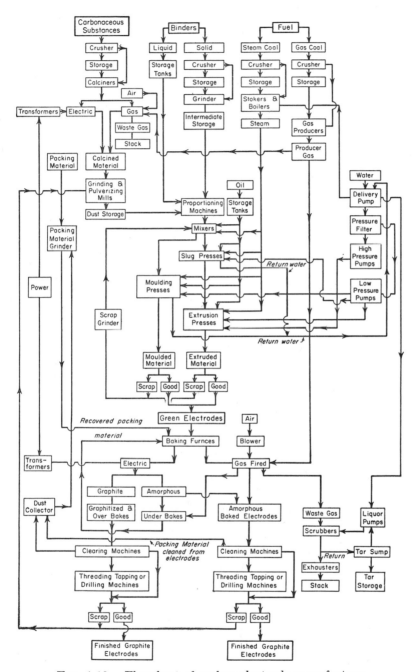

FIG. 1.10. Flowsheet of carbon electrode manufacture.

exception that retort carbon, lampblack, and graphite are often incor-porated for specific purposes.   Modern practice in arc light carbon manu-facture is to add some metallic salts or oxides to the mix before extrusion of the green material, as these oxides increase the brilliance of the light given off by the arc.   The materials used for the production of white light are titanium, thorium, and cerium oxides, monazite sand, ilmenite, lime, ferrotitanium, various metallic oxides, and related materials.

4. *Battery carbons.*   Battery carbons are small-size electrodes.

5. *Carbon specialties.*   Carbon specialties are articles of carbon molded in special shapes to predetermined characteristics or machined out of standard shapes to supply a specified demand.   The nonfusing characteristics of carbon are of importance in the carbon and graphite contacts used on electric elevator controllers, automatic motor starting equipment, high amperage circuit breakers, and the like, where a non-burning material is essential to long life of the contact.

Telephone carbon is a crushed product made of carefully selected coals calcined to determined resistivity, vacuum treated, ground, and sifted to 60 to 80 meshes to the inch in its use for ordinary telephones, and 60 to 120 mesh for some special purposes.   It must be hard material.

6. *Carbon refractories.*   Carbon refractories are the only commercial refractories which will resist very high temperatures.   Elemental carbon has a melting point assumed to be around 4400°C.   It sublimes or volatilizes at approximately 3500°C.   For these reasons it is a very good refractory, except in oxidizing atmospheres.   Carbon begins to oxidize somewhat above 300°C.   In a reducing atmosphere it is better than any of the usual refractories.   It is manufactured into bricks and blocks for furnace, hearth, and retort linings.

7. *Purified carbon for atomic piles.*   Carbon of sufficient purity for use in an atomic pile has been made by cracking of a 65 to 70% methane derived from ammonia synthesis purified over activated carbon and by a Cottrell precipitator at 1500° to 1600°C (induction heated) in a graphite tube, finally the carbon mixture is cooled in an aluminum condenser at atmospheric pressure.   The carbon yield is 70%.[9]

**Other Forms of Carbon.**   There are three other very important indus-trial forms of carbon.   They are wood charcoal, coal, and coke.

*Wood charcoal.*   The purest charcoal is obtained by heating sugar until gases are no longer evolved and igniting the residue in a current of pure chlorine.   The product is black, tasteless, and odorless, conducts

---

[9] F. M. Bosch *et al., Mededel. Koninkl. Vlaam. Acad. Wetenschap. Belg., Kl. Weten-schap.* **15**, (11), 3 (1953).

electricity well, and has a real density of about 1.8.    Charcoal usually floats on water due to the air content of its pores.    Pure carbon is also obtained by burning magnesium in carbon dioxide:

$$2Mg + CO_2 \rightarrow C + 2MgO$$

Wood charcoal is produced by setting fire to a stack of wood covered with turf.    The supply of air is so regulated that most of the heat is produced by the combustion of the volatile matter.    A part of the wood, however, is burned; the rest is converted into charcoal.    By this process charcoal only is obtained and the valuable by-products are lost.    These are saved by the destructive distillation of wood in iron retorts in the absence of air.

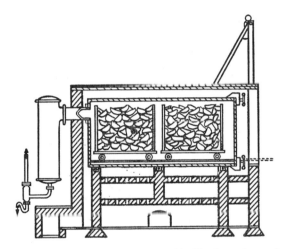

Fig. 1.11.    Plant for the dry distillation of wood.

In a second process charcoal is obtained as before.    The vapors are conducted through a cooled pipe in which a part is condensed to a liquid. The remainder is gaseous.    The gases are used for heating.    Good hardwood yields about a fourth of its weight of charcoal; approximately an equal weight of gaseous products is driven off.    The liquid material makes up the rest.    It consists principally of water, acetic acid, methanol (wood alcohol), a tarry mixture, and a small proportion of acetone.

*Coal.*    Large quantities of coal have been formed in nature by the slow decomposition of vegetable matter without much heating, but in the presence of water and away from air.    Coal consists of free carbon admixed with various carbon compounds and mineral matter.    There are two general kinds: anthracite (hard) coal and bituminous (soft) coal.

From a geologic-time standpoint peat and lignite are forming carbon of more recent origin. The latter is of relatively high water content (about 37%), but serves admirably as a fuel if properly pretreated.

Hard coal contains about 6% of volatile matter. It ignites with some difficulty, but gives out a great deal of heat in burning without producing much smoke or flame. Hence it is suitable for domestic heating and for firing the boilers of ships. Both anthracite and coke are used for making water gas.

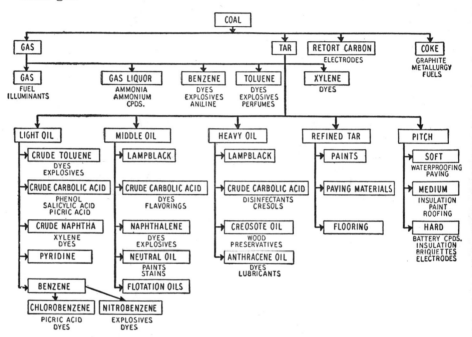

Fɪɢ. 1.12.   Products from coal.

Soft coals contain much volatile matter, but the amount varies. They burn with a bright smoky flame and are used for ordinary fuel. They are of two general kinds, *coking* and *noncoking* coals, according as they do or do not fuse on burning. A variety high in volatile matter is selected for producing coal gas. Coking coals are used for making coke. The world annually produces over a thousand million metric tons of coal, of which about 40% is mined in the United States.

*Coke.* When bituminous coal is heated in *by-product coke ovens* without access to air, many products distill out. Among these are gas for fuel, ammonia, and many other valuable substances (Fig. 1.12). The heating is applied so as to secure a maximum yield of coke, which is left behind in the oven. Coke is used in tremendous quantities for reducing ores of iron and other metals and for fuel.

Formerly beehive coke ovens (Fig. 1.13) were in general use for making coke. These ovens are made of fire brick and are shaped like beehives. They are filled with coal, a part of which is allowed to burn in a limited

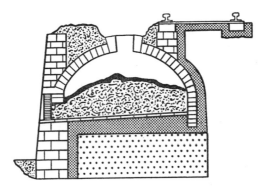

FIG. 1.13. Beehive coke oven.

supply of air. They yield about 66% of coke, whereas the by-product ovens are about 10% more productive. Only coke is obtained from beehive ovens, the gaseous and liquid products being burned. Millions of dollars' worth of these valuable and irrecoverable products were lost each year. Hence for economic reasons the primitive ovens have been largely replaced by modern by-product ovens (Fig. 1.14).

*By-products (Gaseous)*

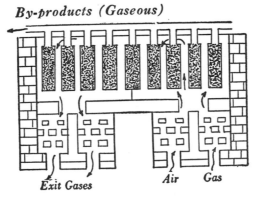

*Exit Gases*      *Air*   *Gas*

FIG. 1.14. By-product coke oven.

A dense grade of coke is required for metallurgical processes because it must be strong enough to resist crushing. The special grades of coal used to make this coke are not suitable for the production of coal gas (artificial or illuminating gas). Temperatures in the coke oven are maintained between 900° and 1200°C for a period of from 11 to 19 hours. Air is of course excluded by sealing the oven doors. At the completion of the heating period the doors at the ends of the oven are opened and the coke is pushed out into cars by a pusher ram.

*Low-temperature carbonization* (500°–700°C) of coal has received a great deal of attention in recent years, but it is still largely in the experimental stages. Coke made in this way is not suitable for metallurgical purposes, and the yield of gas is not as high as that obtained in the high-temperature process. For example, one ton of coal carbonized in the 900° to 1200°C range yields from 11,000 to 13,000 cubic ft of gas, while at 500° to 700°C the yield is only 5000 cubic ft. Since gas and metallurgical coke are the desired products in this country, the low-temperature process has not risen to a position of great importance. In Europe and particularly in Germany, the process is used to a considerable extent because of the larger yields of coal tar. Oils in this distillate may be be *cracked* to form a satisfactory motor fuel.

Heavy residual oils may be coked upon contact at 427° to 704°C with a dense, turbulent, fluidized mass of finely divided metallic carrier solids of a thermal expansion coefficient at least twice that of the resulting coke coating (e.g., powdered copper, brass, or nickel steel). On cooling the coated particles to 25° to 170°C, the coke flakes off.[10]

**Some General Physical and Chemical Properties of Carbon.** The heat of sublimation, $\Delta H$, for carbon is reported as 139 kcal/mole.[11] This value supports the suggestion that in a series of similar bonds, the bond energy is proportional to the reciprocal of the equilibrium interatomic distance or bond length. The condensation coefficient of carbon vapor is 141.7 ± 4 kcal/mole. This experimentally determined value agrees well with the value of 141.26 kcal/mole deduced from the carbon monoxide spectrum.[12] The total cross section of carbon is reported[13] as 380 ± ~ 3% and the absorption cross section as 200 ± ~ 5% mb. The atomic refraction of carbon is 1.09 as derived from a measurement on carbon dioxide.[14]

[10] U.S. 2,700,642, Jan. 25, 1955.
[11] L. Pauling, *J. Phys. Chem.* **58**, 662 (1954).
[12] Th. Doehaerd *et al., Bull. soc. chim. Belges* **62**, 498 (1953).
[13] T. Coor *et al., Phys. Rev.* **98**, 1369 (1955); J. R. Beyster *et al., ibid.* **98**, 1216 (1955).
[14] T. Sameshima, *Rept. Liberal Arts Fac. Shizuoka Univ. Nat. Sci.* No. 4, 31 (1953).

When heated to electric-furnace temperatures, carbon unites with many elements, among which are iron, aluminum, calcium, hydrogen, sulfur, silicon, and boron. A number of the resulting compounds, known as carbides, are of great industrial importance. Several of these were first prepared by Moissan by applying electricity for the production of high temperatures. Tin, lead, arsenic, antimony, and bismuth do not form carbides. A number of carbides, including those of silicon, tantalum, niobium, and tungsten are very hard substances. Boron carbide, $B_4C_3$, is reported to have a hardness very close to that of the diamond. It has been used in the manufacture of extrusion dies, drills, sand-blasting equipment, and grinding instruments.[15] A material reported to have a hardness exceeding that of the diamond is borazon or boron nitride[16] (*vide infra*, Chapter 8). The reaction between hydrogen sulfide and various types of carbon has been reported over a temperature range of $1000°$ to $1600°K$. In addition to unreacted $H_2S$, there is formed a mixture of $CS_2$, sulfur, and hydrogen. The yield of $CS_2$ varies with temperature, the maximum yield is reported as 69.7% at $1600°K$. Other variables are the porosity and general nature of the carbon. A decrease in activity at $1300°K$ is noted for the series

beechwood > coconut > B.C.U.R.A. reactive

chars > coalite > anthracite > coke

The last mentioned material gives 45.4% $CS_2$ at $1500°K$. With some oxygen in the reacting system about 4% COS is formed.[17] Ash-free carbon reduces barium sulfate very rapidly when the two reactants are present in a 4:1 ratio. Both CO and $CO_2$ accelerate the reaction.[18]

Diamond is scarcely attacked by the most active oxidizing agents, such as a mixture of nitric acid and sodium chlorate. Diamond is oxidized by air at about $1600°F$. On the other hand, graphite is slowly oxidized by these reagents, and charcoal is oxidized rapidly. Under ordinary circumstances carbon is very inert, but its activity increases rapidly with rising temperatures until at the intense heat of an electric arc it becomes very active. Its general uses depend upon its property of readily uniting with oxygen to give carbon dioxide. Under certain conditions carbon monoxide is formed. The union of these elements to produce heat is a universal application of this action. The liberation of metals,

---

[15] *Chem. and Eng. News* **34**, 6369 (1956).

[16] *Ibid.* **35**, 28 (1957).

[17] A. J. Owen *et al.*, *Trans. Faraday Soc.* **49**, 1198, 1207 (1953).

[18] V. A. Shushunov *et al.*, *Zhur. Fiz. Khim.* **28**, 1472 (1954); A. M. Ginstling, *J. Appl. Chem. U.S.S.R.* **25**, 303, 559 (1952).

such as iron and copper, from their ores (oxides) is also a familiar use of carbon.   Carbon is insoluble in water and all other common solvents, but it dissolves to a limited extent in molten metals, especially iron.

**Union of Carbon with Hydrogen.**  Under ordinary circumstances carbon and hydrogen unite either not at all or too slowly to be appreciable. When hydrogen is passed over powdered carbon mixed with finely divided nickel as a contact agent, methane, $CH_4$, is obtained.   The reaction is exothermal and reversible.   Some acetylene, $C_2H_2$, is produced by passing hydrogen through an electric arc between carbon poles.

The true carbides might be considered as the salts of $H_4C$, as $Al_4C_3$ which upon reaction with water gives methane.   The commercial calcium salt of $H_2C_2$ or acetylene as an acid is $CaC_2$ which might more properly be called an acetylide (see Part II).

**Calcium Carbide, $CaC_2$[19]**   Calcium carbide is manufactured by heating a mixture of calcium oxide and coke in an electric furnace:

$$CaO + 3C \rightarrow CaC_2 + CO$$

The nature of this reaction between CaO and carbon varies depending upon the type of carbon used.[20]   At reduced pressures (2 to 3 mm) and at temperatures in excess of 1200°C, the reaction between CaO and charcoal (as a carbon source) is reported to result only in the reduction of the oxide to calcium metal.[21]   The activation energy of the reaction is 110.0 kcal/mole.   The commercial product is a dark-gray stony material, whereas pure calcium carbide (made by heating calcium hydride in acetylene) is colorless and crystalline.   The ordinary carbide is of considerable industrial importance.   With water it yields acetylene:

$$CaC_2 + 2H_2O \rightarrow Ca(OH)_2 + C_2H_2 \uparrow$$

When strongly heated with nitrogen it is converted into calcium cyanamide which is used sometimes as a fertilizer and in the commercial preparation of calcium cyanide, as well as the starting point for organic compounds of the melamine type.

Although the cyanamide process for making ammonia does not compete with other processes, acetylene is required in the production of a great many organic chemicals, for oxyacetylene cutting and welding, acetylene black, and vinyl compounds.

[19] See Part II, Chap. 8, This Volume.
[20] T. Mukaibo and Y. Yamanoka, *J. Chem. Soc. Japan, Ind. Chem. Sect.* **57**, 191 (1954).
[21] T. Mukaibo, *ibid.* **56**, 73 (1953).

Carbide furnaces are a combination of the resistance and the direct-arc heating type. Most of the heat is developed by arcing across the charge; the remainder results from the resistance of the raw materials and the product to the passage of the current. As shown in Fig. 1.15, the furnace is essentially a steel box lined with carbon blocks. Carbon is the only refractory able to withstand the action of molten calcium carbide (melting point approximately 1800°C). Furnaces are built large enough so that a thick layer of semisolid carbide forms the working lining of the furnace. Liquid carbide is tapped off and allowed to flow into "chill cars." The solid may be readily dumped from these cars inasmuch as the carbide contracts considerably on cooling. Crude carbide contains about 83% $CaC_2$, 14% $CaO$, and 1% $C$; the small remainder may be a mixture of silicides, sulfides, and phosphides.

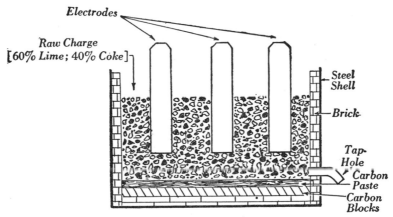

FIG. 1.15.    Electric furnace for making calcium carbide.

**Carbon Disulfide, $CS_2$.** Carbon disulfide is formed by the direct union of its elements. This is brought about by heating sulfur and charcoal away from air in closed retorts, while smaller quantities are made in electric furnaces:

$$C + 2S + 22{,}000 \text{ cal} \rightarrow CS_2$$

The product passes off as a vapor and is condensed.

The velocity of formation of $CS_2$ from sulfur and carbon (sugar-charcoal) is represented by the expression $KP/1 + K'P$, where $P$ is the partial pressure of the sulfur vapor, and $K$ and $K'$ are parameters whose values have been calculated[22] over the temperature range 770° to 900°C.

[22] H. Guerin and J. Adam-Gironne, *Compt. rend.* **238**, 583 (1954).

Carbon disulfide is a colorless heavy liquid (density 1.262 at 20°C), boiling point 46.3°C, freezing point −111.6°C. The liquid is highly flammable (ignition temperature 236°C). It is very poisonous, acting both as a respiratory and cutaneous poison. The dielectric constant[23] is 2.634 (20°C). The critical temperature[24] is 546.1°K.

Carbon disulfide is reactive, forming $CO_2$ and $SO_2$ when burned in air, phosgene when reacted with $Cl_2O$, carbon oxysulfide (COS) when reacted with $SO_3$, and in contact with a platinum catalyst reacts with hydrogen to form methane and hydrogen sulfide. Carbon disulfide when heated to high temperatures is partially converted to a subsulfide, $C_3S_2$. This compound is analogous to carbon suboxide. The subsulfide is a red liquid of 1.27 density. It may be prepared by an electric arc treatment of $CS_2$ vapor.

Carbon disulfide when diluted with nitrogen and fluorinated with elemental fluorine produces mostly $SF_4$ with only traces of $SF_6$ and $CF_4$. Carbon oxysulfide, on the other hand, when fluorinated with $CoF_3$ (using nitrogen as a diluent) yields almost pure $SF_6$ and a liquid mixture of $SF_6$ and $COF_2$. The electrochemical fluorination of $CS_2$ is reported to give $CF_3SF_5$ in 90% yield[25] with only a little $SF_6$. In a special mild fluorination apparatus, other fluorinated compounds are formed,[26] as $CF_2(SF_5)_2$, $F_3SCF_2SF_5$, $CF_3SF_3$, as well as $S_2F_{10}$.

**Carbon Halides.** A large number of carbon-halogen compounds are known, some of which have wide use in industrial chemistry.

1. *Carbon Tetrachloride, $CCl_4$.* Carbon tetrachloride is manufactured by leading dry chlorine into carbon disulfide containing a little iodine or antimony trichloride, $SbCl_3$, as a catalytic agent or as a chlorine carrier:

$$CS_2 + 3Cl_2 \rightarrow CCl_4 + S_2Cl_2$$

It boils at 76.8°C and is separated by distillation from the sulfur monochloride, $S_2Cl_2$ (boiling point 135.6°C). It is a colorless, nonflammable, pleasant-smelling liquid whose specific gravity is 1.595 at 20°C. Nonpolar solutes have a high degree of solubility in $CCl_4$. Thus, fats, greases, waxes, and other organic substances readily dissolve in it. *Carbona* is a commercial, nonflammable cleaning fluid composed of $CCl_4$ and mineral spirits.

As would be expected the solubility of halogens in carbon tetrachloride

[23] J. Timmermans *et al.*, *Bull. soc. chim. Belges* **64**, 5 (1955).
[24] L. Andrussow, *Z. Elektrochem.* **57**, 374 (1953).
[25] G. A. Silvey and G. H. Cady, *J. Am. Chem. Soc.* **74**, 5792 (1952).
[26] A. F. Clifford *et al.*, *J. Chem. Soc.* **1953**, 2372; E. A. Tyczkowski and L. A. Bigelow, *J. Am. Chem. Soc.* **75**, 3523 (1953).

is nearly ideal. The deviation of chlorine as a solute is only slightly less ideal. The solubility curves for $Cl_2$ in $CCl_4$ and in $CH_2CHBr$ are parallel and do not cross as has been previously reported.[27] The following values for the solubility of chlorine (moles per kilogram of solution) in $CCl_4$ are reported: 40°C, 0.793; 50°C, 0.596; 60°C, 0.522; 70°C, 0.425; 80°C, 0.335; and 90°C, 0.296. Acid solutions of radioactive chloride ion have been proved to exchange with the chlorine of carbon tetrachloride. The exchange is accelerated by ultraviolet light. This form of activation has no effect on the exchange in an alkaline solution.[28]

Fire extinguishers of the *Pyrene* type contain carbon tetrachloride. Its high volatility, and the fact that it is a nonconductor of the electric current make carbon tetrachloride especially useful in fighting fires near electrical equipment where water would cause short circuits. However, caution should be exercised in its use because it reacts with water vapor at the temperature of a flame to give, among other things, phosgene. Water vapor is always formed in the combustion of gasoline and other hydrogen-containing organic compounds. Since phosgene is toxic, it is dangerous to leave it in a very small or poorly ventilated space in which a fire has been extinguished by carbon tetrachloride. Extinguishers of the dry powder type appear to be favored in chemical laboratories.

2. *Carbon Fluorides.* The usual preparation of *carbon tetrafluoride* is by the direct union of the elements. A mixture of a number of fluorides is so obtained. A more easily controlled reaction is that between carbon tetrachloride and silver(I) fluoride. Carbon tetrafluoride is a colorless gas with a boiling point of $-128$°C and a melting point of $-183.6$°C. A general preparation resulting, again, in a mixture of fluorides is by passing fluorine with another halogen through a fluidized carbon bed at 315° to 650°C. The normally vigorous reaction may be modified by the presence of the second halogen. Interhalogens may also be used, as $ClF_3$, diluted with nitrogen.[29] A typical run in which $ClF_3$ is diluted with 13 parts of nitrogen and passed through 40 to 100 mesh fluidized Norit at 412°C yields in grams: $CF_4$, 0.56; $CClF_3$, 7.25; $CCl_2F_2$, 0.5; $C_2F_6$, 0.66; $C_2ClF_5$, 1.70; $C_2Cl_2F_4$, 1.31; $C_3F_8$, 1.04; $C_3ClF_7$, 1.37; and $C_4F_{10}$, 1.10. Higher weight compounds are also formed. Increasing the temperature above 412°C tends to decrease the relative amounts of chlorinated products. Fluorination of methane results in carbon tetrafluoride, and the heat of formation of the $CF_4$ from this reaction is re-

[27] T. Smith, *J. Phys. Chem.* **59**, 188 (1955); J. C. Gjaldbeck and J. H. Hildebrand, *J. Am. Chem. Soc.* **72**, 609 (1950).
[28] J. Horiuchi and K. Tanabe, *Proc. Japan Acad.* **29**, 254 (1953).
[29] See Volume III, This Series; R. M. Mantell *et al.*, **U.S. 2,684,987**, July 27, 1954.

ported as $-220.4$ kcal/mole $\pm 2\%$ at $32°C.$[30] The value calculated from the direct reaction of graphite and fluoride at $298.16°K$ is $218.3$ kcal/mole.[31] The effective bond moments for $CF_4$ from the absolute intensities of the fundamental infrared absorption bands as well as the bond moment derivative $\partial\mu/\partial r$, have been calculated as $1.12D$ and $4.88D/A$, respectively.[32]

The bond energies of a number of carbon fluorides are noted in Table 1.1.

TABLE 1.1. BOND ENERGIES OF SOME CARBON FLUORIDES*

| Compound | Bond Energy, kcal/mole | | |
| | C–F | C–X | C–C |
|---|---|---|---|
| $CCl_3F$ | 100 | 70 | — |
| $CCl_2F_2$ | 107 | 78 | — |
| $CClF_3$ | 128 | 100 | — |
| $CF_4$ | 138 | — | — |
| $CF_3Br$ | (95) | 64 | |
| $CH_3F$ | 115 | (104) | — |
| $CH_2F_2$ | (120) | (105) | — |
| $CHF_3$ | (130) | (125) | — |
| $COF_2$ | (115) | — | — |
| $F_3CCF_3$ | (130) | — | 107 |
| $ClF_2CCF_2Cl$ | (120) | (80) | 95 |

* N. W. Luft, J. Chem. Phys. **23**, 973 (1955).

Assuming that $C_2F_4$ is decomposed to carbon and $CF_4$, the heat of decomposition is reported as $61.430$ kcal/mole. The heat of hydrogenation of the same compound to form carbon and HF is $132.720$ kcal/mole, and the heat of combustion is $1,603$ cal/g assuming that in the combustion $0.1178$ mole fraction of $COF_2$ is formed. A value of $1,572$ cal/g is calculated, corrected to zero yield of carbonyl fluoride.[33] The heat of formation of the carbon trifluoride radical, $CF_3$, is $-120.5$ kcal/mole, and the bond dissociation energy, $D(F_2C–F)$, is less than $116$ kcal/mole.[34]

The heats of formation for a number of carbon fluorides are found in Table 1.2 based upon the ignition of the compounds with potassium. Values from several sources are given.[35]

The melting and boiling points of a number of the higher molecular-weight carbon fluorides are, respectively:[36] $C_2F_6$, $-100.6$ and $-78.2°C$;

[30] R. S. Jessup et al., J. Am. Chem. Soc. **77**, 244 (1955).
[31] D. W. Scott et al., J. Am. Chem. Soc. **77**, 245 (1955).
[32] P. N. Schotz and D. F. Hornig, J. Chem. Phys. **21**, 1516 (1953).
[33] H. C. Duus, Ind. Eng. Chem. **47**, 1445 (1955).
[34] B. S. Rabinovitch and J. F. Reed, J. Chem. Phys. **22**, 2092 (1954).
[35] H. v. Wartenberg and J. Schiefer, Z. anorg. u. allgem. Chem. **278**, 326 (1955).
[36] H. Remy, op. cit., p. 439.

$C_3F_8$, $-183$ and $-38°C$; $C_4F_{10}$, $-4.7°C$ (boiling point only); $C_6F_{12}$, $+51$ and $+58°C$.

Electron diffraction studies have given data on the bond distances and structures for a number of carbon fluorides.[37]

The trifluoromethyl derivatives of Group VA and VIA have been prepared and their structures determined (Tables 1.4 and 1.5).

TABLE 1.2. HEATS OF FORMATION OF SOME CARBON FLUORIDES

| Compound | $\Delta H$, kcal/mole, 25°C |
|---|---|
| $CF_4$ | $-225(-212.7)*(218\pm2)\dagger$ |
| $CF_3Cl$ | $-167(-171\pm1)\dagger$ |
| $CF_2Cl_2$ | $-113(-112\pm)\dagger$ |
| $CFCl_3$ | $-67(-70\pm4)\dagger$ |
| $C_2F_4$ | $-164(-151.3)*(-162\pm1)\dagger$ |
| $C_2F_3Cl$ | $-120$ |
| $C_2F_2Cl_2$ | $-77$ |
| $(CF_2Cl)_2$ | $(-213\pm3)\dagger$ |
| $CF_2:CFCl$ | $(126\pm2)\dagger$ |
| $C_2F_6$ | $(-303\pm2)\dagger$ |
| $C_3F_8$ | $(257.8)\dagger$ |

* H. C. Duus, *loc. cit.*
† F. W. Kirkbride and F. G. Davidson, *Nature* **174**, 79 (1954).

TABLE 1.3. STRUCTURES OF SOME CARBON FLUORIDES

| Compound | C–F, A | C–X, A | ∠F–C–F, ° |
|---|---|---|---|
| $CF_4$ | $1.33_7 \pm 0.22$ | | |
| $CF_3Cl$ | $1.32_3 \pm 0.032$ | $1.74_7 \pm 0.040$ | $108.5 \pm 9$ |
| $CF_3Br$ | $1.34_3 \pm 0.021$ | $1.91 \pm 0.033$ | $109.5 \pm 2$ |
| $CF_3I$ | $1.32_8 \pm 0.026$ | $2.12 \pm 0.037$ | $108.3 \pm 2$ |

TABLE 1.4. STRUCTURES OF SOME GROUP VA TRIFLUOROMETHYL COMPOUNDS

| Compound | C–F, A | C–M, A | ∠C–M–C, ° |
|---|---|---|---|
| $P(CF_3)_3$ | $1.34 \pm 0.013$ | $1.93_7 \pm 0.017$ | $99.6 \pm 2.5$ |
| $As(CF_3)_3$ | $1.33_6 \pm 0.012$ | $2.05_3 \pm 0.019$ | $100.1 \pm 3.5$ |
| $Sb(CF_3)_3$ | $1.32_6 \pm 0.009$ | $2.20_2 \pm 0.016$ | $100.0 \pm 3.5$ |

TABLE 1.5. STRUCTURES OF SOME GROUP VIA TRIFLUOROMETHYL COMPOUNDS

| Compound | C–F, A | C–M, A | ∠C–M–C, ° | M–M, A | ∠C–M–M, ° |
|---|---|---|---|---|---|
| $S(CF_3)_2$ | $1.32_8 \pm 0.01$ | $1.82_8 \pm 0.015$ | $105.6$ | — | — |
| $S_2(CF_3)_2$ | $1.33_4 \pm 0.013$ | $1.82_9 \pm 0.017$ | — | $2.05_3 \pm 0.019$ | $105.4 \pm 3$ |
| $S_3(CF_3)_2$ | $1.34_0 \pm 0.011$ | $1.84_8 \pm 0.015$ | — | $2.06_5 \pm 0.016$ | ∠S–S–S $103.8 \pm 3$ |
| $Se(CF_3)_2$ | $1.35_6 \pm 0.015$ | $1.95_8 \pm 0.022$ | $104.4 \pm 5$ | — | — |
| $Se_2(CF_3)_2$ | $1.33_6 \pm 0.012$ | $1.93_4 \pm 0.018$ | — | $2.33_5 \pm 0.032$ | — |

[37] H. J. M. Bowen, *Trans. Faraday Soc.* **50**, 444 (1954).

**Carbon Dioxide, $CO_2$.** In the first half of the seventeenth century (1630) Van Helmont noted that the gas coming from burning wood would extinguish a flame. In 1757 Black obtained the substance from carbonates. Lavoisier showed that it contained carbon and oxygen.

Carbon dioxide is a variable component of the atmosphere. In some places, such as the Grotto del Cane near Naples, it comes from the ground through fissures. The Valley of Death in Java is an old volcanic crater filled with the gas. The waters of some springs and wells are so heavily charged with it that they are effervescent. Good examples of these *carbonated waters* are those of Vichy, Selters, and the Geyser Springs of Saratoga. Natural-gas wells producing carbon dioxide are found in California, Colorado, New Mexico, Utah, and Washington. Measurement of a single well in Mexico showed a daily output of 150,000,000 cubic ft of carbon dioxide.

**Preparation of Carbon Dioxide.** 1. Carbon dioxide is formed by the decay and fermentation of organic matter. It is produced, therefore, during the alcoholic fermentation of sugars:

$$C_6H_{12}O_6 \rightarrow 2C_2H_5OH + 2CO_2 \uparrow$$

2. When carbon burns in an excess of oxygen, carbon dioxide is produced. The same product results from the complete combustion of all carbon compounds and by slow oxidation in the bodies of plants and animals. An impure gas mixed with nitrogen is obtained by burning carbon (for example, coke) in air. If the gas is passed under pressure into a concentrated solution of potassium carbonate, the carbon dioxide is absorbed, with the formation of potassium hydrogencarbonate:

$$CO_2 + H_2O \rightleftharpoons H_2CO_3$$
$$H_2CO_3 + 2K^+ + CO_3^= \rightleftharpoons 2K^+ + 2HCO_3^-$$

On reducing the pressure and heating the solution, the actions are reversed, and carbon dioxide free from nitrogen is liberated. Carbon dioxide obtained from the burning of coal, from cement plants, and from lime-burning plants is conducted into towers filled with coke, over which runs a concentrated solution of sodium or potassium carbonate. The product is sodium or potassium bicarbonate. When this is heated with steam, carbon dioxide is evolved and is then compressed into steel cylinders. This is an industrial method of preparation. Certain basic organic compounds (the aliphatic amines) are said to have more capacity for absorbing carbon dioxide than does an inorganic carbonate; they are more reactive and are easily regenerated.

**3.** Pure carbon dioxide is obtained simply by heating solid sodium hydrogencarbonate:

$$2NaHCO_3 \rightarrow Na_2CO_3 + CO_2 + H_2O$$

Many normal carbonates are decomposed by heat, giving the gas:

$$CaCO_3 \rightarrow CaO + CO_2$$

Advantage is taken of this reaction for making quicklime, CaO, by the process of *lime-burning*.

**4.** Carbon dioxide is obtained by the action of acids on carbonates:

$$2H_3O^+ + CO_3^= \rightarrow 3H_2O + CO_2 \uparrow$$

This method is used in the laboratory. The reaction is often carried out in a Kipp generator in which calcium carbonate (marble) and dilute hydrochloric acid are used:

$$CaCO_3 + 2H_3O^+ \rightarrow Ca^{++} + H_2CO_3 + 2H_2O$$

Carbonic acid, $H_2CO_3$, which is first formed, is unstable and breaks up into water and carbon dioxide.

**Physical Properties.** Carbon dioxide is a colorless, odorless gas with a weakly acid taste due to the formation of carbonic acid in the mouth. The weight of 22.4 liters is 44.28 g; hence the formula $CO_2$, and also the information that the gas is about 1.5 times as heavy as air. Up to about 4 atmospheres the solubility of the gas is in good agreement with Henry's law. A volume of water at 20°C dissolves 0.9 volume of carbon dioxide. The relatively high critical temperature, 31°C, makes it possible to liquefy the gas at ordinary temperatures; the critical pressure is 73 atmospheres. Liquid carbon dioxide freezes at −56.5°C (5.2 atmospheres). The vapor pressure of the solid is 1 atmosphere at −79°C; hence the solid, on exposure to air, vaporizes without melting. Furthermore, the cooling effect of vaporization prevents the temperature from rising to its melting point by the absorption of external heat. When the liquid is allowed to evaporate, it freezes to a snowlike crystalline mass which is used to produce low temperatures.

The constant volume specific heat of carbon dioxide is calculated as 17.4 cal/mole from the equation: $C_v = (T/m)(v/a_c\mu_c)^2$ at the critical point for the gas, where $v$ is the volume, $m$ is the molecular weight, $a_c$ is the sound velocity, and $\mu_c$ is the Joule-Thompson coefficient. There is a wide discrepancy between this calculated value and 50 cal/mole, the only calorimetric specific heat value reported.[38] The difference may be

[38] J. F. Lee, *Z. angew. Math. u. Phys.* **4**, 401 (1953).

attributed to the heat capacity lag, scattering, absorption, and configurational relaxation in the sound velocity.

Some additional thermodynamic properties of gaseous carbon dioxide are: $\Delta H_f^0$ at $0°K = -93.9686$ kcal/mole, at $298.16°K$ the value is $-94.0518$ kcal/mole; $\Delta F_f^0$ at $298.16°K = -94.2598$ kcal/mole; the equilibrium constant of formation at $298.16°K = 69.09124$; the value of $S^0 = 51.061$ cal/deg mole and the heat capacity, $C_p^0 = 8.874$ cal/deg mole (both values at $298.16°K$).[39]

**Chemical Properties.** Toward heat carbon dioxide is about as stable as water. At from $1200°$ to $1300°C$ it decomposes to a small extent into carbon monoxide and oxygen, the dissociation reaching $1.8\%$ at $2000°C$:

$$2CO_2 \rightleftharpoons 2CO + O_2$$

Recombination of oxygen and carbon monoxide takes place when the temperature is lowered, except when the heating is carried out in the presence of some combustible substance such as hydrogen. In this case the whole of the dioxide is reduced to the monoxide. A burning magnesium wire continues to burn in an atmosphere of carbon dioxide, the oxide of the metal and carbon being formed:

$$CO_2 + 2Mg \rightarrow 2MgO + C$$

When the gas is led over heated potassium or sodium, the carbonates of these metals are formed and carbon is set free:

$$3CO_2 + 4K \rightarrow 2K_2CO_3 + C$$

The decomposition of calcium carbonate is a reversible reaction, and hence carbon dioxide unites with calcium oxide to form the carbonate, $CaCO_3$. In a similar way the gas unites with the oxides of other active metals.

With water carbon dioxide forms the unstable acid $H_2CO_3$:

$$H_2O + CO_2 \rightleftharpoons H_2CO_3$$

This compound is carbonic acid.

**Carbonic Acid and Carbonates.** Carbonic acid, formed by dissolving carbon dioxide in water, is a very weak acid. Its solution reddens blue litmus but is a poor conductor of electricity. Like other polyprotic acids it ionizes in steps:

$$H_2CO_3 + H_2O \rightleftharpoons H_3O^+ + HCO_3^-$$
$$HCO_3^- + H_2O \rightleftharpoons H_3O^+ + CO_3^=$$

[39] *N.B.S. Circular 500*, U. S. Government Printing Office, Washington 25, D. C., 1952.

A differentiation should be made between the "true" and "apparent" dissociation constants of carbonic acid. The apparent constant may be described as

$$K_a = \frac{[H^+][HCO_3^-]}{[CO_2 + H_2CO_3]}$$

Thus, the total amount of $CO_2$ is considered, both that combined as $H_2CO_3$ and that dissolved in the water. The molar solubility of $CO_2$ is represented by the equation

$$\text{Log } C = 2385.73/T - 14.0184 + 0.0152642T$$

The true constant is represented by

$$K_t = [H^+][HCO_3^-]/[H_2CO_3]$$

The value of $K_a$ is reported as $4.45 \times 10^{-7}$, whereas the value of $K_t$ is about $5 \times 10^{-4}$. In actual fact a solution of carbonic acid behaves as an acid, but not as strong as the value of $K_t$ would indicate (a value larger than formic and acetic acids). The second dissociation constant of $H_2CO_3$ has been calculated over the temperature range 60° to 90°C. The values follow the equation: $\log K_2 = -2909.10T^{-1} + 6.119 - 0.02272T$. A maximum is observed[40] at the temperature 84.8°C.

The heat of formation (standard state) of aqueous $CO_2$ is $-98.69$ kcal/mole; the value of $\Delta F_f^0$ is $-92.31$; the equilibrium constant of formation is 67.662; and the entropy, $S^0$, is 29.0 cal/deg mole.[41]

Since carbonic acid is diprotic it forms both hydrogencarbonates and normal salts. Thus, when a solution of sodium hydroxide is saturated with carbon dioxide, sodium hydrogencarbonate is formed:

$$OH^- + CO_2 \rightarrow HCO_3^-$$

A solution of sodium hydrogencarbonate is not acid because of the strength of the carbonate ion, $CO_3^=$, as a base. For this reason the reaction

$$HCO_3^- + H_2O \rightarrow H_3O^+ + CO_3^=$$

takes place only to a very slight extent.

Sodium carbonate is formed from the hydrogencarbonate by the addition of an equivalent amount of sodium hydroxide to the solution of the hydrogencarbonate:

$$HCO_3^- + OH^- \rightleftharpoons CO_3^= + H_2O$$

[40] C. Cuta and F. Strafelda, *Chem. Listy* **48**, 1308 (1954).
[41] *N.B.S. Circular 500*, U. S. Government Printing Office, Washington 25, D. C., 1952.

Solutions of the carbonate are distinctly alkaline because of the readiness with which the reverse action takes place in the foregoing system.

The carbonates of ammonium and the alkali metals are soluble. Other carbonates (with the exception of hydrogencarbonates) are difficultly soluble in water. The precipitation of calcium or barium carbonate by passing carbon dioxide into limewater, $Ca(OH)_2$, or barium hydroxide, $Ba(OH)_2$, is used as a test for $CO_2$:

$$Ca^{++} + 2OH^- + CO_2 \rightarrow CaCO_3 \downarrow + H_2O$$

When an excess of the gas is used, the precipitate dissolves because of the formation of $Ca(HCO_3)_2$:

$$CaCO_3 + H_2CO_3 \rightleftharpoons Ca^{++} + 2HCO_3^-$$

It is in this way that natural waters dissolve limestone and other carbonates, such as iron(II) carbonate, $FeCO_3$. The reverse process takes place in nature, which explains the formation of stalactites (downward growth) and stalagmites in caves.

Some information on the nature of crystalline carbonates is available from infrared spectra. Barium carbonate (in Nujol mulls) has been examined between 1.3 and 12.5 $\mu$. The vibrations of the carbonate ions which occur in isotopic isolation as pairs, triplets, and quadruplets are resolvable. From coupling constants the dipolemoment[42] of $BaCO_3$ is 2.1$D$, for $CaCO_3$ 1.8$D$, and for $SrCO_3$ 1.9$D$.

An extensive study has been made of both the alkali and alkaline earth carbonates in relation to the oxygen and carbon dioxide exchange reactions.[43] Two types of exchange are noted. There may be an atomic exchange which takes place apparently almost in pure form during interaction of carbonates with oxygen-containing gases at elevated temperatures, but not at temperatures exceeding the threshold of the heat of ionization of the molecule. A second exchange takes place in aqueous medium when an interaction is possible between the ions in solution. Experiments are reported using tagged metal carbonates ($^{18}O/^{16}O$ from 0.35 to 1%). Carbonates exchange with $CO_2$ and $O_2$ at high temperatures independently of water vapor; thus a different mechanism exists contrasted to ionic exchange. For $BaCO_3$ and $Na_2CO_3$ the gaseous exchange with $O_2$ proceeds easier than with $CO_2$. A general disruption of the oxygen bond in the molecule is assumed followed by intense diffusion of the gas into the carbonate lattice. For $CaCO_3$ the exchange is easier

[42] J. C. Decius, *J. Chem. Phys.* **23**, 1290 (1955).
[43] A. V. Trofirnov, *Doklady Akady. Nauk S.S.S.R.* **96**, 335 (1954).

with $CO_2$ than with $O_2$. Magnesium carbonate shows an intense exchange with $CO_2$ at 400°C. The chemical stability of the C–O bond in carbonates decreases in the series $BaCO_3$, $Na_2CO_3$, $CaCO_3$, and $MgCO_3$ as determined from these exchange processes. Certain specific exchanges reported for gaseous oxygen in a 212-day period using $^{18}O$-enriched carbonates are: $CaCO_3 = 1\%$; $BaCO_3 = 19\%$; $Na_2CO_3 = 71\%$; $MgCO_3 \cdot MgO = 70\%$. Calcium carbonate (chalk) was much more resistant to exchange using $H_2^{18}O$ than was $BaCO_3$.[44]

On electrolysis of potassium carbonate solution at low temperatures utilizing a smooth platinum anode, a peroxycarbonate, $C_2O_6^=$, is formed. This anion probably hydrolyzes[45] slowly to the monoperoxy acid, $H_2CO_4$.

**Uses of Carbon Dioxide.** Carbon dioxide is used chiefly in the manufacture of sodium carbonate, $Na_2CO_3 \cdot 10H_2O$ (washing soda), sodium hydrogencarbonate, $NaHCO_3$ (baking soda), basic carbonate of lead, $Pb_3(OH)_2(CO_3)_2$ (white lead), and aerated beverages such as soda water. Soda water is charged with the gas under a pressure of from 3 to 4 atmospheres.

Carbon dioxide does not burn. Even 2.5% of carbon dioxide in air is sufficient to extinguish a burning candle; hence it is suitable for smothering fires. Many portable fire extinguishers contain liquid carbon dioxide or are devices for generating the gas. Extinguishers of the latter type contain a dilute solution of baking soda and a bottle of sulfuric acid (Fig. 1.16). When ready for use the acid is released into the carbonate solution, and the pressure produced by the liberated carbon dioxide forces a stream of liquid out of the nozzle. Very nearly all of the extinguishing power of this type of device is from water itself.

Fig. 1.16. Portable fire extinguisher.

A modification of the foregoing extinguisher enhances the blanketing effect of carbon dioxide by preventing rapid diffusion of the gas away from a burning surface. Carbon dioxide is generated within the extinguisher by the interaction of solutions of aluminum sulfate and sodium hydrogencarbonate:

$$[Al(H_2O)_6]^{+3} + 3HCO_3^- \rightarrow Al(OH)_3 \downarrow + 3CO_2 \uparrow + 6H_2O$$

[44] *Ibid.* **98**, 237 (1954).

[45] W. Latimer, *Oxidation Potentials*, Prentice-Hall, Inc., New York, 1952, p. 134.

A persistent foam, stabilized by licorice, soaps, or saponin in the original solution, is ejected from the extinguisher. This carbon dioxide-containing foam coats a burning surface and hinders the access of air to the surface. It is especially effective against fires in storage tanks containing gasoline or oils because the foam floats on the surface of the burning liquid and excludes the air. Water, on the other hand, sinks to the botton of the tanks where it is of no value.

Liquid carbon dioxide has been employed to some extent in place of ammonia in refrigeration plants on board ships where the escape of ammonia gas would be dangerous. Solid carbon dioxide (Dry Ice) has come into widespread use. Although its cost is much greater than that of ordinary ice, and although its cooling effect is only twice that of ice, it has a number of special advantages. Its use does not involve the formation of a liquid as does ice because of the direct change of the solid to a gas. Special refrigerator cars have been designed to permit its use in the refrigeration of fish, fruits, and meat in shipment. These foodstuffs have been shown to keep much better in a dry atmosphere of carbon dioxide than they do in moist, cold air.

Dry Ice plants using gas from wells have been built in five western states. However, naturally occurring carbon dioxide is a very small factor in the total sales volume of either liquid or solid carbon dioxide because the wells are so far from the cities where the bulk of the product is consumed. By-product carbon dioxide from cement mills, limekilns, and metallurgical plants is much more important, chiefly because these plants are likely to be located in or near the large centers of population which afford the markets.

One of the more important uses of carbon dioxide is its absorption in sodium chloride and ammonia liquors in the Solvay-Soda process. The absorption of $CO_2$ by ammonia at various concentrations follows the expression: $N = K(P_g - P_l)$ where $N$ is the rate in cubic centimeters per minute, $K$ is the over-all coefficient, and $P_g$ and $P_l$ are partial pressures of $CO_2$ in the gas and liquid states. The assumption is made that a reversible reaction occurs forming $NH_2COONH_4$, which hydrolyzes into $NH_4HCO_3$. The rate of hydrolysis, however, is much less than the rate of formation. A refined rate expression is $N_a = \beta H k_l(P_g - P_l)$, where $k_l$ is the liquid film resistance. Initially $N_a$ is increased by the concentration of $NH_3$ in the solution; however, in the final stages, $N_a$, as a function of the concentration of ammonia, passes through a maximum. Temperature and concentration have about the same effect.[46]

[46] T. A. Sarukhanyan and A. P. Belopol'skii, *Zhur. Priklad. Khim.* **27**, 142, 712 (1954).

Experiments at the University of Minnesota have shown the value of carbon dioxide for the preservation of certain fruits. For the past few years growers in Minnesota have had considerable success in shipping and selling strawberries and raspberries to the surrounding states. Berries gased with carbon dioxide are reported to be firmer in texture, brighter in color, and far less subject to mold than the untreated fruit.

**Physiological Action of Carbon Dioxide.** Low concentrations of carbon dioxide are practically without effect on humans. Increases in concentration cause rapid breathing because of a stimulating effect on the respiratory centers. Thus, when mixed with oxygen, it is administered by pulmotors in treatment of conditions in which a rapid rate of respiration is desirable. Carbon dioxide is given to stimulate respiration during anesthesia.

**Carbon Monoxide, CO.** Carbon monoxide was first obtained in 1776 by Lassone when he heated zinc oxide mixed with carbon. He noted that it burned with a blue flame. Lavoisier (1777) showed that it burned in oxygen to form carbon dioxide, and Cruikshank (1800) proved that it was nothing else than an oxide of carbon. In 1802 Clément and Desormes determined the composition of the oxide.

Carbon monoxide is present in the gases issuing from volcanoes. Aside from this it does not occur in nature except as it is formed by the imperfect combustion of carbonaceous materials and by the reduction of oxides with carbon.

Some thermodynamic properties of carbon monoxide are indicated in Table 1.6.

TABLE 1.6. SOME THERMODYNAMIC PROPERTIES OF CARBON MONOXIDE*

| Property | Value |
|---|---|
| $\Delta H_f^0$, 0°K | $-27.2019$ kcal/mole |
| $\Delta H_f^0$, 25°C | $-26.4157$ kcal/mole |
| $\Delta F_f^0$, 25°C | $-32.8079$ kcal/mole |
| log $k_f$, 25°C | 24.04778 |
| $S^0$, 25°C | 47.301 cal/deg mole |

* *N.B.S. Circular 500*, U. S. Government Printing Office, Washington 25, D. C., 1952.

**Preparation of Carbon Monoxide.** 1. Carbon monoxide may be prepared by heating formic acid or a formate in the presence of concentrated sulfuric acid as a dehydrating agent.

$$HCOOH \rightarrow CO + H_2O$$

When oxalic acid or an oxalate is heated with concentrated sulfuric acid, a mixture of carbon monoxide and carbon dioxide is produced:

$$H_2C_2O_4 \rightarrow CO + CO_2 + H_2O$$

The carbon monoxide may be obtained by collecting the mixture over sodium hydroxide, which absorbs carbon dioxide, or by passing the gases through sodium hydroxide and then collecting the monoxide over water.

2. Carbon monoxide is formed when carbon dioxide is passed over a metal, such as zinc, heated to a relatively high temperature:

$$Zn + CO_2 \rightarrow ZnO + CO$$

3. When oxygen is passed over hot carbon, carbon dioxide is produced:

$$C + O_2 \rightarrow CO_2 + 94{,}380 \text{ cal.}$$

A blue flame of burning carbon monoxide is often seen above a coal fire. This gas is formed by the reduction of carbon dioxide as the latter passes upward through the heated carbon:

$$C + CO_2 \rightarrow 2CO - 41{,}020 \text{ cal.}$$

Thus the heat of formation of the monoxide is 26,680 cal. The reaction varies from zero to first order and is retarded by the carbon monoxide formation.[47] The mechanism of carbon dioxide reduction by carbon has been investigated using carbon-14. Five steps are suggested as being necessary.[48]

1. The reaction between $CO_2$ and C to form a 6-membered C–O cyclic complex on the carbon surface.

2. Decomposition of the cyclic compound to form C*O and a nonactive C–O complex.

3. Decomposition of the cyclic complex (1) to form elemental C* and a nonactive complex (step 2).

4. Decomposition (principal reaction) of the nonactive complex (step 2) to form nonactive CO and free carbon.

5. The reverse of all steps 1 through 4.

A limited supply of air passed through hot coke gives a mixture called *producer gas*. It consists almost entirely of carbon monoxide and nitrogen in the ratio of approximately 1 to 3 by volume. This mixture is readily combustible, but its heating value is comparatively low because of the nitrogen present. However, producer gas is inexpensive to make, and it serves as an economical fuel gas in industrial operations. The mixture

[47] H. Guerin, *Chimie and industrie* **70**, 875 (1953).
[48] I. G. Petrenko, *Izvest. Akad. Nauk S.S.S.R. Otdel Tekh. Nauk* **1955**(5), 157.

of gases escaping from a blast furnace is essentially producer gas; it has almost one half the heating value of the original coke.   Since approximately 100,000,000 cubic ft of this gas are available daily from a large furnace, its use plays an important part in the economy of the process.

If an *excess* of air is forced through a bed of coal or coke, the reactions which occur are those taking place in the ordinary furnace used for domestic heating, and in the large installations used in industry for the generation of steam, and for general heating purposes.   Figure 1.17 shows the sequence and the approximate zones in which the separate reactions

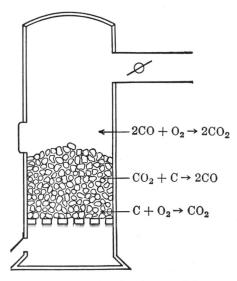

$$2CO + O_2 \rightarrow 2CO_2$$

$$CO_2 + C \rightarrow 2CO$$

$$C + O_2 \rightarrow CO_2$$

Fig. 1.17.   Combustion in a coal furnace.

go on.   At the top, center, and bottom zones, respectively, the following reactions take place:

$$2CO + O_2 \rightarrow 2CO_2$$
$$CO_2 + C \rightarrow 2CO$$
$$C + O_2 \rightarrow CO_2$$

4. One of the methods of preparing hydrogen is by the passage of steam through incandescent coke.   Carbon monoxide is formed at the same time:

$$C + H_2O \rightarrow CO + H_2 - 28.1 \text{ kcal}$$

At relatively low temperatures (25° to 200°C) the heterogeneous reaction between different forms of carbon and water results in the formation of hydrogen and at least two surface oxygen complexes of different stability. One of these decomposes to give $CO_2$, and another more stable complex gives CO. A carbon surface with some sulfur impurity reacts more rapidly than does a pure surface. Some hydrogen sulfide is formed from the impure surface.[49] The high-temperature (745°C) reaction between carbon and water is first order.[50] The mixture of carbon monoxide and hydrogen is known as *water gas*. The action of $H_2O$ on carbon is endothermal, and for this reason the coke soon becomes too cool to act. An air blast is then substituted for steam until the fuel is again heated to bright redness. The two blasts are used alternately. It is common practice to blow a mixture of steam and air continuously through heated coke so as to avoid the intermittent process. The heat of combustion of carbon serves to keep the temperature high enough for the formation of water gas. This fuel is used in large quantities in factories.

In addition to processes involving incomplete combustion of carbon and hydrocarbons and dehydration of formic acid, carbon monoxide may be produced in the thermal decomposition of KNCO. An equilibrium is assumed between KNCO and KOCN. The former dissociates into potassium and an NCO radical. This latter radical then decomposes rapidly into CO and nitrogen. The CO reduces KNCO reversibly to KCN and eventually yields carbon dioxide. Potassium formed in the process reacts with $CO_2$ to form more CO and a KO radical. The cycle is further perpetuated by the KO radical reacting with KOCN to give $K_2O$ and NCO. The latter dissociates into CO as already mentioned. Metals such as copper, arsenic, and iron accelerate the KCNO decomposition very markedly. The energy of activation for the process is reported as 23,000 cal/mole.[51]

**Coal Gas.** The original process for making illuminating gas by heating bituminous coal out of contact with air is still the basis for the present method. Coal is heated in cylindrical retorts, and the products are collected as shown in Fig. 1.18. Since this is essentially the method by which coke is made, the composition of the gas is like that produced in the coke ovens. Carbon monoxide constitutes only about 8% of the mixture; hydrogen (50%), and methane (29%) are the main heat-producing components present.

[49] R. N. Smith et al., J. Phys. Chem. **58**, 298 (1954).
[50] N. M. Ershova, Zhur. Priklad. Khim. **27**, 106 (1954).
[51] V. A. Shushunov and N. K. Serdyuk, Doklady Akad. Nauk S.S.S.R. **89**, 1033 (1953); ibid. **93**, 507 (1953).

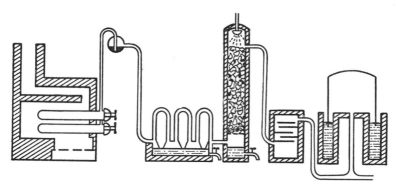

Fɪɢ. 1.18.  Manufacture of coal gas.

**Physical Properties.**  Carbon monoxide is a colorless, odorless, taste-less gas.  It is slightly lighter than air (28:28.96).  It is but slightly soluble in water, 100 volumes of water dissolving 3 volumes of the gas at 0°C.  A liter weighs 1.2501 g at S.T.P.  The critical temperature is −139.5°C; the critical pressure is 35.5 atmospheres.  Liquid carbon monoxide boils at −192°C and freezes at −207°C.  At high pressures $2 < T/T_{critical} < 5$ according to determinations of $c_p$ and $c_v$.[52]

**Chemical Properties.**  An ordinary valence-bond structure for carbon monoxide is usually written as C═O.  No single, electronic fomula fits all the properties of the molecule.  It is probable that its normal state is best represented by resonance among three structures.  These are:

$$\overset{+}{\text{(a) } :\!C:\!\overset{..}{\underset{..}{O}}:^{-}}, \quad \text{(b) } :\!C:\!:\!\overset{..}{O}:, \quad \text{and} \quad \overset{-}{\text{(c) } :\!C:\!:\!:\!\overset{+}{O}:}.$$

All three structures contribute about equally.  The dipole moment of CO is about $0.1D$.  Such a small moment necessitates the third structure (c) to counterbalance the charge effect of (a).  The measured bond distance of 1.13 A is less than that expected for single or double bonds between carbon and oxygen.  The triple bond contribution is further indicated.[53] Electrons assigned in pairs to the sigma orbitals of carbon monoxide are distributed variously as: (1) between the nuclei; (2) on the outer side of the oxygen atom; and (3) on the outer side of the carbon atom.  This distribution differs from that in carbon dioxide (symmetrical) in that there is a projection on the remote side of the bond in carbon monoxide.  This projection is the major cause for the dipole moment of the CO

[52] A. M. Rozen, *Zhur. Fiz. Khim.* **27**, 178 (1953).
[53] L. Gero *et al.*, *Phys. Rev.* **52**, 467 (1937).

molecule.   Ionization of CO from the $s$ sigma or the $s$ mu level implies the removal of an electron mainly from the oxygen or mainly from the carbon, respectively.[54]

From infrared dispersion and absorption intensity measurements (Van Vleck calculations) the atomic polarization of CO is 0.044 cc.   Other data in the literature[55] lead to differing values of 0.045 and 0.077 cc.   There is no predissociation of the electronic states of carbon monoxide below 11.11 ev.   The dissociation energy[56] of CO then is $89{,}620 \pm 50$ cm$^{-1}$. The heat of dissociation, $D_0(CO)$, is 256.19 kcal/mole.[57]   Table 1.7 includes the resonance entropy of carbon monoxide along with the values for a $CO_2$ and several carbon halides.[58]

TABLE 1.7   RESONANCE ENTROPY OF SOME CARBON COMPOUNDS

| Compound | Resonance Entropy, cal/deg mole |
|---|---|
| CO | 1.4 |
| $CO_2$ | 10.7 |
| $COCl_2$ | 3.8 |
| $CF_4$ | 6.1 |
| $CCl_4$ | 2.7 |
| $CBr_4$ | 2.9 |

Carbon monoxide reacts directly with a number of metals to form *carbonyls*.   For example, $Fe(CO)_5$ is a yellow substance which melts at $-20°C$ and boils at 103°C; nickel carbonyl, $Ni(CO)_4$, is colorless, melts at $-23°C$ and boils at 43°C; $Co_2(CO)_8$ is an orange solid which melts at 51°C and sublimes under diminished pressure.   Nickel carbonyl is important in the purification of that metal.   One of the more outstanding differences between the reactions of sodium and potassium is found in the readiness with which the latter reacts with carbon monoxide to form a "carbonyl" of the formula $K_6C_6O_6$.   This compound is actually a benzene derivative in which an $-O-K$ group is associated with each of the carbon atoms of the hexagon.

Carbon monoxide is absorbed by both acidic and ammoniacal solutions of copper(I) chloride.   The nature of the addition compound in the former medium is illustrated by the formula $CuCl \cdot CO \cdot 2H_2O$, and

[54] R. C. Sahni, *Trans. Faraday Soc.* 49, 1246 (1953).

[55] A. P. Altshuller, *J. Chem. Phys.* 23, 256 (1955).

[56] A. E. Douglas, *J. Phys. Chem.* 59, 109 (1955).

[57] M. S. Sodha, *Science and Culture* (India) 19, 45 (1953); J. G. Valatin, *Proc. Phys. Soc.* (*London*) 66A, 1185 (1953); T. E. Brackett, *J. Chem. Phys.* 24, 1103 (1956).

[58] K. Otozai, *Catalyst* (*Japan*) No. 9, 53 (1953); E. Gelles and K. S. Pitzer, *J. Am. Chem. Soc.* 75, 5259 (1953); D. A. Long and A. G. Thomas, *Proc. Royal Soc.* A223, 130 (1954).

$CuCl \cdot CO \cdot NH_3$ in the latter. Ammoniacal solutions absorb more completely than do hydrochloric acid solutions of CuCl and the reaction is utilized in the quantitative analysis of gaseous mixtures,[59] as well as the industrial separation of CO from $H_2$ in ammonia production.

An accurate method for the determination of small amounts of the gas involves its reaction with iodine pentoxide:

$$I_2O_5 + 5CO \rightarrow 5CO_2 + I_2$$

The amount of iodine liberated is determined by its reaction with a standard solution of sodium thiosulfate, and from this result the weight of carbon monoxide is calculated.

Direct combination of carbon monoxide and chlorine takes place in sunlight, or in the presence of a charcoal catalyst, to form carbonyl chloride (phosgene), $COCl_2$. A strongly exothermic reaction takes place when carbon monoxide is burned to the dioxide:

$$2CO + O_2 \rightarrow 2CO_2 + 135,400 \text{ cal}$$

The equilibrium constants for this system have been determined at 1 atmosphere pressure over the temperature range 1205° to 2843°C. The value at the former temperature is $10^{-12.85}$ and for the latter $10^{-1.96}$. At 2606°C the value for K is $10^{-3.00}$ and the degree of dissociation of the carbon dioxide to carbon monoxide is 51.7/100. Above 5000°C, carbon dioxide is almost completely dissociated into CO and oxygen. Equilibrium constants have similarly been reported for the reaction $CO + H_2O \rightleftharpoons CO_2 + H_2$. The values of K at 700°C, 800°C, 830°C, 1000°C, 1200°C, and 1300°C are, respectively, 0.60, 0.90, 1.0, 1.7, 2.6, and 3.45. From these values of K it may be assumed that above 830°C the hydrogen gas is the stronger reducing agent, and below this temperature CO is the stronger.[60]

The reaction between carbon monoxide and hydrogen catalyzed by nickel, cobalt, or iron serves as a basis for the production of very substantial amounts of hydrocarbons. The reaction (Fischer-Tropsch) varies depending upon the catalysts used. On cobalt and nickel it is suggested that the reaction, $CO + 2H_2 \rightarrow (CH_2) + H_2O$, takes place. With iron catalysts a secondary water-gas shift reaction occurs between the water formed and the chemisorbed CO, producing $CO_2$. The formation of $CH_4$ is probably independent of the main hydrocarbon synthesis

[59] K. Onda *et al.*, *J. Chem. Soc. Japan, Ind. Chem. Sect.* **57**, 415 (1954); *ibid.*, *J. Fuel Soc. Japan* **34**, 418 (1955).

[60] H. Remy, *Treatise on Inorganic Chemistry*, Elsevier Publishing Co., 1956, Vol. I, p. 444.

being governed by the active point sites on the catalyst surface. The main reaction is: $2CO + 2H_2 \rightarrow CH_4 + CO_2$. There is probably no carbide intermediate formation insofar as the catalytic reaction is concerned since carbides themselves do not act in a catalytic capacity.[61]

Alcohols are also formed in the above described hydrocarbon syntheses. It is assumed that these alcohols are absorbed on the catalyst, acting as intermediates.[62] At 180° to 280°C and 3000 atmospheres polyhydric alcohols and their derivatives are formed.[63]

Carbon monoxide reacts with ozone in the presence of metals (as silver) according to the following:

$$O_3 + (Ag) \rightarrow O \text{ (bound)} + O_2 \qquad (1)$$

$$O_3 + O \text{ (bound)} \rightarrow Ag + 2O_2 \qquad (2)$$

$$CO + O \text{ (bound)} \rightarrow Ag + CO_2 \qquad (3)$$

Step (1) is slow in contrast to (2) and (3) which have $k$ values of about the same order of magnitude. It is also reported that the reaction mixture of oxygen and nitrogen with small amounts of ozone proceeds as $CO + O + (M) \rightarrow CO_2 + (M)$. Only small amounts of $CO_2$ are formed. No activation energy is needed, and there is a $CO_2$ molecule formed for every 1000th three-body collision.[64]

**Carbon Suboxide, $C_3O_2$.** Malonic acid, $CH_2(COOH)_2$, may be dehydrated with phosphorus pentoxide to give a colorless gas (boiling point 7°C and melting point −107°C) analyzing as $C_3O_2$. When very pure this oxide is fairly stable, but when impure it polymerizes giving a red amorphous substance. The oxide reacts with Grignard reagents to give a mixture of ketones.[65] The infrared bond intensities have been measured. The set of values calculated[66] are $\partial\mu_{CO}/\partial r_{CO} = \pm 8.80 \times 10^{-10}$, $\partial\mu_{CC}/\partial r_{CC} = \pm 5.34 \times 10^{-10}$ cm. Liquid phase Raman measurements indicate a linear model, but the infrared spectrum is not explainable with such a structure. It is presumed that the oxygen atoms are bent out of

[61] H. Kolbel, *Brennstoff-Chem.* **35**, 161 (1954); P. H. Emmett and J. T. Kummer, *Proc. 3rd World Petroleum Cong.* **4**, 15 (1951).

[62] Brit. 689,214, Mar. 25, 1953; C. C. Hall, *Gas World* **139**, No. 3629 *Coking Sect.* 49–54, 60 (1954); H. G. McGrath, U.S. 2,637,739, May 5, 1953.

[63] W. F. Gresham, U.S. 2,636,046, Apr. 21, 1953; Brit. 682,826, Nov. 19, 1952; J. T. Kummer and P. H. Emmett, *J. Am. Chem. Soc.* **75**, 5177 (1953); N. G. Basak and K. K. Bhattacharya, *J. Inst. Fuel* **27**, 195 (1954).

[64] D. Garvin, *J. Am. Chem. Soc.* **76**, 1523, 1581 (1954).

[65] D. J. Cram and R. L. Zimmerman, *J. Am. Chem. Soc.* **74**, 2646 (1952).

[66] R. L. Williams, *J. Chem. Phys.* **22**, 345 (1954).

line with the carbon atoms in a zigzag plane configuration. The O–C–C bond angle is presumed to be 158°C.[67]

**Physiological Action.** Carbon monoxide is *very poisonous*. It is classed as a treacherous poison because it lacks taste and odor to give warning of its presence. Thus, persons exposed to relatively high concentrations of the gas may be rendered unconscious without becoming aware of danger. Unpleasant symptoms, such as headache and nausea, are produced upon breathing air containing 9 parts of the monoxide in 10,000 over a period of an hour; a concentration of 100 parts in 10,000 (1%) is dangerous in ten minutes. The A.S.A. in cooperation with the U. S. Public Health Service sets the limit of CO concentration for 8 hours daily exposure at 100 parts CO per million parts of air.

Exhaust gas from automobiles is a most dangerous source of carbon monoxide. A small car with its engine idling in a closed one-car garage may yield enough monoxide to cause death in *six minutes*. Deaths resulting from the inhalation of illuminating gas are generally caused by the carbon monoxide which it contains.

The action of carbon monoxide as a poison depends upon its property of forming a rather stable combination with hemoglobin, the oxygen-carrying substance of the blood. Thus the oxygen-absorbing capacity of the blood may be reduced to such an extent that the supply of oxygen for life processes is insufficient. Small animals and birds, such as canaries, are more susceptible to this type of poisoning than humans. Therefore, these birds were frequently used to warn rescue workers of the dangerously high concentrations of carbon monoxide which may be present after a mine disaster. A *chemical* test for the gas takes advantage of the green color it produces with a mixture of iodine pentoxide and fuming sulfuric acid absorbed in pumice (hoolamite). Another means of detecting carbon monoxide is by the black color it imparts to a solution of palladium(II) chloride. The latter may be soaked up on filter paper.

Carbon monoxide is adsorbed but very little by the charcoal in the ordinary gas mask. A special mask has been devised in which hopcalite, a mixture of metallic oxides, such as $Ag_2O$, $Co_2O_3$, $MnO_2$, and $CuO$, is employed to catalyze the oxidation of carbon monoxide to dioxide at ordinary temperatures. Masks of this type afford complete protection.

**Carbonyl Halides.** *Carbonyl chloride* or *phosgene* results when carbon monoxide unites with chlorine in direct sunlight. The compound is more conveniently prepared by leading a mixture of the two gases at about 125°C over porous charcoal which acts as a catalyst. The exo-

---

[67] H. D. Rix, *ibid.*, 429; D. A. Long *et al.*, *Proc. Royal Soc.* **A223**, 251 (1954).

thermic reaction is simply represented as

$$CO + Cl_2 \rightarrow COCl_2 + 26.2 \text{ kcal}$$

The gas is highly poisonous with a boiling point of 7.56°C, a melting point of $-118.8$°C, density of 1.41 at 4°C, a critical temperature and pressure of 182°C and 56 atmospheres, respectively.   On hydrolysis carbonic acid is formed slowly as well as HCl.   The low solubility of phosgene accounts for the slow reaction.   On ammonolysis phosgene is converted to urea.

$$COCl_2 + 2NH_3 \rightarrow CO(NH_2)_2 + 2HCl$$

*Carbonyl fluoride* is prepared by the action of silver(II) fluoride on carbon monoxide.   The substance is a colorless, pungent-smelling gas with a boiling point of $-83.1$°C and a melting point of $-114.0$°C.   Its reaction with water is much more vigorous than that of phosgene, giving carbon dioxide and HF.[68]

Resonance structures of carbonyl halides (x–CO–y) are summarized as:

$$\begin{array}{ccc} \overset{x}{\underset{y}{\diagdown}}C\equiv O^+ & \overset{x}{\underset{y}{\diagdown}}C=O & \overset{x}{\underset{y}{\diagdown}}C^+\!\!-\!O^- \\ \text{I} & \text{II} & \text{III} \end{array}$$

The carbonyl vibration frequency has been shown to vary linearly with the arithmetic sum of the electronegativities of x and y.   The structure I predominates when x or y is strongly electronegative.[69]

[68] Remy, *op. cit.*, p. 450.
[69] R. E. Kogarise, *J. Am. Chem. Soc.* **77**, 1377 (1955).

# CHAPTER 2

## SILICON AND ITS SIMPLE COVALENT COMPOUNDS

### BY HAROLD P. KLUG

*Mellon Institute, Pittsburgh, Pa.*

**Introduction.** The chemistry of silicon is modern chemistry. The infusibility of silicon and the silicates, and their general resistance to attack by reagents, greatly retarded the development of the chemistry of silicon. Not until the discovery of hydrofluoric acid, HF, by Scheele[1] in 1771 was a convenient reagent available for studying silicon compounds, and even after this date progress was very slow. Another retarding factor was the great complexity of the natural silicates. The complete systematization of the chemistry and structure of the silicates has been one of the triumphs of modern crystal chemistry. Silicon is one of the most important elements in modern civilization, and new chapters in its chemistry are being written today.

Silicon, the element immediately below carbon in Group IV, stands midway between the more positive metallic elements on its left in the periodic table and the more negative nonmetallic elements on its right. In general, the Group IV elements partake of the properties of both the metals and the nonmetals. However, since positive character within a family increases with increasing atomic weight, silicon should show little if any base-forming tendency. It is, in fact, feebly acidic and forms weak acids. Salts of these acids are of great importance in the mineral kingdom. Truly, silicon may be said to be the *central element* of the inorganic world, just as carbon may be looked upon as holding a similar position in the realm of living things.

Common rocks of the earth's crust are all siliceous with the exception of limestone and dolomite. They are the structural material of which the earth, with its elevations and depressions, is built. Chains of carbon atoms—straight, branched, and ringlike—make up the framework of the organic world. Simple and complex silicates constitute the greater portion of the solid exterior of the earth. After oxygen, silicon is the most abundant element and makes up nearly 28% of the earth's crust.

**History.** Compounds of silicon have been of great importance from antiquity. Implements made from flint, a variety of silicon dioxide,

[1] C. W. Scheele, *Handl. Svenska. Akad.* **33**, 120 (1771).

were among early man's first tools and weapons.   The manufacture of
glass from silicates dates back to ancient times.   In the seventeenth
century, it was found that silica, then infusible, formed a fusible glass
when heated with other oxides.   Davy[2] was unsuccessful in attempts to
prepare the element in 1809.   In this same year, however, it is probable
that Gay Lussac and Thénard[3] obtained amorphous silicon from the
reaction of potassium and silicon tetrafluoride, $SiF_4$, but they failed to
make any examination of the brown powder obtained in the reaction.
The credit for the first preparation of the element, therefore, usually goes
to Berzelius,[4] who produced it by reducing potassium fluosilicate, $K_2SiF_6$,
with potassium.   He also prepared it from potassium and silicon tetrafluoride by following the procedure of Gay Lussac and Thénard.   His
product was impure amorphous silicon with which he determined its
chief properties.   Crystalline silicon was first prepared by Sainte-Claire
Deville[5] in 1854 by crystallization from solutions in molten aluminum.
Shining platelets remained when the aluminum was dissolved away with
acid.   Despite the metallic luster of the crystalline silicon he realized it
was not a true metal.

**Occurrence.**   Silicon never occurs free in nature.   In combination it
is found in a great variety of substances.   Its most abundant compound
is the oxide, $SiO_2$, commonly known as silica, which exists in many more
or less pure varieties (Table 2.1).[6]   Rock crystal, tridymite, and cristobalite are essentially pure silica, $SiO_2$, while the remaining varieties are
more or less impure.   Small amounts of inorganic or organic materials
impart the colors characteristic of many varieties.   In impure frag-
mentary form, silica is common in sand, quartzite, quartzose sandstone,
and quartz-conglomerate.   Pseudomorphous quartz appears in the forms
of many common mineral species, which it has taken through either the
alteration or replacement of crystals of those minerals.   Petrified or
silicified wood is a quartz pseudomorph of wood.

Silica also occurs in the bodies of plants and animals.   It is present
in the ashes of plants; barley, oats, bamboo, and tobacco contain an
appreciable percentage of silica.   The feathers of some birds contain up
to 40 per cent of silica, and sponges and certain other aquatic organisms

[2] H. Davy, *Phil. Trans.* **100**, 16 (1810).

[3] J. L. Gay Lussac and L. J. Thénard, *Recherches Physico-Chimiques* (Paris) **1**, 313
(1811); **2**, 55 (1811); *Ann. Chim. Phys.* (1) **69**, 204 (1809).

[4] J. J. Berzelius, *Gilbert's Ann.* **36**, 89 (1810); *Pogg. Ann.* **1**, 169 (1824).

[5] H. Sainte-Claire Deville, *Compt. rend.* **39**, 321 (1854).

[6] For more detailed information on the various varieties of silica, see E. S. Dana and
W. E. Ford, *A Textbook of Mineralogy*, 4th Edition, John Wiley and Sons, Inc., New
York, 1932.

have skeletons rich in silica. Diatoms and infusoria, when they die, leave their siliceous skeletons on the bottom of the sea as fine-grained, porous silica known as tripolite, kieselguhr, or diatomaceous earth. Such deposits are found in the United States, Denmark, Algeria, and Germany. The material has wide use as a polishing agent and as an adsorbent.

Rocks of the earth's crust are occasionally simple silicates, but usually they are aggregates of minerals. For example, granite is a mixture of quartz, feldspar, and mica. These minerals are usually very stable compounds. At high temperatures the acidic nature of silica increases, and it combines with metallic oxides to form a great variety of silicates.

TABLE 2.1. VARIETIES OF SILICA

| Phenocrystalline (Crystallized, vitreous in luster) | Cryptocrystalline (Flintlike, massive) | Amorphous (Colloidal) |
|---|---|---|
| Quartz (rock crystal) | Chalcedony | Opal (several varieties) |
| Tridymite | Carnelian | Hyalite |
| Cristobalite | Chrysoprase | Siliceous sinter |
| Amethyst | Plasma | Geyserite |
| Rose, yellow, smoky, and milk quartz | Agate | Float-stone |
| | Onyx | Tripolite |
| | Sardonyx | |
| Star-, and sapphire-quartz | Siliceous sinter | |
| | Flint | |
| Sagentic quartz | Hornstone | |
| | Chert | |
| Aventinine | Basanite | |
| Cat's-eye | Jasper | |

Some important natural silicates are the following: garnet, $Ca_3Al_2(SiO_4)_3$; zircon, $ZrSiO_4$; olivine, $(Mg,Fe)_2SiO_4$; topaz, $(AlF)_2SiO_4$; beryl $Be_3Al_2Si_6O_{18}$; asbestos, $H_4Mg_3Si_2O_9$; micas, such as $KAl_2(AlSi_3O_{10})(OH)_2$; talc, $Mg_3(Si_4O_{10})(OH)_2$; zeolites, such as natrolite, $Na_2(Al_2Si_3O_{10})\cdot2H_2O$; feldspars, such as orthoclase, $(K,Na)AlSi_3O_8$; and clay minerals, such as kaolinite, $Al_2Si_2O_5(OH)_4$.

Many silicates have important uses in their native form, as clay and feldspar in the ceramic industry. Because of their great stability, they are seldom used as sources of the metals they contain. An example to the contrary is the mineral calamine, $Zn_2SiO_4\cdot H_2O$, which is an important source of zinc.

**Preparation of Silicon.**   The element is difficult to prepare, because of the great affinity it shows toward oxygen and other nonmetals.   The standard heats of formation, $\Delta H_f^0$, listed in Table 2.2 illustrate the great stability of its commoner binary compounds.[7]   Consequently, the element is set free only under powerful reducing conditions, and only very limited application of direct decomposition methods can be made.   Potassium, sodium, or aluminum at high temperatures reduces silicon tetrachloride or potassium fluosilicate:

$$SiCl_4 + 4Na \rightarrow Si + 4NaCl$$
$$K_2SiF_6 + 4K \rightarrow Si + 6KF$$

TABLE 2.2.   HEATS OF FORMATION OF BINARY COMPOUNDS OF SILICON

| Compound | Physical State | $\Delta H_f^0$ (kcal/mole) |
|---|---|---|
| $SiF_4$ | Gas | −370* |
| $SiCl_4$ | Gas | −145.7 |
| $SiBr_4$ | Liquid | −95.1 |
| $SiI_4$ | Solid | −31.6 |
| $SiO_2$ (α quartz) | Solid | −205.4 |
| $SiH_4$ | Gas | −14.8 |
| $SiC$ | Solid | −26.7 |
| $Si_3N_4$ | Solid | −179.3 |
| $SiS_2$ | Solid | −34.7 |

* The negative sign indicates that heat is evolved in the process.

During either reduction, oxygen must be excluded.   The fused mass, after cooling, is extracted with water to dissolve the soluble salt from the brown silicon powder.

A commoner method is the reduction of silica by magnesium, aluminum, or carbon.   When fine sand and magnesium powder are mixed and heated, two vigorous reactions take place:

$$4Mg + SiO_2 \rightarrow Mg_2Si + 2MgO$$

and

$$2Mg + SiO_2 \rightarrow Si + 2MgO$$

The cooled mixture is treated with hydrochloric acid to decompose the silicide ($Mg_2Si$) and to remove magnesium oxide.   The silicon is left as a brown powder.   The use of aluminum for the reduction produces crystalline silicon, through crystallization in the excess of molten aluminum.

[7] From F. D. Rossini, D. D. Wagman, W. H. Evans, S. Levine, and I. Jaffe, "Selected Values of Chemical Thermodynamic Properties," *N.B.S. Circular 500*, U. S. Government Printing Office, Washington 25, D. C., 1952.

At the high temperature (3100°F) of the electric furnace, silicon dioxide is reduced by carbon:

$$SiO_2 + 2C \rightarrow Si + 2CO$$

This reaction[8] has since developed into the present large-scale commercial process. The raw materials are sand and coke, and the current is introduced through carbon electrodes. Liquid silicon is tapped from the bottom of the furnace and cast into pigs of 600 to 800 lb. A product of 97 to 98% purity is produced by this method at Niagara Falls. An excess of carbon, under the same conditions, leads to the formation of silicon carbide, SiC. When an excess of silica is present, any carbide formed reacts with additional silica to form silicon and carbon monoxide:

$$2SiC + SiO_2 \rightarrow 3Si + 2CO$$

By reducing a mixture of iron oxide and silica by this method, an important alloy known as ferrosilicon is obtained. Calcium carbide will also reduce silica:

$$3SiO_2 + 2CaC_2 \rightarrow 3Si + 2CaO + 4CO$$

Certain metallic silicides can be used for the preparation of silicon. Copper silicide is reduced when heated with sulfur, yielding a sulfide of copper and free silicon. The weakly exothermic silane, $SiH_4$, burns readily in the air and leaves a residue of silicon. By allowing the flame of the burning hydride to impinge on a cold surface an amorphous deposit of the element is obtained.

Silicon can also be produced by decomposition methods. Only the less stable compounds, such as $SiH_4$, $SiI_4$, and SiC, come into consideration for such methods. Some silicon is produced as a by-product during the manufacture of graphite by the Acheson process, the silicon resulting from the decomposition of silicon carbide, SiC, at the high temperature of the process. Its decomposition temperature is reported to be from 2200° to 2240°C. The carbon residue is left with the crystalline form of the silicon carbide, while the silicon volatilizes and sublimes onto the interior of the furnace. Silicon can be obtained by the direct decomposition of silane and other hydrides, either through the action of heat or a spark discharge. van Arkel[9] has discussed the preparation of pure silicon by the decomposition of $SiH_4$, $SiI_4$, and mixtures of hydrogen and $SiCl_4$ in contact with a hot wire.

[8] H. N. Potter, **U.S. 875,285** (1907); **875,672** (1907); **908,130** (1908); *Chem. and Eng. News* **33**, 1948 (1955).

[9] A. E. van Arkel, *Reine Metalle*, Julius Springer, Berlin, 1939, pp. 478–481.

The preparation of high purity silicon has received increasing emphasis because of its use in the fabrication of transistors and solar "batteries." As early as 1927, Tucker[10] succeeded in obtaining the element in 99.94% purity by dissolving the impurities from the pulverized material with suitable solvents. Kroll[11] purified the element by high vacuum distillation. A sample of 99.97% purity was prepared by Lyon, Olson, and Lewis,[12] who reduced silicon tetrachloride with zinc vapor at 950°C. Under these conditions the zinc chloride formed was volatilized, and metallic gray crystals of silicon were obtained. Metallic impurities totaled not over 0.001%, but carbon was present to about 0.03%. Ultra-pure silicon has been obtained by the "zone melting" process.[13,14] An ingot of high purity silicon is drawn through a long, gas filled, quartz tube (Fig. 2.1). Heat from a series of induction coils melts the element

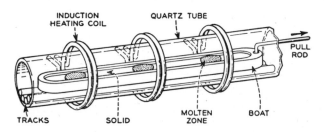

FIG. 2.1. Schematic diagram of the zone melting technique. (*Schumacher, loc. cit.*)

in narrow zones. The impurities, being more soluble in the liquid, remain in the high-temperature zone and are swept to the end of the ingot. The method is capable of reducing the concentration of impurities to the part-per-billion range.

Most silicon is marketed as ferrosilicon, which as the 50-50 alloy is priced at $0.124 per lb of Si, delivered, in carload lots. Silicon of 97% purity sells for $0.185 per lb. Semiconductor grade silicon (very pure) is available at $430 per pound.[15]

**Physical Properties.** The brown powder, known as amorphous silicon, has been shown by X-ray diffraction to be crystalline and to differ

[10] N. P. Tucker, *J. Iron Steel Inst.* **115**, 412 (1927).
[11] W. Kroll, *Metallwirtsch.* **13**, 725 (1934).
[12] D. W. Lyon, C. M. Olson, and E. D. Lewis, *J. Electrochem. Soc.* **96**, 359 (1949).
[13] W. G. Pfann, *J. Metals* **4**, *Trans.*, 747 (1952).
[14] E. E. Schumacher, *ibid.* **5**, 1428 (1953).
[15] D. W. Lyon, *Silicon*, Chap. 19 of *Rare Metals Handbook*, C. A. Hampel, Editor, Reinhold Publishing Corp., New York, 1954, p. 379.

only in its finer state of subdivision from crystalline silicon. When a very slightly volatile and insoluble material, such as silicon, is separated from a medium in which its parent substance was distributed, it produces no easily discernible crystals because the primary particles formed cannot orient themselves as they are set free. The material at first is in a molecular state of subdivision, and finally deposits a dust with only slight orientation. The resulting powder is termed amorphous. Crystals result only when a substance is produced by solution, distillation, or from the melt. An example is the formation of crystals of silicon through crystallization from aluminum. It is reported[16] that amorphous silicon transforms to crystalline silicon in the temperature range of 650° to 750°C.

Massive silicon is a brittle, gray-black, metallic-appearing solid. Its crystals are octahedral, with the diamond type of lattice, and are transparent when in thin sheets. Single crystals can be grown from the melt by the usual controlled cooling, seeding, and withdrawal techniques. The high surface tension of molten silicon, 720 dynes/cm,[17] makes possible a novel method for producing single crystals of exceptionally high purity. In the "floating zone" technique[18] a zone of molten silicon is held stable between two vertically aligned solid silicon rods clamped at the ends, thus eliminating the need for a container for the melt. The rods may be made up of irregular pieces of silicon welded together, or may be pressed from powdered silicon. Heating is supplied by high-frequency induction from outside the cylindrical vacuum chamber surrounding the rods. The liquid zone is pushed slowly along the rod, melting new silicon on the advancing side and crystallizing the material in its wake. Several passes must be made, always in the same direction. With each pass the single-crystal areas increase in size, and single crystals up to 10 cm in length have been prepared. The successive zone melting also effects a certain amount of purification in most samples during the growth process.[13,14] Single-crystal silicon fibers or "whiskers" may be prepared by the reaction of silicon tetrachloride and zinc vapor in a carrier gas (argon or hydrogen) at 800° to 1000°C.[19]

Silicon crystallizes in the diamond structure type (Fig. 2.2) in which each atom is tetrahedrally surrounded by four other atoms to which it is bound by covalent bonds. Each atom contributes one of its four valence electrons to each of the four bonds, and the pair of electrons in

[16] H. Krebs, *Angew. Chem.* **65**, 293 (1953).

[17] P. H. Keck and W. Van Horn, *Phys. Rev.* **91**, 512 (1953).

[18] P. H. Keck, *Physica* **20**, 1059 (1954); P. H. Keck, W. Van Horn, J. Soled, and A. MacDonald, *Rev. Sci. Instruments* **25**, 331 (1954).

[19] E. R. Johnson and J. A. Amick, *J. Appl. Phys.* **25**, 1204 (1954).

the bond is shared equally by the two atoms at its end.   The highly pure and perfect crystal would thus be an insulator, and, indeed, its dielectric constant is 12, nearly as high as that of diamond, and its intrinsic resistivity is $6.36 \times 10^4$ ohm cm.[20]   Most interest in the electronic field centers

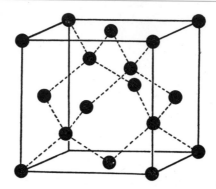

Fig. 2.2.   Crystal structure of diamond and silicon.

around slightly impure silicon crystals.   The chemical impurities are introduced in controlled amounts and are of two kinds, known as donors and acceptors.   Typical donor elements are the members of Group V$A$, such as antimony and arsenic.   Antimony or arsenic atoms, when present in a silicon crystal, substitute themselves in place of silicon atoms in the lattice.   Since an arsenic atom has five valence electrons, it has one too many electrons for its share of the bonds in the silicon lattice.   This becomes an excess electron which wanders throughout the crystal.   Correspondingly there is a localized excess positive charge of $+1$ at the position of the substituting arsenic atom.   Such a specimen containing a relatively large number (typically $10^{15}$ per cc) of donor atoms is known as $n$-type silicon.   It is a semiconductor, and the current is carried by the excess unbound electrons.   Aluminum, gallium, and other Group III$A$ elements are typical acceptors for silicon.   When the trivalent aluminum atom substitutes for a silicon atom there is a deficiency of one electron for the formation of four covalent bonds to the surrounding silicon atoms.   There will thus be a *hole* at one of the bonds which may be filled by migration of an electron from a near-by bond.   This leaves a localized negative charge at the point of the acceptor atom and a hole at the position of the bond which set free the electron.   The behavior of the hole simulates that of the excess electron in the $n$-type material,

[20] E. M. Conwell, *Proc. Inst. Radio Eng.* **40**, 1327 (1952).

except for its positive charge. A specimen of this kind is $p$-type silicon, and it has $p$-type conductivity since the charge carriers are positive. A single crystal may be $p$-type in one region and $n$-type in another, in which case the $p$-$n$ boundary or junction between the two regions has special electrical and optical properties. For additional properties of $n$- and $p$-type silicon, the reader is referred to Conwell's excellent summary.[20]

Straumanis and Aka[21] obtained for the lattice constant of 99.97% pure silicon[12] at 25°C the value $a = 5.43097 \pm 0.00003$ A. This same study gave the density at 20°C (determined by the suspension method) as $2.32831 \pm 0.00031$ g/cm³. The linear thermal expansion coefficient in the range 10° to 50°C is $\alpha = 4.15 \times 10^{-6}/°C$ (see also Table I.1). Straumanis' very precise X-ray and density data lead to a value of $28.083 \pm 0.013$ for the atomic weight. This is to be compared with the chemical value 28.09 recommended by the International Commission of Atomic Weights in September, 1951. Silicon is hard enough to scratch glass (Mohs scale 7), melts at 1420°C, and boils at 2600°C. Its latent heat of fusion is 11.1 kcal/mole, and its latent heat of vaporization at the boiling point is 71.0 kcal/mole. For the range 18.2° to 99.1°C its specific heat has the value 0.181. The critical pressure and critical temperature have been calculated to be 1450 atmospheres and 4920°C, respectively.[22] Silicon's vapor pressure measured in millimeters of mercury is 1 at 1920°K, 10 at 2120°K, and 100 at 2360°K. Its thermal conductivity at 20°C is 0.20 cal/sec cm °C. Table 2.3 presents additional thermodynamic data, and Table 2.4 lists several mechanical properties[15,20] of silicon.

Silicon (atomic number 14) has three stable isotopes (see also Table I.4) and three radioactive isotopes. Of the stable isotopes $^{28}$Si makes up 92.27% of the element, $^{29}$Si is present in 4.68% abundance, and $^{30}$Si in 3.05%. Four of the isotopes have had their nuclear masses measured:[23] $^{28}$Si = 27.9858, $^{29}$Si = 28.9857, $^{30}$Si = 29.9833, $^{31}$Si = 30.9851. Spin moments of the three stable isotopes are 1, $\frac{1}{2}$, 1, respectively. The favorable spin moment of $\frac{1}{2}$ for $^{29}$Si makes nuclear magnetic resonance studies of silicon compounds possible in spite of the low abundance of $^{29}$Si.[24] The proton resonance shifts of organosilicon compounds are large enough for easy analysis of silicones in organic solvents, and direct studies of $^{29}$Si resonances also appear promising. The $n$-$m$-$r$ frequency of $^{29}$Si in megacycles for a 10 kgauss field is 8.460. Its relative sensitivity for equal

[21] M. E. Straumanis and E. Z. Aka, *J. Appl. Phys.* **23**, 330 (1952).

[22] Hampel, *loc. cit.*

[23] C. W. Li, *Phys. Rev.* **88**, 1038 (1952); K. Ogata and H. Matsuda, *ibid.* **89**, 27 (1953).

[24] *Technical Information Bulletin*, Varian Associates, Palo Alto, California, Vol. 1, Nos. 2 and 3.

TABLE 2.3.  ENTROPY, FREE ENERGY, AND HEAT CONTENT OF SILICON*

| Temperature (°K) | Entropy (cal/mole°K) | Free Energy $[-(F - H_{298})/T]$ (cal/mole°K) | Heat Content $(H_T - H_{298})$ (kcal/mole) |
|---|---|---|---|
| **Solid silicon** | | | |
| 298............... | 4.50 | 4.50 | — |
| 500............... | 7.58 | 5.46 | 1.06 |
| 1000............... | 11.85 | 7.70 | 4.15 |
| 1500............... | 15.48 | 10.56 | 7.37 |
| **Liquid silicon** | | | |
| 2000............... | 23.75 | 12.29 | 22.92 |
| **Gaseous silicon** | | | |
| 298............... | 40.13 | 40.13 | — |
| 500............... | 42.76 | 40.63 | 1.065 |
| 1000............... | 46.14 | 42.55 | 3.60 |
| 1500............... | 48.20 | 44.12 | 6.12 |
| 2000............... | 49.66 | 45.31 | 8.70 |

* From L. L. Quill, *The Chemistry and Metallurgy of Miscellaneous Materials*, McGraw-Hill Book Co., New York, 1950, pp. 13–39; see also Table I.2.

TABLE 2.4.  MECHANICAL PROPERTIES OF SILICON

| Quantity | Value |
|---|---|
| Elastic constant $C_{11}$........................... | 16.740 $\times$ 10¹¹ dynes/cm² |
| Elastic constant $C_{12}$........................... | 6.523 $\times$ 10¹¹ dynes/cm² |
| Elastic constant $C_{44}$........................... | 7.957 $\times$ 10¹¹ dynes/cm² |
| Volume compressibility........................ | 0.98 $\times$ 10⁻¹² cm²/dyne |
| Modulus of rupture............................ | 9,046 psi |
| Plasticity number............................. | 89.3 |
| Brinnell hardness............................. | 240 |

numbers of nuclei is $7.85 \times 10^{-2}$ at constant field, and 0.199 at constant frequency.  Magnetic moment measurements give $\mu = -0.5549$ nuclear magneton.[25]  Data on the properties of silicon's radioactive isotopes are summarized in Table I.4.

The total cross section of silicon for both slow and fast neutrons has been investigated over wide ranges of neutron energies.[26]  In the slow neutron range, 0.03 to 200.0 ev, the cross section is constant at 2.25

[25] *Nuclear Magnetic Resonance Table*, Varian Associates, Palo Alto, Calif., July 1953.
[26] For an excellent summary, see D. J. Hughes and J. A. Harvey, *Neutron Cross Sections*, Brookhaven National Laboratory, Upton, New York, 1955, 328 pp.  For sale by U. S. Government Printing Office, Washington 25, D. C.

barns.[27]   From 0.01 to 7.0 mev, the cross section varies irregularly,[28] reaching a minimum of 0.45 barn at 0.14 mev, and a maximum of 12 barns at 0.195 mev.   Values at 0.01 and 7.0 mev, however, are close to 1.8 to 1.9 barns.   At still higher energies the cross section decreases to 1.14 barns for 94.8 mev, and 0.93 barn at 107.9 mev.[29]

The interatomic distance in elemental silicon is 2.35 A, leading to an atomic radius of 1.175 A.   This is also the normal and tetrahedral covalent radius for silicon.   In intermetallic compounds of silicon its metallic radius depends upon the coordination number (CN) in accordance with Pauling's equation,[30]

$$R(1) - R(N) = 0.300 \log N,$$

where $R(1)$ is the single-bond radius, 1.175 A for silicon, and $N$ is the bond number, the quotient of the valence divided by the number of bonds. Thus $R(\text{CN}12)$ for silicon is 1.318 A.   The radius of the ion $Si^{+4}$ for CN6 is 0.41 A.[31]   Silicon's electronegativity on Pauling's scale is 1.8.   Skinner and Pritchard[32] have determined its electron affinity to be 2.2 ev.   The magnetic susceptibility for silicon with 0.085% iron is $-0.13 \times 10^{-6}$ cgs. Esaki's measurements[33] lead to $4.02 \pm 0.02$ ev for its work function.

The experimental value for the energy gap for silicon is 1.12 ev. Several investigators have attempted to calculate theoretically silicon's energy band structure,[34] but all of these lead to values of the energy gap higher than observed experimentally.   Huggins' early attempt to obtain a flame spectrum of silicon is of historical interest only.[35]   With increasing energy of excitation successive stages of ionization of the silicon atom take place, and several sets of optical spectra, Si I, Si II, Si III, etc., result.   Si I, for which the ionization potential is 8.149 v, is the arc spectrum of the neutral atom.   Lines of Si II, I.P. = 16.34 v, begin to appear in the vacuum arc.   The arc spectrum[36] data of early investi-

[27] L. J. Rainwater, W. W. Havens, Jr., J. R. Dunning, and C. S. Wu, *Phys. Rev.* **73**, 733 (1948).
[28] R. E. Fields and M. Walt, *ibid.* **83**, 479 (1951); G. Freier, M. Fulk, E. E. Lampi, and J. H. Williams, *ibid.* **78**, 508 (1950); R. Meier, R. Ricamo, P. Sherrer, and W. Zünti, *Helv. Phys. Acta* **26**, 451 (1953); N. Nereson and S. Darden, *Phys. Rev.* **89**, 775 (1953).
[29] V. Culler and R. W. Waniek, *Phys. Rev.* **95**, 585 (1954).
[30] L. Pauling, *J. Am. Chem. Soc.* **69**, 542 (1947).
[31] L. Pauling, *The Nature of the Chemical Bond*, Cornell University Press, Ithaca, New York, 2nd Edition, 1940, p. 346.
[32] H. A. Skinner and H. O. Pritchard, *Trans. Faraday Soc.* **49**, 1254 (1953).
[33] L. Esaki, *J. Phys. Soc. Japan* **8**, 347 (1953).
[34] J. F. Mullaney, *Phys. Rev.* **66**, 326 (1944); D. K. Holmes, *ibid.* **87**, 782 (1952); E. Yamaka and T. Sugita, *ibid.* **90**, 992 (1953).
[35] W. Huggins, *Proc. Roy. Soc.* **18**, 546 (1870).
[36] C. C. Kiess, *J. Res. Nat. Bur. Std.* **21**, 185 RP1124 (1938).

gators has been surveyed and their work extended by giving revised wavelengths and intensities for 400 lines between 1565 A in the ultra-violet and 12,270 A in the infrared. It is interesting that only a few lines lie in the visible region, and that the leading lines of Si I are strong in the solar spectrum. Si III and higher spectra of silicon are usually spark excited. The most sensitive lines of the silicon spectrum are listed in Table 2.6. Elaborate tables of the atomic energy levels from optical data,[37] and of the ultraviolet multiplets of silicon,[38] have been compiled.

TABLE 2.6. SENSITIVE LINES IN THE SPECTRUM OF SILICON*

| Wavelength (in A) | Intensities | | Sensitivity† |
|---|---|---|---|
| | Arc | Spark | |
| 3905.528 | 20 | 15 | — |
| 2881.578 | 500 | 400 | U1 |
| 2528.516 | 400 | 500 | U2 |
| 2516.123 | 500 | 500 | U3 |
| 2506.899 | 300 | 200 | U4 |

* From G. R. Harrison, *M.I.T. Wavelength Tables*, John Wiley and Sons, Inc., New York, 1939, p. 00.
† Sensitivity decreases in the order U1, U2, . . . etc.

High resistivity specimens of silicon absorb strongly in the visible and near infrared, and are relatively transparent over a range of the longer infrared wavelengths.[39] One process of absorption in silicon is through excitation of electrons from the valence band to the conduction band. The energy quanta required for this transition correspond to wavelengths in the visible and near infrared regions. The reflectance of polished commercial silicon in the visible region is 26 to 35%.[15] It is highest in the blue, and falls off rapidly toward the infrared. In the infrared[40] the reflectance is a nearly constant 0.30 from 2 to 10 $\mu$. The refractive index of silicon is reported to be 3.87.[41] Bond refractions of silicon in the following bonds are: Si–C, 2.52; Si–$C_{aryl}$, 2.93; Si–F, 1.7; Si–Cl, 7.11; Si–Br, 10.08; Si–Si, 5.89; Si–O, 1.80; Si–H, 3.17; Si–S, 6.14; Si–N, 2.16.[42]

[37] C. E. Moore, "Atomic Energy Levels," Vol. I, *N.B.S. Circular 467*, U. S. Government Printing Office, Washington 25, D. C., 1949, pp. 144–162.
[38] C. E. Moore, "An Ultraviolet Multiplet Table," *N.B.S. Circular 488*, Section 1, U. S. Government Printing Office, Washington 25, D. C., 1950, pp. 32–36.
[39] H. B. Briggs, *Phys. Rev.* **77**, 727 (1950).
[40] H. Y. Fan and M. Becker, *Semiconducting Materials*, Proc. Conf. Univ. Reading, 1951, pp. 132–139.
[41] H. von Wartenberg, *Ber. Physik. Ges.* **12**, 105 (1910).
[42] A. I. Vogel, W. T. Cresswell, and J. Leicester, *J. Phys. Chem.* **58**, 174 (1954).

**Chemical Properties.** Silicon is very inert at low temperatures, but is active when heated. It resembles carbon in many of its reactions and almost universally displays an oxidation state of four (see p. 5). Halogens attack it with the formation of such compounds as silicon tetrafluoride, $SiF_4$, and silicon tetrachloride, $SiCl_4$. At high temperatures it burns in air or oxygen to form the dioxide. Sulfur, nitrogen, carbon, boron, and many of the metals combine directly with it. Silicon does not react with acids, except a mixture of nitric and hydrofluoric acids. However, it readily dissolves in hot alkali solutions with the formation of silicates and hydrogen:

$$Si + 2OH^- + H_2O \rightarrow SiO_3^= + 2H_2$$

At red heat, silicon and steam slowly react with the liberation of hydrogen. Many oxides are reduced by silicon at high temperatures. This is the basis of the well-known Pidgeon process[43] for the reduction of magnesium from its oxide. Silicon readily alloys with a number of metals. With molten magnesium, copper, iron, nickel, and others, it forms silicides (Part II). With metals such as antimony, bismuth, gold, lead, silver, tin, and zinc, the alloys contain no compounds. Silicon separates from molten aluminum and silver as crystals on cooling.

**Uses.** When silicon was first produced at Niagara Falls as a by-product in the manufacture of silicon carbide, it had so few uses that no sale could be found for it. The uses of elemental silicon are still not numerous, and the industrial consumption of the free element is relatively small. Several of its uses, however, are extremely important.

One of the widest applications of silicon is in rectifiers and transistors. For rectifier crystals the silicon is melted and cast into an ingot in a vacuum furnace. Boron, aluminum, etc., are frequently introduced as "doping" agents during fusion. Discs are sawed from the ingot, ground to a flat surface, treated with HF, and heated. A conducting surface of nickel is then applied to the disc. A complete description of silicon rectifiers is given by Torrey and Whitmer.[44] The preparation of high purity single crystals of silicon for use in transistors was mentioned on page 64. An important factor in the increasing use of silicon in transistors is its high maximum operating temperature of about 250°C, as compared to 75°C for germanium. Silicon's availability is also a factor, even though

[43] L. M. Pidgeon, *Trans. Can. Inst. Mining Met.* 49, 621 (1946).
[44] H. C. Torrey and C. A. Whitmer, *Crystal Rectifiers*, McGraw-Hill Book Co., New York, 1948, pp. 301–330.

the rarer germanium is more easily purified.    Several detailed treatments of transistors are available.[45]

Another remarkable application of silicon is the solar "battery,"[46] a large-area silicon *p-n* photocell which transforms solar radiant energy directly into electrical energy without going through the heat stage.    All solar wavelengths shorter than 12,000 A are potentially useful for generating electron-hole pairs in silicon.    A 0.0001-in. layer of *p*-type silicon is formed over an *n*-type silicon base.    In the presence of this *p-n* junction barrier, the electron-hole pairs are separated and made to do work in an external circuit.    Cells delivering 60 watts per square meter of surface have been prepared.    This represents 6% conversion efficiency, a value far higher than for any similar device, and it appears that 10% efficiency is attainable.

Silicon can be mixed with ceramic materials or carbon and fired to form heat-resistant and refractory materials in which some of the silicon remains in elemental form.[47]    Chemical ware, pipes, and crucibles cast mainly of silicon have been patented.[48]    The element has been used as an antoxidation catalyst,[49] and as an electrode material in the electrometric titration of acids and bases.[50]    Silicon mirrors formed by electrodeposition find use in dentistry and other fields.[51]

Elemental silicon is the most abundant metal.    It is cheap, light in weight, corrosion- and heat-resistant; yet it finds very limited use. Primarily, this results from its complete lack of ductility, a deficiency there seems little prospect of overcoming, as well as a lack of technological information in its mechanical treatment.

Increasing amounts of silicon, however, are being used as raw material for the synthesis of silicones (Chapter 3), in the production of silicides and alloys of silicon, and as a deoxidizing agent for metals.    It is employed in the casting of steel, copper, and bronze to remove dissolved oxygen and thereby prevent flaws in the finished product.    In the form of the alloy ferrosilicon it is used in the production of about 90% of the steel made in this country.    The tremendous importance of ferrosilicon

[45] Transistor Issue, *Proc. Inst. Rad. Eng.* **40**, 1283–1603 (November, 1952); A. Coblenz and H. L. Owens, *Transistors: Theory and Applications*, McGraw-Hill Book Co., New York, 1955.

[46] D. M. Chapin, C. S. Fuller, and G. L. Pearson, *J. Appl. Phys.* **25**, 676 (1954); M. B. Prince, *ibid.* **26**, 534 (1955); A. Garrett, *J. Chem. Educ.* **33**, 446 (1956).

[47] H. Haeuber, **U.S. 1,916,836** (1933); E. G. Acheson, **U.S. 1,014,199** (1912).

[48] T. B. Allen, **U.S. 1,037,713** (1912); **1,073,560** (1913).

[49] C. Moureu, C. Dufraisse, and P. Laplagne, *Compt. rend.* **187**, 1266 (1928).

[50] Y. A. Boltunov and K. I. Isakova, *J. Gen. Chem.* (*U.S.S.R.*) **7**, 2838 (1937); Y. A. Boltunov and Z. P. Kozmina, *ibid.* **7**, 2899 (1937).

[51] E. D. Tillyer, **U.S. 1,278,521** (1918).

TABLE 2.7.  FERROSILICON—IMPORTS AND PRODUCTION, 1947–1951*

| Year | Imports (Short Tons, Silicon Content) | Production (Short Tons, Ferrosilicon) |
|---|---|---|
| 1947.................... | 2,141 | 769,653 |
| 1948.................... | 734 | 814,297 |
| 1949.................... | 931 | 647,981 |
| 1950.................... | 3,785 | 742,407 |
| 1951 (9 mos.)........... | 8,846 | 675,916 |

* Anonymous, *Iron Age* 169, (1), 434 (Jan. 3, 1952).

is evident from Table 2.7 listing imports and United States production for several years.  Normally only enough silicon is added to the steel to react completely with the dissolved oxygen, but occasionally enough is added to leave an excess of 0.1 to 5% dissolved in the steel, whereupon an alloy steel, known as silicon steel, is produced.  It has especially valuable properties for magnet and transformer cores.  An increase of silicon content to 10 to 15% produces an alloy with strong corrosion-resisting properties.  Duriron and Tantiron are trade names given to such alloys, used in making acid-resisting kettles, tubes, condensers, and other ware employed in chemical manufacture.  These alloys are very hard and brittle, and are very nearly acidproof.  Aluminum alloys containing up to 17% of silicon possess casting qualities superior to those of pure aluminum

**Silicon Dioxide.**  Reference has been made earlier to the great abundance and wide distribution of silicon dioxide in nature (page 60).  Because it is the source of silicon and most of the compounds of this element, and because of its very important uses in both its pure and impure forms, it deserves to be discussed first and at some length.

1. *Polymorphic forms of silicon dioxide.*  Pure $SiO_2$ exists in no less than 11 (and possibly as many as 15) distinct crystalline and vitreous forms and furnishes one of the most outstanding examples of polymorphism known.  Silica crystallizes as quartz, tridymite, and cristobalite.  Each of these forms in turn possesses a high ($\beta$) and low ($\alpha$) temperature modification.  Thus $\alpha$-quartz, stable at ordinary temperatures, passes into the $\beta$-modification at 575°C.  The latter is stable up to 870°C, at which temperature $\beta$-quartz ceases to be stable and changes into $\beta$-tridymite.  Finally, at 1470°C $\beta$-tridymite undergoes transition into $\beta$-cristobalite, which is stable to the melting point, 1710°C.  The room-temperature stable $\alpha$-tridymite changes at 117°C into the $\alpha'$-form

which, in turn, transforms at 163°C to the high-temperature $\beta$-form. Less pronounced temperature-inversion points at 210° and 475°C suggest the possible existence of two additional forms of tridymite.[52]   The $\alpha \rightleftharpoons \beta$ transition temperature for cristobalite is 218 $\pm$ 2°C.   Changes from low-temperature to high-temperature modifications, $\alpha \rightleftharpoons \beta$, for each form take place rapidly and reversibly.   Changes from one type to the other are extremely slow, and tridymite and cristobalite exist as minerals even though they are metastable at ordinary temperatures.   Silica is thus a geologist's thermometer, since it tells, in a way, from its forms something about previous temperature conditions of rock formation.

Coes[53] has reported a new, very dense form of $SiO_2$ having a specific gravity of 3.01 (quartz, 2.655) and insoluble in hydrofluoric acid.   It is formed at 750°C and 35,000 atmospheres and is metastable at ordinary temperatures and pressures.   Another new form of $SiO_2$, prepared by the oxidation of SiO at 1200° to 1400°C, crystallizes in the orthorhombic system and has a fibrous structure.[54]   Still another crystalline phase, obtained under hydrothermal conditions at 380° to 585°C and 5000 to 18,000 psi, has been tentatively named *keatite*.   This phase duplicates the helical structure of quartz, but in tetragonal symmetry instead of trigonal symmetry.[55]   Crystallographic data on silica are summarized in Table 2.8.   X-ray studies of vitreous silica show only a broad peak at 4.15 A and three weak and poorly resolved peaks corresponding to shorter spacings.[56]   Vitreous silica also has been observed to undergo a sharp reversible critical point in its compressibility curve at about 31 to 33 kilobars and a permanent condensation above 100 kilobars.[57]

2. *Structure of silica.*   In contrast to carbon dioxide, in which the unit of structure in the solid is the $CO_2$ molecule, the molecule of $SiO_2$ is nonexistent in its various forms.   Invariably a silicon atom is surrounded tetrahedrally by four oxygen atoms, and the $SiO_2$ tetrahedra are linked together by sharing the oxygen atoms at the corners between two tetrahedra.   The four crystalline forms of silica arise from different ways in which tetrahedra are linked together to form a three-dimensional network.

[52] J. B. Austin, *J. Am. Chem. Soc.* **76**, 6019 (1954).

[53] L. Coes, Jr., *Science* **118**, 131 (1953); R. B. Sosman suggests the name *coesite* for this new phase: *ibid.* **119**, 738 (1954).

[54] A. Weiss and A. Weiss, *Z. anorg. allgem. Chem.* **276**, 95 (1954).

[55] P. P. Keat, *Science* **120**, 328 (1954); Sosman, *loc. cit.*; P. A. Vaughn, J. Shropshire, and P. P. Keat, *Abstracts*, Am. Cryst. Assn. Meeting, Pasadena, Calif., June 27–July 2, 1955.

[56] B. E. Warren, H. Krutter, and O. Morningstar, *J. Am. Ceram. Soc.* **19**, 202 (1936).

[57] P. W. Bridgman, *Am. J. Sci.* **237**, 7 (1939); P. W. Bridgman and I. Simon, *J. Appl. Phys.* **24**, 405 (1953).

TABLE 2.8. CRYSTALLOGRAPHIC DATA ON SILICA

| Form of Silica | Symmetry | Space Group | Lattice Constants (in A) | $SiO_2$ per Cell |
|---|---|---|---|---|
| $\alpha$-Quartz[a] | Rhombohedral | $P3_121$, or $P3_221$ | $a = 4.913$ $c = 5.405$ (25°C) | 3 |
| $\beta$-Quartz[b] | Hexagonal | $P6_222$, or $P6_422$ | $a = 4.989$ $c = 5.446$ (575°C) | 3 |
| $\alpha$-Tridymite[b] | Orthorhombic | ? | $a = 9.88$ $b = 17.1$ $c = 16.3$ | 64 |
| $\beta$-Tridymite[b] | Rhombohedral or hexagonal | $P62c$, or $P6_3/mmc$ | $a = 5.03$ $c = 8.22$ (above 200°C) | 4 |
| $\alpha$-Cristobalite[c] | Tetragonal | $P4_12_12$, or $P4_32_12$ | $a = 4.971$ $c = 6.929$ (23°C) | 4 |
| $\beta$-Cristobalite[c] | Cubic | $Fd3m$ | $a = 7.143$ (541°C) | 8 |
| Fibrous[d] | Orthorhombic | $Icma$ | $a = 4.7$ $b = 5.1$ $c = 8.3$ | 4 |
| Keatite[e] | Tetragonal | $P4_12_12$, or $P4_32_12$ | $a = 7.46$ $c = 8.59$ | 12 |

[a] H. E. Swanson, R. K. Fuyat, and G. M. Ugrinic, *Nat. Bur. Stand. Circular 539*, Vol. III (1954).

[b] W. L. Bragg, *Atomic Structure of Minerals*, Cornell University Press, Ithaca, New York, 1937.

[c] W. Johnson and K. W. Andrews, *Trans. Brit. Ceram. Soc.* 55, 227 (1956).

[d] Weiss and Weiss, *loc. cit.*

[e] Vaughn *et al.*, *loc. cit.*

The difference between the high- and low-temperature forms of each mineral is entirely of another kind. The change from a high-temperature to a low-temperature form does not alter the mode of linking of the tetrahedra. Instead the tetrahedra are displaced and rotated without breaking any bonds. The resulting structure has a different symmetry. In all cases the symmetry of the high-temperature form is higher than that of the low-temperature modification. The relation between $\beta$-quartz which is hexagonal and $\alpha$-quartz which has only trigonal symmetry is readily observed in the diagrams of Fig. 2.3. A most interesting feature of the structure of $\alpha$-quartz is the grouping of the tetrahedra to form spirals along the $c$-axis. In right-handed quartz all of the spirals twist

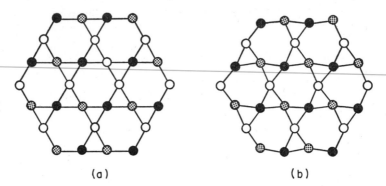

FIG. 2.3.   Symmetry relations between (a) $\beta$-quartz and (b) $\alpha$-quartz.   Silicon atoms only are shown.   (Bragg, *Atomic Structure of Minerals;* courtesy *Cornell University Press.*)

in the same direction, and in left-handed quartz in the opposite sense. Beta tridymite has hexagonal symmetry, and $\beta$-cristobalite is cubic.   The structure becomes more open in passing from quartz, tridymite, through keatite and to cristobalite as evidenced by their densities, 2.655, 2.501, 2.26, and 2.32 to 2.20, respectively.   The orthorhombic variety[54] has a density of only 1.97, melts at 1420°C, and probably contains infinite chains of $SiO_4$ tetrahedra in the direction of the $b$ axis, analogous to the chains in fibrous $SiS_2$ and $SiSe_2$ (page 103).   The Si–O distance in the tetrahedra is uniformly 1.60 ± 0.01 A,[58] except for fibrous silica where it appears to be somewhat larger.   Vitreous silica has a structure based on the $SiO_4$ tetrahedra of quartz, tridymite, and cristobalite but linked in a completely random three-dimensional network.[56]   The density of fused silica is 2.19 to 2.20.

3. *Optical, elastic, and electrical properties.*   The $\alpha$-form of quartz is uniaxial positive, with $N_\omega = 1.544$ and $N_\epsilon = 1.553$ for the D line.   Its optical rotatory power for a section 1 mm thick is 21.71° (D line).[59] Gutowsky[60] also has observed the optical rotation of quartz in the infrared from 2.2 to 9.7 $\mu$ and found anomalous rotatory dispersion at wavelengths longer than 3.7 $\mu$.   The refractive indices of $\beta$-quartz measured at 580°C are $N_\omega = 1.533$ and $N_\epsilon = 1.540$.   Tridymite in its $\alpha$-form is biaxial positive, its indices being $N_\alpha = 1.478$, $N_\beta = 1.479$, and $N_\gamma = 1.481$.   Alpha cristobalite is uniaxial negative, with $N_\omega = 1.487$ and $N_\epsilon = 1.484$.   The $\beta$-form of cristobalite, being cubic, is isotropic with $N = 1.466$.   Vitreous

[58] J. V. Smith, *Acta Cryst.* **7**, 479 (1954).
[59] Dana-Ford, *op. cit.*, p. 471.
[60] H. S. Gutowsky, *J. Chem. Phys.* **19**, 438 (1951).

silica, in the form of natural lechatelierite, has an index of $N = 1.458$.[61] Quartz twins according to four different laws briefly described by Bragg.[62] The intensity of light scattering by optical quality fused quartz has been found to be about 28% of that of pure dust-free ether.[63]

Numerous studies of the infrared spectrum have been made on the various crystalline varieties of silica and on fused silica, opal, and silica gel.[64] By means of reflection and absorption techniques the region from 2 to 24 $\mu$ has been investigated. The spectra of the various forms of silica are characterized by a strong band at 9.0 to 9.5 $\mu$ which is assigned as a valence stretching $\overline{Si}$–$\overline{O}$–$\overline{Si}$ vibration. Raman studies of $\alpha$-quartz at a variety of temperatures are reported in a review by Narayanaswamy.[65,66] Investigation of $\beta$-quartz has disclosed that its Raman frequencies are not greatly different from those of $\alpha$-quartz.[67] The Raman spectrum of vitreous silica excited by Hg 2536 A has been studied.[63,68]

An examination[69] of earlier data on the elastic constants of quartz, indicates that the best average values for the six elastic moduli are as follows:

| $C_{11}$ | $C_{33}$ | $C_{44}$ | $C_{12}$ | $C_{13}$ | $C_{14}$ | |
|------|-------|------|------|------|-------|---|
| 8.63 | 10.63 | 5.76 | 0.68 | 1.28 | $-1.76$ | all $\times 10^{11}$ dynes/cm$^2$ |

Elasticity data for vitreous silica are numerous.[70] Young's modulus, $C_{11}$, has a minimum value of 6.8–7.0 $\times 10^{11}$ dynes/cm$^2$ at 65°K. Its value at room temperature is about 7.30 $\times 10^{11}$ dynes/cm$^2$, and increases linearly by about 6% between 25° to 1000°C. The torsion or shear modulus at 65°K and 25°C is 3.04 $\times 10^{11}$ and 3.20 $\times 10^{11}$ dynes/cm$^2$.

---

[61] "Data on Chemicals for Ceramic Use," *National Research Council Bulletin No. 107*, National Academy of Sciences, Washington, D. C., 1943.

[62] Bragg, *op. cit.*, p. 86.

[63] R. S. Krishnan, *Proc. Indian Acad. Sci.* **37A**, 377 (1953).

[64] J. M. Hunt, M. P. Wisherd, and L. C. Bonham, *Anal. Chem.* **22**, 1478 (1950); W. Brügel, *Z. Physik* **128**, 255 (1950); I. Simon, *J. Opt. Soc. Am.* **41**, 336 (1951); I. Simon and H. O. McMahon, *J. Chem. Phys.* **21**, 23 (1953); M. Haccuria, *Bull. soc. chim. Belges* **62**, 428 (1953).

[65] P. K. Narayanaswamy, *Proc. Indian Acad. Sci.* **26A**, 521 (1947).

[66] C. V. Raman, *ibid.* **34A**, 61 (1951); J. P. Mathieu and L. Couture-Mathieu, *Compt. rend.* **234**, 1961 (1952).

[67] P. K. Narayanaswamy, *Proc. Indian Acad. Sci.* **28A**, 417 (1948); B. D. Saksena and H. Narain, *ibid.* **30A**, 128 (1949).

[68] M. Harrand, *Compt. rend.* **238**, 784 (1954).

[69] R. F. S. Hearmon, *Brit. J. Appl. Phys.* **3**, 120 (1952).

[70] For instance: R. S. Krishnan et al., *Current Sci.* **19**, 89 (1950); K. Vedam, *Phys. Rev.* **78**, 472 (1950); J. W. Marx and J. M. Sivertsen, *J. Appl. Phys.* **24**, 81 (1953); M. J. McSkimin, *ibid.* **24**, 988 (1953); M. E. Fine et al., *ibid.* **25**, 402 (1954).

Values of both moduli are independent of frequency.    Elastic constants of $SiO_2$ gel have been determined by an ultrasonic method.[71]

Quartz when cleaved with a knife in a vacuum of $10^{-4}$ to $10^{-5}$ mm Hg is reported to emit 120-kv electrons, whereas fused quartz does not show electron emission.[72]    Dielectric constant values for quartz vary from 3.8 to 5.0 for a wide range of frequencies.    Fused silica[73] has slightly lower values, 3.2 to 4.4.    The calculated dipole moment of silica is 1.0 debye, and the observed moment of the Si–O bond is 0.86 debye.    Most important of the electrical properties of quartz is its piezoelectricity.    By measurements of equivalent circuits of long thin bars driven electrically at frequencies near resonance, the piezoelectric constants $d_{11}$ and $d_{14}$ have been measured.[74]    For $\alpha$-quartz at 25°C, $d_{11} = 6.95 \times 10^{-8}$ and $d_{14} = -2.21 \times 10^{-8}$ cm/esu of potential.    Between room temperature and 571.5°C, $d_{11}$ decreases by about one half, whereas $d_{14}$ increases by a factor of three.    On further increase in temperature $\beta$-quartz appears at 573°C, and $d_{11}$ vanishes.    The value of $d_{14}$ for $\beta$-quartz then remains approximately constant at $-5.69 \times 10^{-8}$ cm/esu of potential over the range 584°–626°C.

4. *Color centers in silica.*    The coloring induced in quartz and vitreous silica by X-rays and nuclear radiations has received much attention.[75,76] Crystalline quartz becomes smoky in color on irradiation with X-rays, whereas vitreous specimens become violet.    Fast and slow neutrons and the $\gamma$-rays from $^{60}Co$ exert a similar action.[77]    The color is easily removed by heating the specimens to 350°–500°C.    Natural smoky quartz and amethyst probably received their coloration through long irradiation by neighboring or occluded radioactive minerals.    Evidence strongly supports the theory that these color centers are usually associated with the presence of impurities in the silica.[78,79]    Smoky quartz also exhibits a paramagnetic resonance spectrum whose intensity is proportional to the

[71] A. M. Srivastava, *Proc. Natl. Acad. Sci. India* **18A**, 51 (1949).

[72] N. A. Krotova and V. V. Karasev, *Doklady Akad. Nauk S.S.S.R.* **92**, 607 (1953).

[73] J. Takubo, *Mem. Coll. Sci. Kyoto Univ. Ser. B* **16**, 95 (1941); S. K. K. Jatkar and B. R. Y. Iyengar, *Indian J. Phys.* **23**, 145 (1949); G. D. Burdun, *Zhur. Tekh. Fiz.* **20**, 813 (1950); A. L. Khodakov, *ibid.* **20**, 529 (1950); W. L. de Keyser, *Rev. gen. sci. appl. (Brussels)* **1**, No. 3, 84 (1952); A. Pavlovic and R. Pepinsky, *J. Appl. Phys.* **25**, 1344 (1954).

[74] A. C. Lynch, *Proc. Phys. Soc. (London)* **63B**, 890 (1950); R. K. Cook and P. G. Weissler, *Phys. Rev.* **80**, 712 (1950).

[75] For a summary of pertinent earlier references, see F. S. Dainton and J. Rowbottom, *Trans. Faraday Soc.* **50**, 480 (1954).

[76] S. P. Choong, *Proc. Phys. Soc. (London)* **57**, 49 (1945).

[77] P. W. Levy, *J. Chem. Phys.* **23**, 764 (1955).

[78] C. S. Brown and L. A. Thomas, *Nature* **169**, 35 (1952).

[79] M. C. M. O'Brien, *Proc. Roy. Soc. (London)* **231A**, 404 (1955).

optical absorption, and both are explained by O'Brien[79] as associated with small quantities of aluminum as an impurity. Each aluminum atom replaces a silicon atom in the structure. The resonance spectrum is then attributed to an unpaired electron in a localized orbital on an oxygen atom next to the aluminum atom. The mechanism of the bleaching action of heat is still not understood. Additional support is given to the impurity theory by observations that some exceptionally pure quartz and fused silica samples do not become colored on irradiation.[77,78,80] An absorption band at 214 m$\mu$ observed in the latter may be associated with the silica network itself.

5. *Synthesis of large quartz crystals.* Because of their optical and piezoelectric properties, quartz crystals find major applications in optics, in frequency stabilization and control in radio, and in other electronic fields. Quartz crystal plates are also used in ultrasonic devices. Most of the optical- or electronic-grade quartz in the past has come from Brazil, but research initiated during World War II has demonstrated that synthetic quartz crystals, purer than natural quartz and more advantageous to use, can be grown on a production basis.

Earliest experiments in crystallizing quartz were made by Schäfhautl in 1845, and about 110 experiments of this type are recorded up to 1943.[81] The first synthetic quartz crystals large enough to produce resonator plates were obtained by Nacken in Germany in 1944. Progress has now reached the point where crystals weighing more than 1 lb each can be grown in a period of sixty days or less.[82] The synthesis is hydrothermal and carried out in a steel autoclave or bomb (Fig. 2.4) at temperatures from 300°–500°C and pressures to 15,000 psi. Seed crystals of special shape and orientation are supported in an alkaline solution (commonly 1 $N$ sodium hydroxide or 0.83 $M$ sodium carbonate[83]), and a supply of crushed quartz at the bottom of the autoclave serves as nutrient. A thermal gradient of as much as 20°C may exist between the bottom and top of the autoclave. Several crystals are grown at one time, growth being faster for the seeds at the top of the bomb.

6. *Thermodynamic data on silica.* Various thermodynamic data on the different forms of silica are tabulated in Table 2.9.

7. *Solubility of silica.* Quartz is so insoluble at ordinary temperatures and pressures, and in common solvents, that natural quartz crystals show

[80] A. J. Cohen, *J. Chem. Phys.* **23**, 765 (1955); A. J. Cohen, private communication to the author.

[81] P. F. Kerr and E. Armstrong, *Bull. Geol. Soc. Am.* **54**, Suppl. 1, 1–43 (1943).

[82] A. C. Walker, *J. Am. Ceram. Soc.* **36**, 250 (1953).

[83] R. Bechmann and D. R. Hale, *Brush Strokes* **4**, No. 1, September (1955), Brush Electronics Company, Cleveland, Ohio.

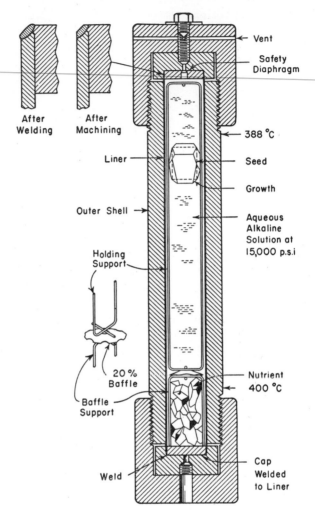

After
Welding

After
Machining

Vent

Safety
Diaphragm

388 °C

Liner

Seed

Growth

Outer Shell

Aqueous
Alkaline
Solution at
15,000 p.s.i

Holding
Support

20 %
Baffle

Nutrient
400 °C

Baffle
Support

Weld

Cap
Welded
to Liner

Fig. 2.4.   Diagram of a bomb for growing quartz crystals.   (Walker, *J. Am. Ceram. Soc.* **36**, 250.)

sharp interfacial edges and angles in spite of having been exposed to weathering for untold thousands of years.   Solubility studies indicate that quartz is essentially insoluble in water below 150°C, but above this temperature the solubility increases linearly with temperature.[84,85,86]

[84] G. C. Kennedy, *Econ. Geol.* **45**, 629 (1950).
[85] L. V. Gardner, *A.I.M.E., Tech. Pubs.*, No. 929 (1938).
[86] V. Lenher, *J. Am. Chem. Soc.* **43**, 391 (1921).

TABLE 2.9. THERMODYNAMIC DATA ON SILICA AT 25°C

| Form of SiO₂ | State | $\Delta H_f^0$ kcal/mole | $\Delta F_f^0$ kcal/mole | $\log_{10} K_f$ | $S^0$ cal/deg mole | $C_p^0$ cal/deg mole |
|---|---|---|---|---|---|---|
| α-Quartz | Crystalline | −210.3* | −197.3* | 144.62* | 10.00 | 10.62 |
| α-Tridymite | Crystalline | −204.8 | −191.9 | 140.66 | 10.36 | 10.66 |
| α-Cristobalite | Crystalline | −209.3* | −196.4* | 143.96* | 10.19 | 10.56 |
| Vitreous | Glass | −202.5 | −190.9 | 139.92 | 11.2 | 10.60 |

* Based on $\Delta H$ measurements by G. H. Humphrey and E. G. King, *J. Am. Chem. Soc.* **74**, 2041 (1952). Remaining data are from Rossini *et al.*, *op. cit.*

The solubility of coarse-particle quartz is about 0.0006% at room temperature[80] and increases to 0.003% with decrease in particle size to 4 μ.[86] Amorphous silica is more soluble than quartz. At room temperature Gardner[85] found 0.0126%. In the form of silica gel the solubility at 94°C is about 0.04%. No dissolution data are available on tridymite and crystobalite, but their solubilities[87] bear a direct relationship to their densities and thus are intermediate between amorphous silica and quartz. The solubility of all forms of silica increases with decrease in particle size, and above pH 9 there is a rapid increase in solubility with alkalinity.[88]

When silica passes into solution in pure water, the mechanism appears to involve a simultaneous hydration and depolymerization:

$$(SiO_2)_n + 2n(H_2O) \rightleftharpoons n\, Si(OH)_4$$

The "soluble silica" is believed to exist in solution in water as this monomeric hydrated form, $Si(OH)_4$. If the pH is high enough, additional silica passes into solution as silicate ions on the basis of the equilibrium:

$$Si(OH)_4 + OH^- \rightleftharpoons (HSiO_3)^- + 2H_2O$$

Assuming that the concentration of $Si(OH)_4$ in solution does not change with pH, the equilibrium constant, $K$, for this reaction is calculated as $1.85 \times 10^4$. In a study of the association[89] of silicate ions in the $CaO/SiO_2/H_2O$ system, a value of $K = 1.5 \times 10^4$ at 30°C was obtained. Evidence for increased solubility at low pH is inconclusive except when fluoride ion is present, whereupon silica is taken into solution as $SiF_6^=$ ion.

The presence of certain impurities may reduce the solubility. A finely divided amorphous silica with a solubility of 0.017% at 37°C dissolved

[87] R. K. Iler, *The Colloid Chemistry of Silica and Silicates*, Cornell University Press, Ithaca, New York, 1955, p. 7.

[88] W. Klemm, *FIAT Review of German Science*, 1939–1946, Part I, "Inorganic Chemistry" (Washington, D. C., 1948), p. 265.

[89] P. S. Roller and G. Ervin, Jr., *J. Am. Chem. Soc.* **62**, 461 (1940).

to the extent of only 0.003 to 0.0097% when aluminum oxide was added to the sample, and to less than 0.0001% in the presence of powdered aluminum.[90] It seems likely, here, that a very insoluble layer of aluminum silicate may form on the surface of the silica and prevent the underlying silica from dissolving. Possibly a similar action of magnesium or other polyvalent metal ions in sea water assists the diatoms in concentrating silica from natural waters. These organisms use the extracted silica for their cell walls and must have some means to prevent the silica from redissolving in the surrounding water, which is far from saturated.

**Chemical Properties of Silica.** Silica is very resistant to chemical action, but is attacked by a few reagents. It is scarcely affected by hydrogen at any temperature. The halogens, except for fluorine, do not attack it directly, but chlorine forms silicon tetrachloride, $SiCl_4$, when passed through a mixture of silica and carbon at about 1000°C:

$$SiO_2 + 2F_2 \rightarrow SiF_4 + O_2$$
$$SiO_2 + 2C + 2Cl_2 \rightarrow SiCl_4 + 2CO$$

Carbon at the temperature of the electric furnace reduces silica, and this reaction is the basis for the large-scale commercial preparation of silicon. The only metals that reduce $SiO_2$ alone are the alkali and alkaline earth metals, and, imperfectly, aluminum. Other metals reduce silica in the presence of carbon to form silicides. Calcium carbide also reacts with silica at high temperatures to give silicon, calcium oxide, and carbon monoxide.

Hydrofluoric acid acts on silica, with the formation of silicon tetrafluoride, $SiF_4$:

$$SiO_2 + 4HF \rightarrow SiF_4 + 2H_2O$$

This compound is a gas, and by its formation silica is separated from other oxides. Hot alkalies and fused alkali carbonates convert silica into soluble silicates:

$$SiO_2 + 4OH^- \rightarrow SiO_4^{-4} + 2H_2O$$
$$SiO_2 + Na_2CO_3 \rightarrow Na_2SiO_3 + CO_2$$

Fusion of $SiO_2$ and insoluble silicates with $Na_2CO_3$ or $K_2CO_3$ is the basis of the procedure for the analysis of rocks. Silicon dioxide is a true acidic oxide, but because of its insolubility it forms no acid with water.

The great chemical inertness of $SiO_2$ makes its detection in mixtures

[90] C. M. Jephcott and J. H. Johnston, *Arch. Ind. Hyg. and Occupational Med.* **1**, 323 (1950).

with the mineral silicates difficult. Procedures involving HF yield the total silica in the sample and do not readily distinguish between free silica and silicate silica. The former, when crystalline, can be identified and quantitatively determined by powder X-ray diffraction techniques. This is the standard method for determination of quartz, tridymite, and cristobalite in industrial dusts in the evaluation of the silicosis hazard.[91] Measurement of the heat effect of the $\alpha$-$\beta$ inversion by differential thermal analysis has also been demonstrated as a fairly exact method for determination of crystalline varieties of silica in mixtures.[92] No satisfactory method for accurately estimating the amorphous silica content has been worked out to date (1957).

Microdetection of silica is readily possible through change to soluble silicate and treatment with molybdate in acid solution. The yellow solution of silicomolybdic acid formed gives a blue solution on addition of benzidine in sodium acetate solution. The limit of this test is 0.1 gamma of $SiO_2$.[93]

**Silicic Acids, Colloidal Silica, and Silica Gel.** A voluminous literature exists on the silicic acids and their polymerization and aggregation to form colloidal silica sols and gels which are of very considerable economic importance.[94] The simplest silicic acid, monosilicic (orthosilicic) acid, $Si(OH)_4$ or $H_4SiO_4$, is obtained as a dilute saturated solution, containing about 0.01% $SiO_2$, when pure amorphous silica is equilibrated with water at room temperature. More concentrated (supersaturated) solutions can be obtained by the action of cold dilute acids on soluble orthosilicates:

$$SiO_4^{-4} + 4H^+ \rightarrow H_4SiO_4$$

Hydrolysis of such compounds as $SiCl_4$ and orthosilicic acid esters will also yield aqueous solutions of monosilicic acid. Monosilicic acid is most stable at a pH around 2 to 3,[95] and 0.1-molar (0.6% $SiO_2$) solutions of the acid can be prepared at pH 3 and 0°C.

When a supersaturated solution of $Si(OH)_4$ is permitted to age, an amorphous silica phase is eventually formed. This silica may appear as

[91] H. P. Klug, L. Alexander, and E. Kummer, *J. Ind. Hyg. Toxicol.* **30**, 166 (1948); H. P. Klug and L. E. Alexander, *X-Ray Diffraction Procedures for Polycrystalline and Amorphous Materials*, John Wiley and Sons, Inc., New York, 1954, pp. 390–439.

[92] R. W. Grimshaw, *Clay Minerals Bull.* **2**, No. 9, 2 (1953); H. Sauzeat, *Rev. ind. minéraux* **34**, 500 (1953).

[93] F. Feigl, *Spot Tests—Vol. I. Inorganic Applications*, Elsevier Publishing Co., 4th Edition, 1954, pp. 307–308.

[94] For an excellent introduction to these topics, see Iler, *op. cit.*, Chaps. III, V, VI, and VIII.

[95] H. Kraut, *Ber.* **64**, 1709 (1931).

either colloidal particles, a precipitate, or a gel.   The over-all reaction for this polymerization may be represented as follows:

$$n \, Si(OH)_4 \rightarrow (SiO_2)_n + 2nH_2O$$

Weyl[96] visualizes this process as proceeding through the formation of dimeric, trimeric, and ultimately, chainlike polymeric units built out of $Si(OH)_4$ molecules by the sharing of $OH^-$ ions between different silicon atoms which are octahedrally coordinated by six $OH^-$ ions.   A second step in the process involves a condensation with the elimination of water, so that adjacent silicon ions become linked directly through oxygen ions. The reactions may be pictured as follows:

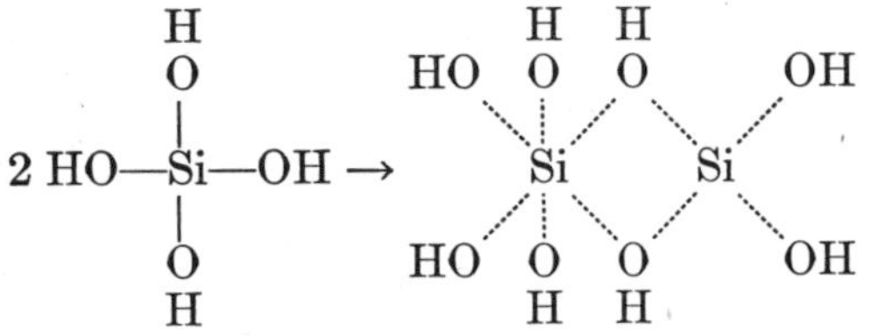

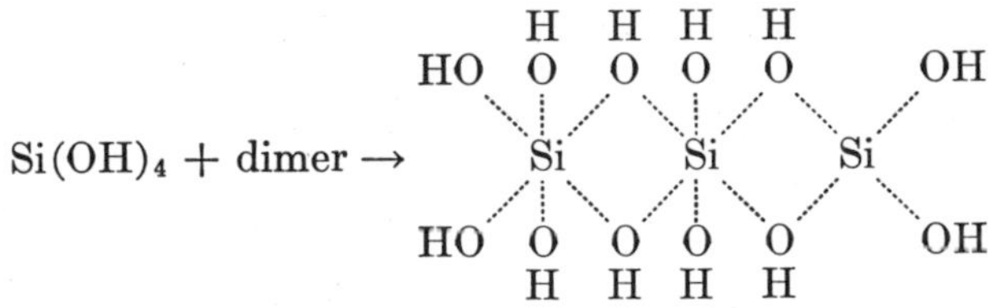

By loss of a water molecule the dimer would become disilicic acid, $H_6Si_2O_7$:

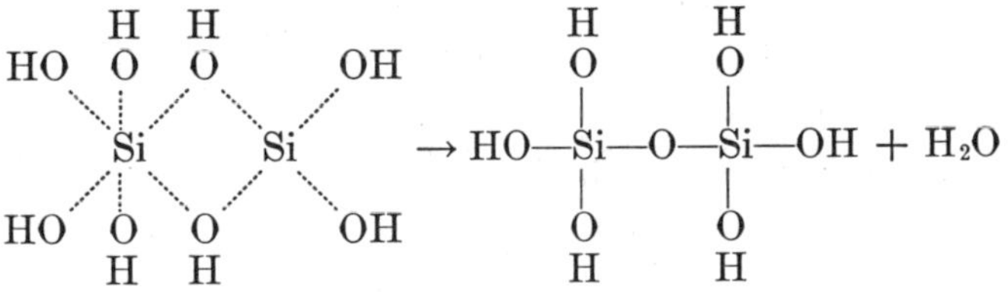

Justification for the postulated sixfold coordination of $OH^-$ around $Si^{+4}$ is very reasonable in view of the long established sixfold coordination of $F^-$ ion in $SiF_6^=$ ion, and the well-known equivalence of $OH^-$ and $F^-$ ions in many structures.

[96] W. A. Weyl, *A New Approach to Surface Chemistry and to Heterogeneous Catalysis,* Mineral Industries Exp. Sta. Bull. No. 57, Pennsylvania State University, University Park, Pa., 1951, pp. 46–52.

Carman[97] has presented a picture in which polymerization has proceeded to the point that a large mass of pure silica (the colloidal particle) has formed, built up of $SiO_4$ tetrahedra in a three-dimensional network. The outer surface of such a particle of exact composition $SiO_2$ will have its bonding incomplete, and in contact with moisture will strive to complete the tetrahedral configuration by the formation of OH groups on the surface. Depending only upon particle size, such colloidal silica could achieve every degree of hydration in the composition range from $H_4SiO_4$ to anhydrous crystalline or amorphous masses of silica. Electron microscope evidence suggests that these colloidal particles[98] are not necessarily compact spheres of $SiO_2$ but may be spongy in character, being aggregates of tiny silica particles. Indeed, there appear to be many different types of polymeric silica particles, made up of many different polysilicic acids, with structures ranging from meshworks of chains and rings to highly condensed spherical units.

The polymerization of silicic acid is catalyzed by small amounts of alkali to form a stable sol of colloidal particles. Similarly, in acid solution, silica gel is formed. Bird[99] prepared relatively stable sols containing up to 18% $SiO_2$ by removing $Na^+$ ions from a dilute solution of sodium silicate, stabilizing the sol by the addition of a small amount of alkali, and then concentrating the sol by evaporation. By stabilization with alkali and careful control of the particle size, stable aqueous dispersions containing 30% or more of silica have been produced.[100]

The relation between sol stability and pH has been summarized in a graph (Fig. 2.5) by Iler.[101] Above pH 6–7 the strong negative charge on the silica particles retards or prevents gelling of the sols, provided soluble salts are absent. At pH 5–6 gel formation is most rapid. In the range pH 2–5 the charge on the silica is low, but rate of condensation depends on the concentration of $OH^-$ ions, and experimental evidence[102] shows a maximum sol stability at pH 2–3. Below pH 2 the rate of gelling increases, and the rate[103] is proportional to the concentrations of hydrogen ions and fluoride ions present. The effect of the $F^-$ ion is marked, even when present to the extent of only a few parts per million.

[97] P. C. Carman, *Trans. Faraday Soc.* **36**, 964 (1940).

[98] O. E. Radczewski and H. Richter, *Kolloid-Z.* **96**, 1 (1941).

[99] P. G. Bird, **U.S. 2,244,325** (National Aluminate Co., 1941).

[100] M. F. Bechtold and O. E. Snyder, **U.S. 2,574,902** (1951); J. M. Rule, **U.S. 2,577,484–2,577,485** (1951).

[101] Iler, *op. cit.*, p. 45.

[102] R. Willstätter, H. Kraut, and K. Lobinger, *Ber.* **58B**, 2462 (1925); **61**, 2280 (1928); **62**, 2027 (1929); Kraut, *op. cit.*; W. D. Treadwell, *Trans. Faraday Soc.* **31**, 297 (1935).

[103] R. K. Iler, *J. Phys. Chem.* **56**, 680 (1952).

Commercial silica gel is usually an *xerogel*, a gel from which the liquid phase has been evaporated. During evaporation of the liquid phase the surface tension of the liquid in the pores of the gel exerts a strong compression on the gel mass. This compression is resisted by the strength

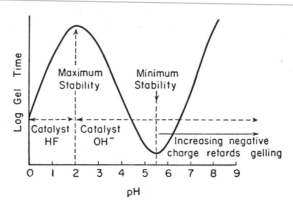

FIG. 2.5. Sol stability: relation between gelling time and pH. (Iler, *Colloid Chemistry of Silica and Silicates;* courtesy *Cornell University Press.*)

of the gel framework, and the equilibrium between the two determines the final density, shrinkage, pore diameter, and specific surface of the dried gel. For use as catalyst bases, strong hard gels are desired which will not shrink and crack when dried. On the other hand, gel technologists also have the problem of producing light, friable, easily powdered gels for use as fillers.

A strong coherent gel which withstands red heat without disintegration or loss of absorptive power can be produced by mixing strong solutions of 3.3 ratio sodium silicate with excess hydrochloric acid.[104] After the gel forms, it is washed and dried slowly. The drying must be slow to keep the gel masses from shattering because of greater shrinkage of the surface layers. Mechanically strong and dense gels result from high concentration of silica (up to 15 g/100 ml) in the gelling solution. A pulverulent, low-density, finely divided gel is produced by treating precipitated gel with water-miscible organic liquids such as alcohols or ketones and then air drying.[105]

It is possible to replace the liquid phase of a gel by a gaseous phase in such a way as to avoid the shrinkage that would occur if the gel had been dried directly from a liquid, resulting in an *aerogel*. Silica aerogels were

[104] J. McGavack, Jr., and W. A. Patrick, *J. Am. Chem. Soc.* **42**, 946 (1920); W. A. Patrick, U.S. **1,297,724** (1919).

[105] K. K. Kearby, U.S. **2,429,319** (Standard Oil Development Co., 1947).

prepared by Kistler[106] by replacing the water in the gel with alcohol. The alcohol was then removed by heating the gel in an autoclave above the critical temperature of alcohol and venting the vapors. This technique removes the liquid phase without subjecting the gel framework to the compressive forces due to the surface tension of the liquid-gas interface. The aerogel thus produced has an open structure closely resembling the structure of the original wet gel. One aerogel prepared by Kistler contained only 0.02 g/cc of silica, and was a very light, transparent, faintly opalescent solid.

Extremely fine silica powders may be prepared by several methods: by pulverizing an aerogel, by vaporizing $SiO_2$ at high temperatures, and by burning a volatile compound such as ethyl silicate or $SiCl_4$ and collecting the "silica fume." The latter procedures are analogous to the preparation of carbon black. Finely divided silica can also be precipitated from aqueous solution under a variety of conditions.[107]

Many of these amorphous silica gels and powders have the power to physically adsorb water to a degree which depends on the relative humidity. Most of the physically adsorbed water is removed by drying in air at 150° to 200°C. Similarly, silica gel adsorbs large volumes of other gases, such as $NH_3$, $SO_2$, $NO$, and organic vapors. When saturated the adsorbed material may be driven off by heating and the gel is ready for a new cycle. The properties of several commercial silica gels and aerogels have been reported[108] and are summarized in Table 2.10.

TABLE 2.10.   ADSORPTIVE PROPERTIES OF SEVERAL SILICA GELS AND POWDERS

| Silica Gels and Powders | BET Area, $m^2/g$ | $V_s$, Gas Adsorbed at $p_0$, cc/g | $P_g$, Pore Volume (from $V_s$) cc/g | Average Pore Radius $(r = 2P_g/A)$ A |
|---|---|---|---|---|
| Davison silica xerogel.......... | 809 | 285 | 0.44 | 11 |
| Silica Aerogel "S"............. | 796 | 2525 | 3.91 | 98 |
| Silica Aerogel "S", wetted and dried..................... | 813 | 425 | 0.66 | 16 |
| Silica bead aerogel............ | 504 | 3700 | 5.71 | 227 |
| "Santocel" C................. | 216 | 2550 | 3.94 | 365 |
| Linde nonporous silica......... | 180 | — | — | — |
| Diatomaceous earth ("Celite" 337)............... | 22 | — | — | — |

---

[106] S. S. Kistler, *J. Phys. Chem.* **36**, 52 (1932); U.S. **2,093,454** (1937); U.S. **2,249,767** (1941); *Nature* **127**, 741 (1931); S. S. Kistler, E. A. Fischer, and I. R. Freeman, *J. Am. Chem. Soc.* **65**, 1909 (1943).

[107] Iler, *op. cit.* ref. 87, pp. 159–165.

[108] H. E. Ries, Jr., *Advances in Catalysis and Related Subjects*, Academic Press, Inc., New York, 1950, IV, p. 87.

**Uses of Silica.** The use of crystalline quartz plates as piezoelectric oscillators for frequency stabilization and control in radio, and for ultrasonic devices, has been mentioned. Thin plates of crystalline quartz elastically bent are used as monochromators in X-ray diffraction. Optical grade crystalline quartz has been for many years the preferred material for lenses and prisms of spectrographs and other optical instruments used in the ultraviolet region. Limited success has been reported in the use of optically active quartz as a resolving agent for optical isomers of coordination compounds. The scarcity of large high-grade quartz crystals and the inconvenience caused by its rotatory power, however, are leading to its gradual replacement by fused-quartz optics.

Quartz melts metastably at 1430°C but not sharply, and the material is in a soft, plastic condition just below the ultimate point of fusion. While in the plastic condition, it is worked into various shapes. Tubes, rods, and various pieces of apparatus are readily fashioned from the fused oxide. Gases in the silica are set free during fusion as microscopic bubbles and cause a milky appearance of the final product.

Transparent fused quartz has very desirable properties. If very pure $SiO_2$ is melted in an electric vacuum furnace, the bubbles become enlarged and most of them come to the surface and escape. When the molten material is allowed to cool under a high pressure of about 200 atmospheres, the few remaining bubbles are compressed to negligible size. The resulting product is clear and transparent. Not only is it transparent to light of the visible spectrum, but also, unlike glass, permits the passage of the shorter ultraviolet rays. For this reason, quartz glass is employed in optical instruments used in the ultraviolet, in the construction of mercury vapor lamps, and in windows of hospitals and sun rooms, in order that the healthful, shorter wavelengths of sunlight may come indoors. Straight and bent rods of fused quartz are used to convey light and heat by internal reflection to inaccessible parts of the body such as the nose and throat.

Quartz apparatus, in addition to permitting irradiation of materials by ultraviolet light, possesses many other very desirable properties. It has a very low coefficient of expansion—0.000000449 between 0° and 1000°C. As a result, a quartz vessel may be heated to redness and plunged into ice water without danger of cracking.

Fine specimens of certain natural forms of silica are used as gems and decorative stones. The more impure varieties also find important commercial uses: as quartz and flint in the manufacture of porcelain and glass, and as an abrasive; as sand in mortars, cements, and concrete; as quartzite, sandstone, etc., for building stone; as an acid flux in certain smelting operations. Tripolite or diatomite is used in metal polishes and scouring soaps, and, because of its porous nature, for adsorbing colored matter in oil refining. Likewise, diatomaceous earth is a polishing agent and an adsorbent. Silica is used in paints and as a wood filler. The presence of colloidal silicic acid in the soil is believed to make phosphate ions more available to plants. Colloidal silica sols find use in paper making, floor waxes, and textiles. An extremely fine-particle sol (Du Pont Ludox; 17 m$\mu$) confers soil-retarding properties to painted walls, wall paper, rugs, and upholstery fabrics. Colloidal silica smaller than 30 m$\mu$ is employed for modifying the characteristics of organic polymers, particularly elastomers and resins. Specially prepared silica sols are used as an aid to flocculation of impurities in water purification.[109] Among the uses of silica gels and powders are the following: as catalysts and catalyst bases; as filter aids; as fillers for plastics and rubber; as heat insulation; and as thickeners in greases, pastes, creams, pharmaceuticals, inks, and paints.

**Silicosis.** Silicosis is a chronic disease of the lungs resulting from prolonged breathing of air containing free silica dust. Dusts from other siliceous materials and from glass and diamond do not produce silicosis. The disease rarely develops on less than three years' exposure to the silica dust, and in most cases workmen have been exposed for seven years or longer before its appearance. Evidence seems to indicate that silicosis results from very small particles of silica undergoing chemical action in the lungs. Investigations place special emphasis on the so-called "respirable dust," that part of air borne dust which is made up of particles 5 $\mu$ and less in diameter. These very small particles may succeed in passing the natural filters of the respiratory tract more readily than the larger particles. Industry, science, and labor are united in efforts to prevent and control this serious occupational disease.

**Silicon Monoxide.** Divalent silicon is exceedingly rare, but the existence of gaseous silicon monoxide has been firmly established by spectral investigations[110] and mass spectrometric studies.[111] The existence of a thermodynamically stable solid SiO, however, is still confused at this writing, in spite of much research.[112] Potter[113] first reported the existence

---

[109] For additional applications and references, see Iler, *op. cit.* ref. 87, pp. 114–120.

[110] W. Jevons, *Proc. Roy. Soc. (London)* **106A**, 174 (1924); K. F. Bonhoeffer, *Z. physik. Chem.* **131**, 363 (1928); P. G. Saper, *Phys. Rev.* **42**, 498 (1932); D. Sharma, *Proc. Nat. Acad. Sci. India* **A14**, 37 (1944); A. Lagerqvist and U. Uhler, *Arkiv Fysik* **6**, 95 (1953); H. C. Rowlinson and R. F. Barrow, *J. Chem. Phys.* **21**, 378 (1953).

[111] R. F. Porter, W. A. Chupka, and M. G. Inghram, *J. Chem. Phys.* **23**, 216 (1955).

[112] For extensive bibliographies of earlier work see: C. A. Zapffe and C. E. Sims, *Iron Age* **149**, [4] 29–31, [5] 34–39 (1942); G. Hass, *J. Am. Ceram. Soc.* **33**, 353 (1950).

[113] H. N. Potter, *Trans. Am. Electrochem. Soc.* **12**, 191 (1907).

of SiO, but his product, a light-brown opaque powder, was later proved by X-ray diffraction to be a finely divided mixture of silicon and cristobalite.[114]   By close control of vacuum, temperature, and rate of condensation, several reactions definitely yield a metastable, black, resinous-looking product with a composition corresponding to SiO :[115,116]

$$SiO_2 + Si \rightarrow 2SiO$$
$$SiO_2 + H_2 \rightarrow SiO + H_2O$$
$$SiO_2 + C \rightarrow SiO + CO$$
$$Si + MO \rightarrow M + SiO$$
$$xMO \cdot ySiO_2 + ySi \rightarrow xMO + 2ySiO$$

The first reaction is considered to be the most suitable for preparing SiO, either as a thin film or in quantity.   The black SiO condensate is characterized by complete solubility in hydrofluoric acid, and by amorphous type X-ray and electron diffraction patterns whose principal halo corresponds to a Bragg spacing of about 3.60 A.[117]   On heating it begins to disproportionate at temperatures as low as 400° to 700°C into Si and SiO$_2$.   This decomposition product is light brown or tan colored and dissolves to the extent of only 68% in hydrofluoric acid, the residue being silicon which is insoluble in HF.

Brewer and Edwards[116] have critically examined the thermodynamic data on SiO.   The pure gas has a $\Delta H^0{}_{298}$ of formation of $-21,411 \pm 570$ cal.   They conclude that solid SiO is unstable below 1450°K, but that at some higher temperature it probably becomes stable and has a melting point higher than 1975°K.   At least three investigators, however, have reported diffraction data for crystalline SiO, each based on a cubic lattice but with different cell sizes: Inuzuka[118] found $a = 6.4$ A; Beletskii and Rapoport[119] found $a = 5.16$ A; and Hoch and Johnston[120] reported $a = 7.135$ A at 1300°C, which was subsequently demonstrated to be due to $\beta$-cristobalite,[121] $a = 7.14$ A at 500°C.   Only further investigation can establish the existence of crystalline SiO.

[114] H. N. Baumann, Jr., *ibid.* **80**, 95 (1941).
[115] H. deWet Erasmus and J. A. Persson, *J. Electrochem. Soc.* **95**, 316 (1949); Hass, *loc. cit.*
[116] L. Brewer and R. K. Edwards, *J. Phys. Chem.* **58**, 351 (1954).
[117] The first strong diffraction line of silicon is at $d = 3.15$ A, and the strong halo of silica glass is at $d = 4.15$ A.
[118] H. Inuzuka, *Mazda Kenkyu Ziho* **15**, 305 (1940).
[119] M. S. Beletskii and M. B. Rapoport, *Doklady Akady. Nauk S.S.S.R.* **72**, 699 (1950).
[120] M. Hoch and H. L. Johnston, *J. Am. Chem. Soc.* **75**, 5224 (1953).
[121] G. Geller and C. D. Thurmond, *ibid.* **77**, 5285 (1955).

Silicon monoxide, because of its relatively high vapor pressure and the adherent films it forms, is especially suitable for producing protective coatings on first-surface mirrors and for preparing replica and support films for electron microscope studies. Hass and Salzberg[122] have reported on the optical properties of silicon monoxide films in the wavelength region from 0.24 to 14.0 $\mu$.

**Silicon Carbide.** At the temperature of the electric furnace, carbon reduces silicon dioxide. If an excess of carbon is used, the product is silicon carbide[123] instead of elemental silicon:

$$SiO_2 + 3C \rightarrow SiC + 2CO$$

Acheson[124] discovered this substance in 1891 during a famous experiment in which he heated a mixture of clay and powdered coke in an improvised electric furnace consisting of a little iron bowl and a carbon electrode. Recognizing immediately the possibilities of the hard crystals and thinking that they were composed of corundum and carbon, he devised the trade name *carborundum* for the material and soon had his own company incorporated for commercial production of grinding wheels. It was not until 1905 that Moissan[125] found SiC to occur naturally as small green hexagonal plates in the meteorites from Cañon Diablo, Arizona.

In modern commercial practice the furnace may be 40 ft in length by 10 ft high and 10 ft wide. The charge consists of a mixture of 60% sand and 40% coke with a little sawdust and sodium chloride added. A core of graphite or granular carbon carries the powerful electric current at 200 to 300 v. The sawdust burns out and leaves a porous mass through which gases easily escape. The salt forms volatile chlorides with iron and aluminum impurities. During a run the temperature reaches a maximum of over 2400°C after about 18 hours. Then until the end of the 36-hour run it falls slowly to become constant at about 2040°C. The cooled charge, after a run, consists of an outer zone of unreacted or partially reacted mixture which is separated and refurnaced with another charge. The next zone, where the temperature has reached the reaction range, contains the crystalline silicon carbide which is removed for processing. The central zone where the core was placed contains only

[122] G. Hass and C. D. Salzberg, *J. Opt. Soc. Am.* **44**, 181 (1954).

[123] For an excellent detailed summary of the production, properties, and uses of silicon carbide, see *Facts about Silicon Carbide*, The Carborundum Co., Niagara Falls, New York, May 1953, 52 pp.

[124] E. G. Acheson, *A Pathfinder: Discovery, Invention and Industry*, The Press Scrap Book, 1910, p. 97.

[125] H. Moissan, *Compt. rend.* **140**, 405 (1905).

graphite which may be used again as core material. Baumann[126] has confirmed that the reaction is a vapor phase reaction that proceeds in two steps:

$$SiO_2 + 2C \rightarrow Si + 2CO$$
$$Si + C \rightarrow SiC$$

The second step is almost instantaneous, and begins at about 1500°C. Operating furnace temperatures are much higher in order that the reaction may go on at a reasonable rate.

Silicon carbide comes from the furnace in beautiful iridescent blue-black crystals. The iridescence is due to a thin surface layer of silica resulting from superficial oxidation of the carbide. The pure compound, however, is colorless. The crystallography of silicon carbide provides the most remarkable case of polymorphism known. Its low-temperature form, β-SiC, is cubic, and occurs only as fine crystals. The major constituent of commercial abrasive grain, the high-temperature form, crystallizes in the hexagonal system, and has several forms in both the hexagonal and rhombohedral classes. Early investigators designated the various forms as Type I, II, III, etc., in order of their discovery, but Ramsdell[127] has proposed a new nomenclature that gives structural relationships between the forms. The β-form has the zinc blende structure, B3, which is simply the diamond structure with one half of the atoms different from the other half. The same Si–C layers found parallel to the (111) planes of β-SiC become the basal (0001) layers of the hexagonal forms. This leads to a series of hexagonal and rhombohedral varieties whose hexagonal cells have a constant $a = 3.073$ A and whose $c$ directions vary with the repeat distance in the stacking sequence of the layers. Table 2.11 lists the 15 crystalline forms of silicon carbide that are well established, using the Ramsdell designation which indicates the number of layers in the repeating sequence in the $c$ direction. Type 6H is the most abundant form in commercial silicon carbide, and is followed in order of decreasing frequency by 15R, 4H, 21R, and 8H. Two additional rhombohedral types have been reported, one of 270 layers[128] and one of 594 layers.[129] This one-dimensional polymorphism (also known as polytypism[130]) has had theoretical treatment as a cooperational phenomenon analogous to order-disorder phase transformations.[131]

[126] H. N. Baumann, Jr., *J. Electrochem. Soc.* 99, 109 (1952).
[127] L. S. Ramsdell, *Am. Mineralogist* 32, 64 (1947).
[128] G. S. Zhdanov and Z. V. Minervina, *J. Exp. Theor. Phys.* 17, 3 (1947).
[129] G. Honjo, S. Miyake, and T. Tomita, *Acta Cryst.* 3, 396 (1950).
[130] H. Baumhauer, *Z. Krist.* 55, 249 (1915).
[131] R. Gevers, *Acta Cryst.* 5, 518 (1952); H. Jagodzinski, *ibid.* 7, 300 (1954); C. J. Schneer, *ibid.* 8, 279 (1955).

TABLE 2.11. CRYSTALLINE FORMS OF SILICON CARBIDE*

| Cubic | Hexagonal | Rhombohedral |
|-------|-----------|--------------|
| $\beta$-SiC (old Type IV) | $4H$ (old Type III) | $15R$ (old Type I) |
| | $6H$ (old Type II) | $21R$ |
| | $8H$ | $27R$ |
| | $10H$ | $33R$ |
| | $19H$ | $51R_{(a)}$ (old Type V) |
| | | $51R_{(b)}$ |
| | | $75R$ |
| | | $84R$ |
| | | $87R$ |

* L. S. Ramsdell and J. A. Kohn, *Acta Cryst.* 5, 215 (1952); L. S. Ramsdell and R. S. Mitchell, *Am. Mineralogist* 38, 56 (1953).

Silicon carbide is one of the hardest substances known (9.15 on the Mohs scale, diamond 10). The mean indices of refraction for $\alpha$-type SiC in sodium light are $N_0 = 2.648$ and $N_e = 2.691$. Beta SiC, being cubic, is isotropic and has an index $N = 2.63$ in lithium light. The specific gravity for all varieties is close to 3.21.[132] Silicon carbide is a semiconductor, and its electrical properties depend greatly on factors such as temperature, voltage, degree of purity, and prior history of the crystal. Thus the specific resistance of black SiC crystals was determined as 2.13 ohms/cm and of green crystals as 0.41 ohm/cm. Selected thermodynamic data[133] for SiC at 25°C are: heat of formation, $\Delta H_f^0 = -26.7$ kcal/mole; free energy of formation, $\Delta F_f^0 = 26.1$ kcal/mole; equilibrium constant of formation, $\log_{10} K_f = 19.13$; entropy, $S^0 = 3.935$ cal/deg mole; heat capacity, $C_p^0 = 6.37$ cal/deg mole. Beta SiC is stable to about 2100°C and then transforms monotropically to the $\alpha$-form in the range 2100° to 2300°C. At about 2250°C it begins to dissociate, without fusing, and its melting point is reported as >2700°C. Studies of the infrared spectrum of silicon carbide have derived the number of normal modes, the symmetry types, and the selection rules for $\beta$-SiC and the $4H$ and $15R$ modifications.[134] The Hg 4358-A radiation[135] produces a strong Raman shift of 818 cm$^{-1}$ from a thin plate of SiC of the hexagonal class. This frequency is thought to be a fundamental mode in which the carbon atoms oscillate against the silicon atoms.

Silicon carbide is acted upon by only a few chemical agents. The one violent reaction recorded is on heating with a mixture of potassium

[132] A. Taylor and D. S. Laidler, *Brit. J. App. Phys.* 1, 174 (1950).
[133] Rossini *et al.*, *op. cit.* ref. 7.
[134] A. K. Ramdas, *Proc. Indian Acad. Sci.* 37A, 571 (1953).
[135] P. S. Narayanan, *Current Sci.* 21, 239 (1952).

dichromate and lead chromate. It is stable to acids, even to fuming nitric acid, and to boiling sulfuric, hydrochloric, and hydrofluoric acids. Most of its reactions occur at relatively high temperatures. Fused alkalies, borax, and cryolite decompose it. Sodium silicate attacks it above 1300°C, and CaO and MgO react with it above 1000°C. Air and the oxyhydrogen blast slowly oxidize it above 1000°C, and it forms silicon tetrachloride and carbon when treated with chlorine at 900°C. The U. S. Bureau of Standards provides a standard sample of silicon carbide with an analysis.[136]

Silicon carbide finds extensive use as an abrasive. The crystals are crushed, sifted to size, mixed with a binder of clay or sodium silicate, molded into various shapes (grinding wheels, whetstones, etc.), and fired. In addition to bonded abrasives, quantities of it are used as loose grain abrasive, and in coated abrasives. Silicon carbide is used as a refractory in furnaces, as an ignition baffle in oil burners, as heating elements in electric furnaces, as catalyst carriers, and as a deoxidizer in the metallurgy of iron and steel. The production of SiC in the United States and Canada in 1953 amounted to 62,301 short tons valued at $8,190,431.[137]

**Halogen Compounds of Silicon.** The halogens react exothermically with silicon to form tetrahalides. The energy of the reaction, however, decreases rapidly with increasing size of the halogen atom. In an atmosphere of fluorine, silicon ignites spontaneously at room temperature, whereas with iodine the reaction occurs only at red heat:

$$Si + 2F_2 \rightarrow SiF_4$$
$$Si + 2I_2 \rightarrow SiI_4$$

The series of tetrahalides shows the same general increase in melting point and boiling point exhibited by the tetrahalides of carbon. In general, they are less stable than the corresponding carbon compounds, especially toward water. Except for the tetrafluoride they hydrolyze completely in water to form silicic acid and the hydrogen halide. Table 2.2 lists the heats of formation of the tetrahalides, and additional physical properties are reported in Table 2.12.

Silicon tetrafluoride is more simply prepared by the action of hydrofluoric acid on calcium metasilicate glass, $CaSiO_3$:

$$CaSiO_3 + 6HF \rightarrow CaF_2 + SiF_4 + 3H_2O$$

A portion of the fluorine content of phosphate rock is evolved as $SiF_4$ or

[136] U. S. Bureau of Standards, Analysis of Standard Sample 112, Silicon Carbide (1937).
[137] Bureau of Mines, Mineral Market Report, MMS No. 2397 (May 24, 1955).

TABLE 2.12. PHYSICAL PROPERTIES OF THE SILICON TETRAHALIDES

| | Color and State | Melting Point, °C | Boiling Point, °C | Refractive Index | Density g/l |
|---|---|---|---|---|---|
| $SiF_4$ | col. gas | $-77^{2\ atm}$ | $-65^{181\ mm}$ | . . . | 4.67 |
| $SiCl_4$ | col. fum. liq. | $-70$ | 57.57 | 1.412 | 1.483 |
| $SiBr_4$ | col. fum. liq. | 5 | 153 | 1.579 | 2.814 |
| $SiI_4$ | col. cubic | 120.5 | 290 | . . . | . . . |

fluosilicic acid, $H_2SiF_6$, when the rock is acidified in the production of phosphate fertilizers and chemicals. Domestic phosphate rock carries from 3 to 4% fluorine as calcium fluoride and fluorapatite, and from 10 to 30 lb of fluorine are evolved per ton of rock treated.[138] The reaction with fluorspar and silica is:

$$3CaF_2 + SiO_2 + 3H_2SO_4 \rightarrow 3CaSO_4 + H_2SiF_6 + 2H_2O$$

Silicon tetrafluoride is a highly stable and incombustible gas, but is partially hydrolyzed to form silicic acid and fluosilicic acid:

$$3SiF_4 + 4H_2O \rightarrow H_4SiO_4 + 2H_2SiF_6$$

Solid $SiF_4$ sublimes without melting, but melts at $-77°C$ under a pressure of 2 atmospheres. Early crystal structure studies[139] revealed tetrahedral $SiF_4$ molecules in the solid, and Atoji and Lipscomb's[140] precise single crystal analysis has determined the bond distance Si–F to be 1.56 $\pm$ 0.01 A. This represents a shortening of 0.12 A from the normal Si–F single-bond distance and is best explained (following Pitzer[141]) by the difference in type of repulsive effect predominating in Si–Si from that in F–F and by the large electronegativity of F.

Fluosilicic acid may also be obtained by the action of hydrofluoric acid on freshly precipitated silicic acid:

$$H_4SiO_4 + 6HF \rightarrow H_2SiF_6 + 4H_2O$$

It is unstable and is obtained only in aqueous solution:

$$H_2SiF_6 \rightleftharpoons SiF_4 + 2HF$$

This water solution, however, is a stronger acid than sulfuric acid. Most of the fluosilicates are soluble in water; conspicuous exceptions are those

[138] C. A. Hampel, *Chem. Eng. News.* **27**, 2420 (1949).
[139] G. Natta, *Gazz. chim. ital.* **60**, 911 (1930).
[140] M. Atoji and W. N. Lipscomb, *Acta Cryst.* **7**, 597 (1954).
[141] K. S. Pitzer, *J. Am. Chem. Soc.* **70**, 2140 (1948).

of sodium, potassium, barium, and calcium, which dissolve sparingly. The solubility of $Na_2SiF_6$ in water is 0.435 g/100 cc solution at 0°C, and 1.822 g/100 cc solution at 78°C. Hydrolysis in water causes its solutions to have a pH in the range 3.5 to 4.0. Solid $Na_2SiF_6$ has a density of 2.679 and crystallizes in pseudohexagonal prisms belonging to the orthorhombic system. Potassium, rubidium, cesium, $\alpha$-ammonium, and thallium fluosilicates crystallize cubic with the $K_2PtCl_6$ arrangement; $\beta$-ammonium fluosilicate is hexagonal with the $CdI_2$ structure; and $BaSiF_6$ has a rhombohedral structure of the type $TlSbF_6$.[142]

Sodium fluosilicate is the most available salt of fluosilicic acid. Some 80,000 tons of the salt could be produced annually from phosphate rock, but the domestic consumption is very much less than this figure. The 1955 price of $Na_2SiF_6$ was 7 cents per lb. The largest use of the salt is in laundering as a "sour" to protect laundered fabrics from alkali damage due to soaps. It is also used in glass and enamel making and, to some extent, as an insecticide. Aqueous solutions of magnesium fluosilicates are applied to concrete surfaces and plastered walls to reduce dusting and to increase hardness.

Silicon tetrachloride results from the direct union of the elements or by passing chlorine over a heated mixture of silica and coke:

$$Si + 2Cl_2 \rightarrow SiCl_4$$

or

$$SiO_2 + 2C + 2Cl_2 \rightarrow SiCl_4 + 2CO$$

Higher members of the series, $Si_nCl_{2n+2}$, are also present in small amounts in the products of these reactions. In contact with moist air $SiCl_4$ fumes strongly because of the formation of hydrogen chloride and a dense smoke of finely divided silicic acid:

$$SiCl_4 + 4H_2O \rightarrow 4HCl + H_4SiO_4$$

It has important uses in military maneuvers for the production of smoke screens, and when used with ammonia the amount of smoke is increased by the simultaneous formation of ammonium chloride. These smoke curtains closely resemble natural fog in appearance. Sulfur trioxide reacts with the tetrachloride to form the oxychloride, $Si_2OCl_6$, and also $SiO_2$:

$$2SiCl_4 + 2SO_3 \rightarrow Si_2OCl_6 + S_2O_5Cl_2$$

and

$$SiCl_4 + 4SO_3 \rightarrow SiO_2 + 2S_2O_5Cl_2$$

Silicon tetrachloride reacts with dry ammonia forming a silazane:

$$SiCl_4 + 8NH_3 \rightarrow Si(NH_2)_4 + 4NH_4Cl$$

[142] R. W. G. Wyckoff, *Crystal Structures*, Interscience Publishers, Inc., New York, 1951, Vol. II.

The Si–Cl bond is also highly reactive to alcohol, organic acids, and other reagents containing hydroxyl groups. The chlorine is readily replaced by organic groups by the use of sodium or organometallic compounds. These reactions and their products form the subject matter of Chapter 3. The Si–Cl distance in $SiCl_4$ from electron diffraction measurements is 2.02 A.[143] This value, as in $SiF_4$, represents a decrease of 0.14 A from the expected single-bond distance. The boiling point of $SiCl_4$ is lower (about 29°) than that of $CCl_4$, a property found generally among the Si–Cl compounds, but not in the other halides nor in the hydrides or alkyls.

The corresponding $SiBr_4$ and $SiI_4$ are readily prepared by direct union of the elements, and mixed halogen compounds of the type $SiF_3Cl$, $SiCl_2Br_2$, $SiClI_3$, $SiFCl_2Br$, etc., are also known.[144] More complex silicon halides are formed by treating silicon tetrahalides with silicon, silver, and certain compounds :[145]

$$3SiCl_4 + Si \rightarrow 2Si_2Cl_6$$
$$2SiI_4 + 2Ag \rightarrow Si_2I_6 + 2AgI$$

Some of the best-known complex halides are $Si_2F_6$, $Si_2Cl_6$, $Si_3Cl_8$, $Si_2Br_6$, $Si_2I_6$, and $SiI_2$. They are colorless except for $SiI_2$ which is orange red. High temperatures split them :

$$Si_2I_6 \rightarrow SiI_4 + SiI_2$$

Water readily decomposes them, leading to interesting products of hydrolysis which are more fully discussed in a later section of this volume :

$$Cl_3Si–SiCl_3 + 4H_2O \rightarrow 6HCl + \quad HO_2Si–SiO_2H$$
$$\text{(silico-oxalic acid)}$$

Oxyhalides of silicon, such as $(SiOCl_2)_4$, $Si_2OCl_6$, $Si_3O_2Cl_8$, $Si_4O_3Cl_{10}$, $Si_5O_4Cl_{12}$, $Si_6O_5Cl_{14}$, $Si_7O_6Cl_{16}$, and $Si_2OF_6$, are formed by the action of a halogen and oxygen on red hot silica.[146] Several mixed oxyhalides, e.g., $Si_2OF_4Cl_2$ and $Si_2OF_3Cl_3$, have been prepared.[147]

The halogen derivatives of the silicon hydrides are considered in the next section.

[143] L. O. Brockway and F. T. Wall, *J. Am. Chem. Soc.* **56**, 2373 (1934).

[144] W. C. Schumb and E. L. Gamble, *ibid.* **54**, 3943 (1932); H. S. Booth and C. F. Swinehout, *ibid.* **54**, 4750 (1932); W. C. Schumb and H. H. Anderson, *ibid.* **58**, 994 (1936); *ibid.* **59**, 651 (1937).

[145] W. C. Schumb and E. L. Gamble, *ibid.* **54**, 583 (1932); G. Martin, *J. Chem. Soc.* **105**, 2836 (1914); A. Besson and L. Fournier, *Compt. rend.* **149**, 34 (1909); C. Friedel and A. Ladenburg, *Ann.* **203**, 241 (1880).

[146] W. C. Schumb and D. F. Holloway, *J. Am. Chem. Soc.* **63**, 2753 (1941).

[147] H. S. Booth and R. A. Osten, *ibid.* **67**, 1092 (1945).

**Silicon Hydrides.** Silicon, like carbon, forms series of hydrides, but to a much more limited extent. Analogous to methane, $CH_4$, is monosilane (or simply silane),[148] $SiH_4$. Higher silanes, disilane, $Si_2H_6$, trisilane, $Si_3H_8$, etc., corresponding to the paraffin hydrocarbons, are known in a series up to $Si_6H_{14}$. In many physical properties, such as boiling and melting points, they resemble the respective hydrocarbons, but their chemical properties are decidedly different. Thus no prediction of the chemistry of the silanes by analogy to the hydrocarbons is likely to succeed, and silane chemistry, although structurally similar at many points to organic chemistry, is much less rich in the variety and complexity of its compounds than is hydrocarbon chemistry. Indeed, the silanes bear a closer relation to the hydrides of boron in accordance with the well-known diagonal subgroup relationships within the periodic table.

Hydrochloric acid reacts with magnesium silicide to form monosilane:

$$Mg_2Si + 4HCl \rightarrow SiH_4 + 2MgCl_2$$

Other silica hydrides are formed at the same time, the total yield representing up to one fourth of the silicon contained in the silicide. One set of conditions reported by Stock[149] yielded the following mixture: 40% $SiH_4$, 30% $Si_2H_6$, 15% $Si_3H_8$, 10% $Si_4H_{10}$, and the remainder as higher silanes. Better yields are obtained by the action of the corresponding silicon chloride on lithium aluminum hydride:[150]

$$LiAlH_4 + SiCl_4 \rightarrow SiH_4 + LiCl + AlCl_3$$

The silanes resemble the hydrides of arsenic or antimony in many respects. Like these they are very poisonous, and lead to headache and sickness when inhaled in small quantities. In low concentrations their odor is described as stupefying, highly nauseating, and chocolatelike; in higher quantities it resembles hydrogen sulfide. The colorless monosilane is rather stable and decomposes only at red heat into hydrogen and silicon. The higher silanes dissociate at progressively lower temperatures: $Si_2H_6$ breaks up at 400° to 500°C, and $Si_6H_{14}$ decomposes at room temperature over a period of a few months. The decomposition of the higher silanes is not complete, but results in mixtures of simple gaseous hydrides and

[148] Recommendation of the American Chemical Society Committee on Nomenclature of Silicon Compounds, E. J. Crane, *Chem. Eng. News* 24, 1233 (1946).

[149] A. Stock and C. Somieski, *Ber.* 49, 111 (1916); A. Stock, *ibid.* 50, 170 (1917); A. Stock, P. Stiebeler, and F. Zeidler, *ibid.* 56, 1695 (1923). An excellent general reference to this entire topic is: A. Stock, *Hydrides of Boron and Silicon*, Cornell University Press, Ithaca, N. Y., 1933.

[150] A. E. Finholt, A. C. Bond, Jr., and H. I. Schlesinger, *J. Am. Chem. Soc.* 69, 1199 (1947); A. E. Finholt, A. C. Bond, Jr., K. E. Wilzbach, and H. I. Schlesinger, *ibid.* 69, 2692 (1947).

solid unsaturated hydrides:

$$Si_5H_{12} \rightarrow 2(SiH) + Si_2H_6 + SiH_4$$

Melting and boiling points of several silanes are reported in Table 2.13.

TABLE 2.13. MELTING AND BOILING POINTS OF SOME SILANES
AND SILANE DERIVATIVES

| Compound | Melting Point, °C | Boiling Point, °C | Compound | Melting Point, °C | Boiling Point, °C |
|---|---|---|---|---|---|
| $SiH_4$ | $-185$ | $-111.9$ | $SiH_2Br_2$ | $-70.1$ | 66 |
| $Si_2H_6$ | $-132.5$ | $-14.5$ | $SiHBr_3$ | $< -60$ | 109 |
| $Si_3H_8$ | $-117.4$ | 52.9 | $SiH_3I$ | $\cdots$ | 45.4 |
| $Si_4H_{10}$ | $-93.5$ | 80 | $SiH_2I_2$ | $\cdots$ | 149.5 |
| $SiH_3Cl$ | $-118.1$ | $-30.4$ | $SiHI_3$ | 8 | 220 |
| $SiH_2Cl_2$ | $-122$ | 8.3 | $SiHF_3$ | $ca.$ $-110$ | $-80.2$ |
| $SiHCl_3$ | $-126.6$ | 33 | $SiHF_2Cl$ | $\cdots$ | $ca.$ $-50$ |
| $SiH_3Br$ | $-94$ | 1.9 | $SiHFCl_2$ | $\cdots$ | $-18$ |

Silicon hydrides are very reactive and react with air immediately, usually explosively. It is suggested that the explosion results from the reaction of oxygen with hydrogen formed in the preliminary reaction:[151]

$$2SiH_4 + O_2 \rightarrow 2H_2SiO + 2H_2$$

Solutions of potassium permanganate and of mercury(II), iron(III), and copper(II) salts oxidize silanes. Water also oxidizes the Si–H bond when catalyzed by OH⁻ ions:

$$Si-H + H_2O \rightarrow Si-OH + H_2$$

The alkali dissolved by water from ordinary glass laboratory equipment is sufficient to bring about this reaction, and dilute alkali solutions will liberate quantitatively one molecule of $H_2$ from most Si–H bonds.

Free chlorine and bromine react violently with the silanes. The direct reaction with bromine must be carried out at low temperatures and at great dilution:

$$SiH_4 + Br_2 \rightarrow SiH_3Br + HBr$$

Controlled halogenation is accomplished by the action of the halogen acids in the presence of the corresponding aluminum halide as a catalyst:[152]

$$SiH_4 + HCl \rightarrow SiH_3Cl + H_2$$
$$SiH_3Cl + HCl \rightarrow SiH_2Cl_2 + H_2$$

[151] A. Stock and C. Somieski, *Ber.* **55**, 3961 (1922).
[152] A. Stock and C. Somieski, *ibid.* **52**, 695 (1919).

Higher hydrides may be chlorinated with chloroform, $CHCl_3$, using aluminum chloride as a catalyst:[153]

$$Si_3H_8 + 4CHCl_3 \rightarrow Si_3H_4Cl_4 + 4CH_2Cl_2$$

Table 2.13 lists the melting and boiling points of several halosilanes.

Silico-chloroform, $SiHCl_3$, is most easily prepared by heating crystalline silicon or a metallic silicide in a current of hydrogen chloride at 350° to 450°C.  Trichlorosilane is characterized by rather remarkable stability toward heat, but at red heat it decomposes reversibly:

$$4SiHCl_3 \rightleftharpoons Si + 3SiCl_4 + 2H_2$$

The ease with which $SiHCl_3$ can be obtained has led to its wide use as an intermediate in preparing more complex derivatives of silane.

The halosilanes react with ammonia to form amines:

$$3SiH_3Cl + 4NH_3 \rightarrow (SiH_3)_3N + 3NH_4Cl$$

and

$$SiH_2Cl_2 + 3NH_3 \rightarrow SiH_2NH + 2NH_4Cl$$

Trisilylamine, $(SiH_3)_3N$, is a volatile, spontaneously flammable liquid, whereas $SiH_2NH$ polymerizes to a material resembling silica.  The hydrolysis of the halosilanes is closely analogous:

$$2SiH_3Cl + H_2O \rightarrow H_3Si\text{–}O\text{–}SiH_3 + 2HCl$$

and

$$SiH_2Cl_2 + H_2O \rightarrow H_2SiO + 2HCl$$

The product of the first reaction is disiloxane, $(SiH_3)_2O$, a volatile low-boiling substance analogous to dimethyl ether.  The compound $H_2SiO$, known as prosiloxane, corresponds to formaldehyde and exists temporarily as the monomer which soon polymerizes to liquid and solid forms. Among these are a benzene-soluble hexamer, $(H_2SiO)_6$, and solid polymers resembling silica.[154]

**Siloxanes.**  Prosiloxane and disiloxane are two of the simpler members of a group of oxygen-containing silanes that are similar to the oxygen-containing organic derivatives of the hydrocarbons.  In chemical behavior, however, these compounds are very different from the analogous carbon compounds.  They are characterized by an unusual ability to polymerize.  Silica, $SiO_2$, the simplest silicon-oxygen compound, is known

---

[153] A. Stock and P. Stiebeler, *ibid.* **56**, 1087 (1923).
[154] A. Stock, *ibid.* **50**, 1769 (1917); A. Stock, C. Somieski, and R. Wintgen, *ibid.* **50**, 1764 (1917); Stock and Somieski, *loc. cit.* ref. 149.

only in the very-high-melting polymerized form (quartz, tridymite, cristobalite, etc.), whereas carbon dioxide is gaseous and forms a molecular lattice. Indeed, Stock reports that $(SiH_3)_2O$ and $H_2SiO$ are the only siloxanes known as monomers.

Other siloxanes are formed by the careful hydrolysis of halosilanes:

$$Si_2Cl_6 + 4H_2O \rightarrow 6HCl + SiO_2H \cdot SiO_2H \quad \text{Silico-oxalic acid}$$
$$\text{(polymerized)}$$

and

$$Si_3Cl_8 + 5H_2O \rightarrow 8HCl + SiO_2H \cdot SiO \cdot SiO_2H \quad \text{Silico-mesoxalic acid}$$
$$\text{(polymerized)}$$

Silico-mesoxalic acid explodes on slight friction and is less stable than silico-oxalic acid, which explodes on warming. In like fashion, silanetriol, $HSi(OH)_3$, the primary hydrolysis product of $SiHCl_3$, condenses spontaneously to a silicalike polymer with the composition $(HSiO_{3/2})_x$, in contrast to methanetriol which dehydrates to the volatile, slightly associated formic acid, HCOOH. A similar hydrolysis takes place with many halogen derivatives of the hydrocarbons, but much less readily. With increasing oxygen content the siloxanes depart more and more from their organic counterparts, regardless of the other constituents. In the presence of permanganate or solutions of the compounds of the noble metals siloxanes are mild reducing agents, but concentrated nitric acid is without reaction on them. The organic siloxane derivatives and polymers include the commercially important silicones (Chapter 3).

**Siloxens.** When $CaSi_2$ is treated with dilute HCl, a polymerized siloxane of the composition $Si_6O_3H_6$ is formed.[155] This compound, known as siloxen, is the parent substance for a group of compounds of unusual properties and has been assigned the following structural formula:

[155] H. Kautsky, *Z. Electrochem.* **32**, 349 *et seq.* (1926).

Siloxen is a powerful reducing agent.  It decomposes water with the liberation of hydrogen and is spontaneously flammable in the air.  The siloxen ring is a chromophore, and introduction of auxochrome groups leads to compounds which absorb in the visible spectrum.  The hydrogen can be substituted by halogens, atom for atom, to give compounds that are greenish to bright yellow in color:

$$Si_6O_3H_6 + I_2 \rightarrow Si_6O_3H_5I + HI$$
$$Si_6O_3H_6 + 3Br_2 \rightarrow Si_6O_3H_3Br_3 + 3HBr$$

The halogen compounds react with water or ammonia to form intensely colored hydroxy- and amino-compounds:

$$Si_6O_3H_5I + H_2O \rightarrow Si_6O_3H_5OH + HI$$
$$Si_6O_3H_3Br_3 + 6NH_3 \rightarrow Si_6O_3H_3(NH_2)_3 + 3NH_4Br$$

These compounds show strong fluorescence and extra-bright chemiluminescence.  Hexahydroxysiloxen is deep black in color and very explosive.

Physically these substances are built up of lamellae with their basal planes parallel in a fashion similar to graphitic acid.  During reactions, which all take place very quickly and completely, the solid structure does not change.  In this respect they resemble the zeolites.  Each molecule of the siloxen derivative is reported to yield the theoretical number of molecules of product by practically instantaneous diffusion.  Their large specific surface permits them to adsorb large quantities of gases, and, since they are almost all surface, they may contribute important knowledge of surface phenomena in the future.

**Miscellaneous Simple Compounds of Silicon.**  Nitrogen derivatives of silane, silazanes, have already been mentioned.  One of these, $Si(NH_2)_4$, on heating, successively loses ammonia with the formation of silicon nitride, $Si_3N_4$:

$$Si(NH_2)_4 \rightarrow Si(NH_2)_2NH + NH_3$$
$$Si(NH_2)_2NH \rightarrow Si(NH)_2 + NH_3$$

and on prolonged heating

$$3Si(NH)_2 \rightarrow Si_3N_4 + 2NH_3$$

This is apparently the compound prepared by Vigouroux and Hugot in 1903, who reported it to be stable at the melting point of glass.[156]  The Si–N bond is, indeed, very stable toward heat, and the melting point of $Si_3N_4$ is 1900°C.  In spite of its high thermal stability, the nitride is

---

[156] E. Vigouroux and Hugot, *Compt. rend.* **136**, 1670 (1903).

slowly hydrolyzed, thus reflecting the even greater stability of the oxide.

$$Si_3N_4 + 6H_2O \rightarrow 3SiO_2 + 4NH_3$$

Silicon disulfide, $SiS_2$, and diselenide, $SiSe_2$, may be prepared by heating the elements together. The disulfide forms long, colorless, silky needles, and the diselenide is described as an iridescent solid. Both are stable in dry air, but are slowly hydrolyzed by water. The great contrast between corresponding compounds of carbon and silicon is again evident in the disulfides; carbon disulfide, $CS_2$, is unimolecular with a boiling point of 46.25°C, whereas $SiS_2$ has a fibrous structure and is difficult to volatilize. X-ray diffraction has demonstrated the crystal structure of $SiS_2$ to consist of infinite chains of $SiS_4$ tetrahedra sharing opposite edges in common:[157]

Halogenated compounds, $SiSCl_2$ and $SiSBr_2$, are formed at red heat from $SiS_2$ and the appropriate halogen, or from $SiCl_4$ and $H_2S$. The colorless needles of the chloro-sulfide melt at 75°C, the bromo-sulfide at 93°C. The compound $SiCl_3 \cdot SH$ is a colorless liquid boiling at 96°C. Water decomposes the silicon halosulfides.

Disilyl sulfide, $(SiH_3)_2S$, and selenide, $(SiH_3)_2Se$, analogous to disilyl ether, $(SiH_3)_2O$, have been prepared, characterized, and some of their physical properties studied.[158] The reaction of $SiH_3I$ with phosphorus, phosphine, arsenic, and arsenides has been studied, leading to the isolation of $P(SiH_3)I_2$ and $As(SiH_3)I_2$ and to evidence for the existence of $P(SiH_3)_2I$, $P(SiH_3)_3$, $P(SiH_3)_4I$, $As(SiH_3)_2I$, $As(SiH_3)_3$, and $As(SiH_3)_4I$.[159]

[157] E. Zintl and K. Loosen, *Z. physik. Chem.* **174A**, 301 (1935); W. Büssem, H. Fischer, and E. Gruner, *Naturwiss.* **23**, 740 (1935).

[158] H. J. Eméleus, A. G. MacDiarmid, and A. G. Maddock, *J. Inorg. Nuclear Chem.* **1**, 194 (1955).

[159] B. J. Aylett, H. J. Eméleus, and A. G. Maddock, *ibid.* **1**, 187 (1955).

# CHAPTER 3

## ORGANOSILICON COMPOUNDS

**Introduction.** Although silica is known to be present in many common plant and animal tissues, including the stems of grasses and grains, in the hulls or shells of nuts, in bamboo, in tropical woods, in the spines of stinging nettles, in feathers, diatoms, and certain sponges, the occurrence of organic compounds of silicon in nature has rarely, if ever, been unequivocally demonstrated. In the *Equisetum* genus (horsetail), Viehoever and Prusky[1] concluded that the silica occurred in the epidermis in organic combination with cellulosic material. Similarly, Engel[2] has reported organic complexes of silica with galactose in rye straw. It is believed that the silica in animal tissues[3] is in combination with lipoid substances and cholesterol.

In contrast to the limited studies of natural organic silicon compounds is the "laboratory" chemistry of organosilicon[4] compounds dating back for more than a century. The great variety and unusual properties of these new synthetic substances, which include the commercially important silicones, justify their separate treatment.

**History.** About the first to prepare an organic compound containing silicon was Ebelmen,[5] who treated silicon tetrachloride with ethyl alcohol:

$$SiCl_4 + 4C_2H_5OH \rightarrow Si(OC_2H_5)_4 + 4HCl$$

The product obtained was ethyl silicate, a volatile liquid of pleasant odor, which is still prepared commercially by the same reaction.

Friedel and Crafts prepared the first compounds containing an organic radical directly attached to silicon.[6] Treating $SiCl_4$ with zinc diethyl, $Zn(C_2H_5)_2$, for some hours in a sealed tube at 160°C produced tetraethyl silicon, now called tetraethylsilane:

$$2Zn(C_2H_5)_2 + SiCl_4 \rightarrow Si(C_2H_5)_4 + 2ZnCl_2$$

[1] A. Viehoever and S. C. Prusky, *Am. J. Pharm.* **110**, 99 (1938).

[2] W. Engel, *Angew. Chem.* **64**, 601 (1952).

[3] L. Holzapfel, *Kolloid-Z.* **115**, 137 (1949).

[4] The term *organosilicon* is frequently reserved solely for those compounds in which carbon is linked directly to silicon. In this chapter, however, brief treatment of the esters or *ethers* of silicic acid, wherein organic groups are linked through oxygen to silicon, has been included.

[5] J. J. Ebelmen, *Compt. rend.* **19**, 398 (1844).

[6] C. Friedel and J. M. Crafts, *ibid.* **56**, 590 (1863); *Ann.* **136**, 203 (1865).

In a similar fashion, tetramethylsilane, $Si(CH_3)_4$, was obtained using zinc dimethyl, $Zn(CH_3)_2$. Both are commercial compounds today, but are prepared by simpler processes. Later the successive substitution of one, two, three, and four ethyl ($-C_2H_5$) groups for the ethoxy ($-OC_2H_5$) groups in ethyl silicate was achieved.[7] It was observed that the product, $(C_2H_5)_2Si(OC_2H_5)_2$, containing two ethyl and two ethoxy groups, would react with acidified water, liberating alcohol and forming a very viscous, heat-stable oil with a melting point of $-15°C$.[8] This, indeed, was the forerunner of today's silicone fluids.

A short time later, Ladenburg[9] prepared triethylphenylsilane and found the phenyl group to be more easily split off from the silicon by acids and alkalies than were the ethyl groups. This observation is important today in explaining some of the reactions of silicones.

In the period 1900–1940 the outstanding exponent of organosilicon chemistry was Kipping, who published 57 papers on the subject. Kipping started out to demonstrate that the chemistry of silicon was really similar to that of carbon, and, in 8 years of work, prepared the first organosilicon compound with an asymmetric silicon atom. As expected, the compound rotated the plane of polarized light and served to strengthen the analogy between silicon and carbon. In this work it was observed that phenyl ($-C_6H_5$) groups attached to silicon were split off by strong acids, but were stable to alkalies. On the other hand, benzyl ($-CH_2C_6H_5$) groups attached to silicon were stable to acids but unstable to alkalies.[10] Kipping introduced the recently discovered Grignard reaction as a means for attaching organic groups to silicon.[10] Some of the messy oils and sticky materials obtained in the studies he recognized as polymers formed by reactions of the type:

$$\begin{array}{ccccc} R & & R & R & R \\ | & & | & | & | \\ -SiOH & + & HOSi- & \rightarrow & -Si-O-Si- + H_2O \\ | & & | & | & | \\ R & & R & R & R \end{array}$$

Kipping investigated the use of sodium for substituting organic radicals for halogens attached to silicon. He showed that silicon and carbon were never joined by a double bond, and he studied the stability of the Si–O–Si and Si–Si bonds. Indeed, the breadth of Kipping's contribution to

[7] C. Friedel and A. Ladenburg, *Ann.* **159**, 259 (1871).
[8] A. Ladenburg, *ibid.* **164**, 300 (1872).
[9] A. Ladenburg, *ibid.* **173**, 143 (1874).
[10] F. S. Kipping, *J. Chem. Soc.* **91**, 209 (1907).

organosilicon chemistry can be fully appreciated only by a reading of his numerous papers.[11]

This brief historical treatment must end here.   Since 1940 the literature has increased greatly, as has also the commercial interest in these compounds.   After consideration of the Si–C bond, the remainder of the chapter will summarize the chemistry of some of the important groups of organosilicon compounds.

**The Silicon-Carbon Bond.**   The properties of the Si—C bond can best be understood from a combination of theory and observation.   The similarity in electronic structure of carbon $(1s^2, 2s^2 2p^2)$ and silicon $(1s^2, 2s^2 2p^6, 3s^2 3p^2)$ suggests that Si–C bonds may closely resemble C–C bonds.   A comparison of the cubic form of silicon carbide (diamondlike structure) with diamond, however, discloses the greater bond distance, lower density, and lower melting point of SiC, and points to a weaker bond in SiC than in diamond.   The fact that the Si–C bond is a bond

|         | $a$     | Bond Distance | Density | Melting Point |
|---------|---------|---------------|---------|---------------|
| SiC     | 4.35 A  | 1.88 A        | 3.21    | >2700°C       |
| Diamond | 3.56 A  | 1.54 A        | 3.51    | >3500°C       |

between dissimilar elements must also be considered.   Although both silicon and carbon belong to the same family of the periodic table, they are in different periods, and silicon is more electropositive in nature than carbon.   In terms of Pauling's electronegativity, silicon is 1.8 compared to 2.5 for carbon.[12]   The Si–C bond, therefore, is slightly polar, and calculations based on the electronegativity difference, 0.7, indicate approximately 12% ionic character.[13]   This polarity is enhanced or diminished by the nature of the atoms or groups attached to the silicon and carbon atoms and, in turn, exerts important directive forces in reactions with attacking molecules.[14]   Silicon-carbon bonds thus range widely in stability; tetraphenylsilane, $(C_6H_5)_4Si$, distills unchanged in air at 430°C, whereas cold water easily disrupts the structure CH≡C–Si.

**Silicic Acid Esters or Ethers.**   The early preparation (1844) of ethyl silicate by Ebelmen has been mentioned previously (p. 104).   Isoamyl

[11] These papers are briefly abstracted in essentially chronological order in: H. W. Post, *Silicones and Other Organic Silicon Compounds*, Reinhold Publishing Corp., New York, 1949, Chap. 3.

[12] L. C. Pauling, *The Nature of the Chemical Bond*, Cornell University Press, Ithaca, N. Y., 1939, p. 64.

[13] Pauling, *op. cit.*, p. 69.

[14] E. G. Rochow, *Chemistry of the Silicones*, John Wiley and Sons, Inc., New York, 2nd Edition, 1951, pp. 21–28.

orthosilicate was also prepared by the same method. Later the methyl compound, halogen containing esters, and mixed esters were prepared:[15]

$$SiCl_4 + 4CH_3OH \rightarrow 4HCl + Si(OCH_3)_4$$

$$SiCl_4 + 3CH_3OH \rightarrow 3HCl + ClSi(OCH_3)_3$$

$$ClSi(OCH_3)_3 + C_2H_5OH \rightarrow HCl + C_2H_5OSi(OCH_3)_3$$

Indeed, this reaction, by which a polyhalogen compound reacts with an alcohol, is the most practical for preparing these silicoorthoesters and is merely an adaptation of the Williamson ether synthesis. The consideration of these compounds as esters of orthosilicic acid, $H_4SiO_4$, is a purely formal one. Silicic acid does not yield hydrogen ions and, therefore, is not acidic. On the other hand, the alcohol used may be decidedly acidic, as when phenol is used in preparing phenyl silicate, $Si(OC_6H_5)_4$. Accordingly, some have suggested the name *ether* as more appropriate than ester for these products.

The preparation of alkoxyhalosilanes is facilitated by using benzene as an inert solvent.[16] Moist alcohol introduces a certain amount of high boiling product containing an oxygen bridge, $(RO)_3Si-O-Si(OR)_3$. These alkoxysiloxanes probably are formed by hydrolysis of the ester and subsequent condensation of the resulting silicols. Stepwise, controllable hydrolysis is characteristic of the silicon orthoesters, and condensed esters of higher and higher molecular weights are readily formed. Some of these produced from ethyl silicate have found uses as paint vehicles, preservatives for stone, and as heat-resistant coatings.[17] In the presence of suitable catalysts all silicon esters hydrolyze completely to silica:

$$Si(OR)_4 + 2H_2O \rightarrow SiO_2 + 4ROH$$

Most of the commercial interest in these esters stems from this easily controlled ability to precipitate silica in a desired form. Grignard reagent reacts stepwise with the ester's alkoxy groups to form compounds with organic groups directly attached to silicon:[18]

$$C_3H_7MgBr + Si(OC_2H_5)_4 \rightarrow C_3H_7Si(OC_2H_5)_3 + Mg(OC_2H_5)Br$$

In the same fashion, silicoesters and zinc alkyls yield organosilicon type

[15] C. Friedel and J. M. Crafts, *Ann.* **127**, 28 (1863); *Ann. chim. phys.* [4] 9, 5 (1866).

[16] M. Kalinin, *Compt. rend. acad. sci.* (*U.S.S.R.*) **18**, 433 (1938).

[17] G. King, *Paint Varnish Production Mgr.* 15, 26, 28–30, 32 (Dec., 1936); H. A. Auden and H. P. Staudinger, **British 494,848** (1937).

[18] R. R. McGregor and E. L. Warrick, **U.S. 2,380,057** (1945).

compounds :[19]

$$Zn(C_2H_5)_2 + Si(OCH_3)_4 \rightarrow C_2H_5ZnOCH_3 + C_2H_5Si(OCH_3)_3$$

For more detailed treatment of the silicoesters, additional methods of preparation, and other known types of esters, the reader is referred to Post's monograph.[20] Physical constants of some silicoorthoesters are listed in Table 3.1.

TABLE 3.1.  PHYSICAL CONSTANTS OF SILICOORTHOESTERS*

| Ester | Melting Point, °C | Boiling Point, °C | Density | Refractive Index |
|---|---|---|---|---|
| $Si(OCH_3)_4$ | $\cdots$ | 121–122 | $1.028\dfrac{22}{4}$ | 1.3677 $(H_D)$ |
| $Si(OC_2H_5)_4$ | $-82.5$ | 165.5 | $0.933\dfrac{20}{4}$ | 1.3821 $(20°/D)$ |
| $Si(OC_3H_7)_4\ n$ | $\cdots$ | 204–206 (17 mm) | $1.0328\dfrac{25}{4}$ | 1.5431 $(25°/D)$ |
| $Si(OC_3H_7)_4\ iso$ | 33.5 | 176–178 (13 mm) | $1.0099\dfrac{25}{4}$ | 1.5350 $(35°/D)$ |
| $Si(OC_4H_9)_4\ n$ | $\cdots$ | 273–277 | 0.913 | 1.4128 $(20°/D)$ |
| $Si(OC_4H_9)_4\ iso$ | $\cdots$ | 256–260 | 0.953 | $\cdots$ |
| $Si(OC_5H_{11})_4\ n$ | $\cdots$ | 145–150 (3 mm) | $0.8933\dfrac{25}{4}$ | $\cdots$ |
| $Si(OC_5H_{11})_4\ iso$ | $\cdots$ | $\cdots$ | 0.8854 | 1.4183 $(20°/D)$ |
| $Si(OC_6H_5)_4$ | 47–48 | $\cdots$ | $\cdots$ | $\cdots$ |
| $Si(OOCCH_3)_4$ | 110 | 148 (5 mm) | $\cdots$ | $\cdots$ |

* Chiefly from Post, *op. cit.* ref. 20, Chap. 12.

The silicon esters exert a hemolytic effect, similar to that of ether and chloroform, when taken into the human body. Breathing air containing 9 to 20 mg/l of ethyl silicate leads to fatal hemolysis in experimental animals.[21] Methyl silicate vapors are reported to cause severe irritation of the cornea of the eye.[22] No silicosis or physiological action attributable to the silicon content of these materials has been demonstrated, however.

**Silicon Alkyls.** Silicon alkyls[23] of the type $SiR_4$, where $R$ is any

[19] A. Ladenburg, *Ann.* **173**, 143 (1874).

[20] H. W. Post, *The Chemistry of the Aliphatic Orthoesters*, A.C.S. Monograph 92, Reinhold Publishing Corp., New York, 1943, Chaps., 9–10.

[21] J. A. Kasper, C. P. McCord, and W. G. Fredrick, *Report of Detroit Department of Health*, Oct. 1, 1937.

[22] Anonymous, *Chem. Eng. News* **24**, 1690 (1946).

[23] The term *alkyl* is here used to designate both aliphatic and aromatic hydrocarbon radicals, as is common in organometallic chemistry.

hydrocarbon radical, are numerous. The simple $Si(CH_3)_4$ and $Si(C_2H_5)_4$, the first organosilicon compounds to be prepared, were obtained by the action of zinc alkyls on the silicon halides.[24] A more convenient method is to treat $SiCl_4$ with an excess of Grignard reagent.[25] Halogen replacement proceeds very easily until the last which requires heating to 100°C:

$$4CH_3MgBr + SiCl_4 \rightarrow Si(CH_3)_4 + 4MgBrCl$$

Tetramethyl silicon is a colorless, volatile, unreactive liquid with only a faint odor; bp = 26.5°C. The ethyl derivative boils at 153.7°C.

Silicon tetraphenyl has been prepared from $SiCl_4$ and chlorobenzene by sodium condensation:[26]

$$SiCl_4 + 4C_6H_5Cl + 8Na \rightarrow Si(C_6H_5)_4 + 8NaCl$$

The tetraphenyl is also easily prepared from the Grignard reagent with either $SiCl_4$ or $Na_2SiF_6$,[27] and by treatment of triphenylsilane with phenyllithium.[28] It is an extraordinarily stable substance, melting at 237°C and boiling undecomposed at 430°C. Hydrogen at 75 atmospheres and 450°C has no action on it in 200 hours. Fuming nitric acid, although it nitrates the phenyl groups, does not split them off. Bromine, phosphorus pentachloride, and aluminum chloride, however, on heating remove the phenyl groups stepwise:

$$Si(C_6H_5)_4 + AlCl_3 \rightarrow (C_6H_5)_3SiCl + C_6H_5AlCl_2$$

Tetrabenzyl silicon, $Si(CH_2 \cdot C_6H_5)_4$, is another exceptionally stable compound; it is said to boil undecomposed above 550°C.

Mixed alkyls with up to four different groups on a silicon atom are prepared by means of the Grignard reagent. Among these are compounds in which silicon forms part of a ring as in:[29]

$$CH_2 \begin{array}{c} CH_2-CH_2 \\ \diagup \qquad \diagdown \\ \qquad \qquad Si \\ \diagdown \qquad \diagup \\ CH_2-CH_2 \end{array} \begin{array}{c} C_2H_5 \\ \diagup \\ \diagdown \\ C_2H_5 \end{array}$$

[24] Friedel and Crafts, *loc. cit.* ref. 6.

[25] F. S. Kipping, *Proc. Chem. Soc.* **20**, 15 (1904); W. Dilthey (reported to P. Pfeiffer and K. Schnurmann), *Ber.* **37**, 319 (1904); A. Bygden, *ibid.* **44**, 2640 (1911).

[26] A. Polis, *Ber.* **18**, 1540 (1885).

[27] E. M. Sochestvenskaja, *J. Gen. Chem. (U.S.S.R.)* **8**, 294 (1938); Z. Manulkin and F. Yakubova, *ibid.* **10**, 1300 (1940).

[28] H. Gilman and H. W. Melvin, Jr., *J. Am. Chem. Soc.* **71**, 4050 (1949).

[29] G. Grüttner and M. Wiernik, *Ber.* **48**, 1473 (1915).

As a class, the silicon tetra-alkyls are very stable. In the cold, in water, concentrated potassium hydroxide and concentrated sulfuric acid have no affect on them. The halogens, if they react at all, normally only replace hydrogen on the carbons. Exceptionally large and highly branched alkyl groups introduce sufficient steric hindrance as to prevent complete tetra-substitution, even though the silicon atom radius is 50% larger than that of carbon. For instance, only three cyclohexyl groups can be accommodated around silicon,[30] and the tertiary butyl radical will replace only two of the chlorine atoms of $SiCl_4$.[31] Physical data on more than 80 silicon alkyls and organopolysilanes, and for over 100 organosilanes with substituted alkyl groups have been tabulated by Rochow.[32]

**Alkylsilanes.** Derivatives of $SiH_4$ in which the hydrogens are only partly replaced by alkyl groups are readily obtained from the corresponding halosilanes by the methods used in preparing the silicon tetra-alkyls:[33]

$$2SiH_3Cl + Zn(CH_3)_2 \rightarrow 2CH_3SiH_3 + ZnCl_2$$
$$SiHCl_3 + 3C_6H_5MgBr \rightarrow (C_6H_5)_3SiH + 3MgBrCl$$

The alkylsilanes[34] can also be made by the action of lithium hydride or lithium aluminum hydride on the alkylhalosilanes:[35]

$$(C_2H_5)_2SiCl_2 + 2LiH \rightarrow (C_2H_5)_2SiH_2 + 2LiCl$$

The hydrogen of the alkylsilanes is easily attacked by oxygen and the halogens. Methyl silane, $CH_3SiH_3$, although not spontaneously flammable, explodes if shaken with mercury in an oxygen atmosphere. Triethylsilane, $(C_2H_5)_3SiH$, is stable in air and to concentrated sulfuric acid; but fuming acid oxidizes it to the ether, $(C_2H_5)_3Si–O–Si(C_2H_5)_3$, and bromine immediately forms $(C_2H_5)_3SiBr$ and HBr. Alkalies cleave the Si–H bond in alkylsilanes, and the rate in trialkyl derivatives in alcoholic potash solution decreases with increase in size of the alkyl groups.[36] Rochow has listed physical properties of various alkylsilanes that have been obtained in a pure state.[37]

[30] W. H. Nebergall and O. H. Johnson, *J. Am. Chem. Soc.* **71**, 4022 (1949).

[31] L. J. Tyler, L. H. Sommer, and F. C. Whitmore, *ibid.* **70**, 2876 (1948).

[32] Rochow, *op. cit.* ref. 14, pp. 171–176.

[33] F. Taurke, *Ber.* **38**, 1661 (1905); H. H. Reynolds, L. A. Bigelow, and C. A. Kraus, *J. Am. Chem. Soc.* **51**, 3067 (1929); A. G. Taylor and B. V. de G. Walden, *ibid.* **66**, 842 (1944); H. J. Eméleus *et al.*, *J. Inorg. Nuclear Chem.* **1**, 194 (1955).

[34] Compounds containing two or more different substituent groups are named as derivatives of silane in the recommended system of nomenclature, reserving the term *silicon tetra-* for the completely substituted compound with four like groups.

[35] A. E. Finholt *et al.*, *J. Am. Chem. Soc.* **69**, 2692 (1947).

[36] F. P. Price, *ibid.* **69**, 2600 (1947).

[37] Rochow, *op. cit.*, p. 173.

**Alkylhalosilanes.** The alkylhalosilanes deserve special emphasis, since many are intermediates in the preparation of silicone polymers. All three types, $R_3SiX$, $R_2SiX_2$, and $RSiX_3$, have reactive halogen linkages through which they are easily converted into silicols, alkoxysilanes, or organosiloxane polymers. Table 3.2 lists melting points and boiling points for selected examples of each type.

TABLE 3.2. PHYSICAL CONSTANTS OF ORGANOHALOSILANES*

| Compound | Melting Point, °C | Boiling Point, °C | Compound | Melting Point, °C | Boiling Point, °C |
|---|---|---|---|---|---|
| $CH_3SiF_3$ | −72.8 | −30.2 | $C_2H_5SiCl_3$ | −105.6 | 97.9 |
| $(CH_3)_2SiF_2$ | −87.5 | 2.7 | $(C_2H_5)_2SiCl_2$ | −96.5 | 129 |
| $(CH_3)_3SiF$ | −74.3 | 16.4 | $(C_2H_5)_3SiCl$ | · · · | 143.5 |
| $C_2H_5SiF_3$ | −113.3 | −4.2 | $C_6H_5SiCl_3$ | · · · | 201.5 |
| $(C_2H_5)_2SiF_2$ | −78.7 | 60.9 | $(C_6H_5)_2SiCl_2$ | · · · | 305.2 |
| $(C_2H_5)_3SiF$ | · · · | 109 | $(C_6H_5)_3SiCl$ | 88–89 | 378 |
| $(C_6H_5)SiF_3$ | · · · | 102 | | | |
| $(C_6H_5)_2SiF_2$ | · · · | 247 | $CH_3SiBr_3$ | · · · | 133.5 |
| $(C_6H_5)_3SiF$ | 64 | 205 (10 mm) | $(CH_3)_2SiBr_2$ | · · · | 112.3 |
| | | | $(CH_3)_3SiBr$ | · · · | 80 |
| $CH_3SiCl_3$ | −77.8 | 65.7 | $(C_2H_5)_3SiBr$ | · · · | 66.5 (24 mm) |
| $(CH_3)_2SiCl_2$ | −76.1 | 70.0 | $(C_6H_5)_2SiBr_2$ | · · · | 180 (12 mm) |
| $(CH_3)_3SiCl$ | −57.7 | 57.3 | $(C_6H_5)_3SiBr$ | 119 | · · · |

* Selected from a table of data on more than 150 organohalosilanes: Rochow, *op. cit.* ref. 14, pp. 177–179.

A variety of *trialkylfluorosilanes* can be prepared by the action of the appropriate Grignard reagents on silicon tetrafluoride[38] or sodium fluosilicate.[39] Even with an excess of the Grignard reagent, alkylation does not proceed beyond the trisubstitution stage. Apparently the remaining F atom becomes much less reactive than the final Cl or Br atom in $R_3SiCl$ and $R_3SiBr$. Hexamethyl- and hexaethyldisiloxane, when treated with HF, yield $(CH_3)_3SiF$ and $(C_2H_5)_3SiF$.[40] The Swarts reaction,[41] employing $SbF_3$ and $SbCl_5$, has been widely used to prepare organofluorosilanes from chlorosilanes.[42]

[38] F. M. Jaeger and D. W. Dykstra, *Z. anorg. u. allgem. Chem.* **143**, 233 (1925); J. A. Gierut, F. J. Sowa, and J. A. Nieuwland, *J. Am. Chem. Soc.* **58**, 897 (1936); H. V. Medoks and N. Z. Kotelkov, *J. Gen. Chem. (U.S.S.R.)* **7**, 2007 (1937) and **8**, 291 (1938).
[39] E. M. Sochestvenskaja, *ibid.* **8**, 294 (1938) and **10**, 1689 (1940).
[40] E. A. Flood, *J. Am. Chem. Soc.* **55**, 1735 (1933); C. A. Burkhard *et al.*, *Chem. Revs.* **41**, 97 (1947); F. C. Whitmore *et al.*, *J. Am. Chem. Soc.* **68**, 1881 (1946); **70**, 433 (1948).
[41] F. Swarts, *Acad. Roy. Belg.* [3] *Bull.*, No. 9–10, 309, *Bull.*, No. 11, 474 (1892).
[42] H. S. Booth *et al.*, *J. Am. Chem. Soc.* **68**, 2650, 2652, 2655, 2658, 2660, 2662 (1946).

Trialkylchlorosilanes from $(CH_3)_3SiCl$ to $(C_6H_5CH_2)_3SiCl$ are known,[43,44] and the corresponding bromo analogs up to $(C_6H_5)_3SiBr$ have been prepared. These, in general, are readily synthesized by the action of limited amounts of the appropriate Grignard reagent on the silicon tetrahalide. Successive treatment with different Grignard reagents will yield mixed trialkylhalosilanes.[45]

Most characteristic of the trialkylchlorosilanes is their hydrolysis to trialkylsilanols, $R_3SiOH$, which in turn may condense to organodisiloxanes:

$$R_3SiCl + H_2O \rightarrow R_3SiOH + HCl$$

$$2R_3SiOH \rightarrow R_3Si-O-SiR_3 + H_2O$$

The larger the R group the slower the rate of condensation. Thus $(C_6H_5)_3SiOH$ does not condense when distilled at 170–180°C and 1 mm pressure, but pure $(CH_3)_3SiOH$ can only be isolated by special means.[46]

Numerous *dialkyldihalosilanes* have been made for use as intermediates in the formation of polymeric silicones. They are easily prepared by the direct action of the alkyl halide on elementary silicon at 300°C in the presence of a copper or silver catalyst.[47] Yields as high as 70% are obtainable, the net reaction being:

$$2RX + Si \rightarrow R_2SiX_2$$

The Grignard synthesis is also suitable for the preparation of the dihalides. The dialkyldihalosilanes form esters when treated with alcohols:

$$R_2SiX_2 + 2R'OH \rightarrow R_2Si(OR')_2 + 2HX$$

Of most interest is the hydrolysis of these esters to form dialkylsilanediols or dialkylsilicols, $R_2Si(OH)_2$. As in the case of the trialkylsilanols, these diols also condense to form polymeric organosiloxanes at rates which decrease as the size of the R group increases. Monomeric dimethylsilanediol requires exceptional care in its preparation because minute traces of acid or base catalyze its condensation; whereas diphenylsilanediol separates easily as a stable, white, crystalline compound on adding $(C_6H_5)_2SiCl_2$ to a mixture of water, toluene, and *t*-amyl alcohol.[48]

[43] Taylor and Walden, *op. cit.*; W. F. Gilliam and R. O. Sauer, *J. Am. Chem. Soc.* 66, 1793 (1944).

[44] G. Martin and F. S. Kipping, *J. Chem. Soc.* 95, 302 (1909).

[45] F. S. Kipping, *ibid.* 91, 717 (1907).

[46] R. O. Sauer, *J. Am. Chem. Soc.* 66, 1707 (1944).

[47] E. G. Rochow *et al.*, *ibid.* 67, 963, 1057, 1773 (1945).

[48] C. A. Burkhard, *J. Am. Chem. Soc.* 67, 2173 (1945); J. F. Hyde, *ibid.* 75, 2166 (1953); S. W. Kantor, *ibid.* 75, 2712 (1953).

Phenyl- and *p*-tolyltrichlorosilanes, the first *alkyltrihalosilanes* to be synthesized, were prepared by treating $SiCl_4$ with the respective mercury alkyls.[49] More suitable for preparing all such trihalides is the action of the appropriate Grignard reagent on $SiX_4$. A fair yield of trihalosilane may also be had in the reaction of alkyl halides with silicon, if carried out under conditions favoring the pyrolysis of the free radicals:[50]

$$3RX + Si \rightarrow RSiX_3 + 2R \text{ (followed by pyrolysis of R)}$$

The alkyltrihalides hydrolyze supposedly to form silanetriols, $RSi(OH)_3$, but no such monomeric compounds have been isolated. Loss of water from a single molecule of triol would lead to a "siliconic acid" analogous to a carboxylic acid:

$$CH_3Si(OH)_3 \rightarrow H_2O + CH_3SiOOH$$

The condensation products of all silanetriols, however, are obviously polymeric substances, being either viscous, glassy, or silica-like materials. Evidently, condensation proceeds until a three-dimensional silicon-oxygen network results. This property is the basis of the silicone polymer industry.

The methylchlorosilanes show another most spectacular property—the ability to make certain surfaces water-repellent. Their vapors react rapidly at room temperature with hydrophilic surfaces to leave a submicroscopic film which renders the surface water-repellent for a considerable period of time. Filter paper exposed to the vapors for less than one second is no longer wet by water. Cotton and wool may be treated in the same way. Glass and ceramic surfaces are not acted on by the methylchlorosilanes if they are completely dry, as after baking in a vacuum. However, under ordinary conditions the adsorbed film of water on their surfaces will react with these compounds and leave a water-repellent organosilicon film. Neutral solvents and detergents wet the film but do not remove it.

Allyl-[51] and vinylchlorosilanes[51,52] have been prepared and their properties investigated. Numerous derivatives of the halosilanes, in which the alkyl groups are halogenated, have been described.[53] The preparatory methods previously discussed may also be used to synthesize

[49] A. Ladenburg, *Ann.* **173**, 143 (1874).
[50] Rochow, *op. cit.* ref. 47.
[51] D. T. Hurd, *J. Am. Chem. Soc.* **67**, 1813 (1945).
[52] C. A. Burkhard and R. H. Krieble, *ibid.* 69, 2687 (1947).
[53] For instance: R. H. Krieble and J. R. Elliott, *ibid.* **67**, 1810 (1945); L. H. Sommer and F. C. Whitmore, *ibid.* **68**, 485 (1946); C. L. Agre, *ibid.* **71**, 300 (1949).

"mixed" alkylhalosilanes containing Si–H as well as Si–X linkages:

$$CH_3MgCl + SiHCl_3 \rightarrow CH_3SiHCl_2 + MgCl_2$$
$$2CH_3Cl + Si \rightarrow CH_3SiHCl_2 + C + H_2$$

(under pyrolyzing conditions)

Such compounds may be hydrolyzed or esterified without cleaving the Si–H bond, but the hydrogen retains its silane vulnerability to oxidation by aqueous alkalies.

**Alkylalkoxysilanes.** The action of alcohols on the dialkyldihalosilanes to form alkylsilicic esters is characteristic of all types of alkylhalosilanes:

$$R_3SiX + R'OH \rightarrow R_3SiOR' + HX$$
$$R_2SiX_2 + 2R'OH \rightarrow R_2Si(OR')_2 + 2HX$$
$$RSiX_3 + 3R'OH \rightarrow RSi(OR')_3 + 3HX$$

The alkylalkoxysilanes may also be obtained by direct action of the Grignard reagent[54] or of zinc alkyls[55] on orthosilicates. Common to these esters is their hydrolysis followed by condensation to form polymeric materials, among them the commercially important silicone polymers. Physical data on more than 60 alkoxyorganosilanes have been listed by Rochow.[56]

A number of cyclic alkoxy derivatives have been prepared by the action of ethylene glycol or polyethylene glycols on $(CH_3)_2SiCl_2$;[57] for instance:

Dimeric dimethylethylenedioxysilane

$$(CH_3)_2Si \underset{O-CH_2-CH_2-O}{\overset{O-CH_2-CH_2-O}{\diagup\diagdown}} Si(CH_3)_2$$

Dimethyl-(trimethylene-1,3-dioxy)-silane

$$(CH_3)_2Si \underset{O-CH_2}{\overset{O-CH_2}{\diagup\diagdown}} \overset{CH_2}{\underset{}{}}$$

[54] McGregor and Warrick, *op. cit.* ref. 18.
[55] Ladenburg, *op. cit.* ref. 19.
[56] Rochow, *op. cit.* ref. 14, pp. 180–181.
[57] R. H. Krieble and C. A. Burkhard, *J. Am. Chem. Soc.* **69**, 2689 (1947).

Tetramethyl-1,3-(2,2'-oxydiethoxy)-disiloxane

$$O-CH_2-CH_2-O-CH_2-CH_2-O$$

$$(CH_3)_2Si\text{————}O\text{————}Si(CH_3)_2$$

Water-soluble alkylsilicic esters with fair hydrolytic stability are obtained when one or more 2-methoxyethoxy groups are attached to methyl-, phenyl-, and benzylchlorosilanes.[58]   On standing 30 minutes an aqueous solution of dimethyl *bis*-2-methoxyethoxysilane is merely cloudy from hydrolysis, but after 24 hours a dimethyl silicone oil has separated.

**Alkylsilylamines.**   The alkylhalosilanes, like the silicon halides, react with ammonia and amines, the products being substituted silylamines or silazanes.   One, two, or all three of the hydrogens of the ammonia molecule may be replaced by alkylsilyl groups, but not with equal ease. With trimethylchlorosilane and ammonia, only hexamethyldisilazane is obtained:[59]

$$2(CH_3)_3SiCl + 3NH_3 \rightarrow (CH_3)_3SiNHSi(CH_3)_3 + 2NH_4Cl$$

The N–H bond of this compound is unexpectedly stable, as evidenced by failure to isolate the tertiary amine, $[(CH_3)_3Si]_3N$, during the ammonolysis of $(CH_3)_3SiCl$, and by the inactivity of metallic sodium when applied for 16 hours at 125°C.   In water or in basic solutions it yields ammonia and trimethylsilanol:

$$(CH_3)_6Si_2NH + 2H_2O \rightarrow 2(CH_3)_3SiOH + NH_3$$

In acids, however, hexamethyldisiloxane is produced.

$$(CH_3)_6Si_2NH + H_3O^+ \rightarrow (CH_3)_6Si_2O + NH_4^+$$

Alkyl substituted amines have an action similar to ammonia, but large R groups on the amines may prevent substitution of part of the hydrogen:

$$(CH_3)_3SiCl + (C_2H_5)_2NH \rightarrow (CH_3)_3SiN(C_2H_5)_2 + HCl$$

Larger R groups on the silicon may also sterically hinder the ammonolysis reaction.

Dialkyldihalosilanes and ammonia react to form diamines, $R_2Si(NH_2)_2$, which polymerize with loss of ammonia:

$$\begin{array}{ccc} R & R & R \\ | & | & | \\ 2H_2N-Si-NH_2 \rightarrow H_2N-Si-NH-Si-NH_2 + NH_3 \\ | & | & | \\ R & R & R \end{array}$$

---

[58] C. A. Burkhard, *J. Org. Chem.* **15**, 106 (1950).
[59] R. O. Sauer and R. H. Hasek, *J. Am. Chem. Soc.* **68**, 241 (1946).

This reaction is analogous to the polymerization of the silanediols to form siloxanes. Cyclic trisilazanes and tetrasilazanes have been prepared and described.[60] Properties of 26 organosilazanes have been tabulated by Rochow.[61]

**Organosilicon Esters.** The term *ester* in this section is used to indicate compounds containing an organosilicon group attached to a ternary inorganic or organic acid radical, such as sulfate, phosphate, acetate, benzoate, etc.

Trialkylsilyl chlorides and hexalkyldisiloxanes react with concentrated or fuming sulfuric acid to yield trialkylsilyl sulfates:[62]

$$2R_3SiCl + H_2SO_4 \rightarrow (R_3Si)_2SO_4 + 2HCl$$

$$R_3SiOSiR_3 + SO_3 \rightarrow (R_3Si)_2SO_4$$

Trimethylsilyl sulfate, $[(CH_3)_3Si]_2SO_4$, is a white crystalline solid, mp 56°–58°C, and triethylsilyl sulfate, $[(C_2H_5)_3Si]_2SO_4$, is a liquid, bp 170°C (12 mm), $n^{20}D = 1.4442$. Phosphoric anhydride likewise reacts with hexamethyldisiloxane to produce trimethylsilyl phosphate, $[(CH_3)_3Si]_3PO_4$, bp 85°–87°C (4 mm), $n^{20}D = 1.4090$.[63] Water easily hydrolyzes these esters to silanols or disiloxanes.

Silicon tetracetate was first prepared in 1867 by treating $SiCl_4$ with acetic anhydride,[64] and more recently by reaction of organic acetates with $SiCl_4$.[65] Substituted acetoxysilanes, silyl acetates, can be made by a variety of methods,[66] most convenient of which is perhaps the reaction of anhydrous sodium acetate with alkylchlorosilanes:[67]

$$(CH_3)_3SiCl + CH_3COONa \rightarrow (CH_3)_3SiOCOCH_3 + NaCl$$

Trimethylacetoxysilane, trimethylsilyl acetate, boils at 30° to 31°C under a pressure of 35 mm. When long-chain alkyl groups are present these compounds have the property of imparting water-repellent films to tex-

---

[60] S. D. Brewer and C. P. Haber, *ibid*. **70**, 3888 (1948).

[61] Rochow, *op. cit.* ref. 14, p. 186.

[62] N. Patnode and F. C. Schmidt, *J. Am. Chem. Soc.* **67**, 2272 (1945); L. H. Sommer *et al.*, *ibid.* **68**, 156, 2282 (1946); *ibid.* **70**, 445 (1948).

[63] R. O. Sauer, *ibid.* **66**, 1707 (1944).

[64] C. Friedel and A. Ladenburg, *Ann.* **145**, 174 (1868).

[65] J. N. Volnov, *J. Gen. Chem. (U.S.S.R.)* **9**, 2269 (1939).

[66] C. Friedel and J. M. Crafts, *Am. J. Sci. Arts.* [2] **43**, 331 (1867); A. Ladenburg, *Ber.* **5**, 319 (1872); *Ann.* **164**, 300 (1872); R. O. Sauer and W. Patnode, *J. Am. Chem. Soc.* **67**, 1548 (1945).

[67] A. J. Barry, U.S. **2,405,988** (1946); H. A. Schuyten, J. W. Weaver, and J. D. Reid, *J. Am. Chem. Soc.* **69**, 2110 (1947).

tiles, paper, and hydrophilic surfaces in general.[68] The compounds react with hydroxyl groups on the surface and attach their alkylsilyl groups to the fiber surface. The acetic acid liberated in the process is less damaging to most fibers than the hydrochloric acid set free when the methylchlorosilanes are used.

**Derivatives of the Polysilanes.** Since organic derivatives of monosilane are so numerous, it would be expected that similar derivatives of the polysilanes could be prepared. This is indeed the case; short organosubstituted silicon chains are known and may be regarded, in a sense, as polymers based on simple silyl groups. Because of the fundamental instability of the longer silicon chains, preparation of the higher alkyl polysilanes is more difficult than for monosilane derivatives.

Hexachlorodisilane has been successfully alkylated by means of Grignard reagents or sodium alkyls,[69] but octachlorotrisilane has one Si–Si bond broken when treated with $C_6H_5MgBr$, resulting in the formation of tetraphenylsilane and hexaphenyldisilane. Indeed, it is rather common to encounter some cleavage of the lone Si–Si bond of halogenated disilanes during alkylation.[70]

Both cyclical and open-chain tetramers have been synthesized by the reaction of sodium on dichlorosilanes substituted by phenyl, tolyl, or benzyl groups:[71]

$$4(C_6H_5)_2SiCl_2 + 8Na \rightarrow 8NaCl + \begin{array}{c} Si(C_6H_5)_2-Si(C_6H_5)_2 \\ | \qquad\qquad | \\ Si(C_6H_5)_2-Si(C_6H_5)_2 \end{array}$$

Evidence for the corresponding open-chain tetramer is chiefly a marked unsaturation exhibited by one modification of the product. Molten sodium is reported to react with $(CH_3)_2SiCl_2$ to form a mixture of substances from which the cyclic hexamer, $[(CH_3)_2Si]_6$, has been isolated.[72] These materials have no practical applications in polymer technology because they readily oxidize, hydrolyze, or dissociate thermally.

**Silicon-Carbon Chains.** The stability of the Si—C bond in certain compounds suggests the possibility of compounds containing Si–C–Si

[68] Barry, *op. cit.*

[69] W. C. Schumb and C. M. Saffer, Jr., *J. Am. Chem. Soc.* **61**, 363 (1939); **63**, 93 (1941).

[70] C. Friedel and A. Ladenburg, *Compt. rend.* **68**, 920 (1869); *Ann. chim. phys.* [5] **19**, 390 (1880); *Ann.* **203**, 241 (1880); L. Gattermann and K. Weinlig, *Ber.* **27**, 1943 (1894); G. Martin, *ibid.* **46**, 2442, 3289 (1913).

[71] F. S. Kipping et al., *J. Chem. Soc.* **119**, 830, 848 (1921); **123**, 2590, 2598 (1923); **1928**, 1931; **1929**, 360, 1176, 2545.

[72] C. A. Burkhard, *J. Am. Chem. Soc.* **71**, 963 (1949).

groups and, indeed, polymers with chains of alternate carbon and silicon atoms. A single carbon bridge may be inserted between two silicon atoms by treating a halogen substituted silicon alkyl with a trialkyl-halosilane in the presence of sodium:[73]

$$R_3SiCH_2Cl + ClSi(R_3) + 2Na \rightarrow R_3Si-CH_2-Si(R_3) + 2NaCl$$

Starting with $ClR_2SiCH_2Cl$ either the Grignard reaction or sodium may be used to effect a polymerization that, theoretically, can continue indefinitely:

$$\underset{\overset{|}{R}}{\overset{R}{|}} \qquad \underset{\overset{|}{R}}{\overset{R}{|}}$$

Cl–Si–CH$_2$Cl + Mg → Cl–Si–CH$_2$MgCl

Cl–Si–CH$_2$ ⸨ MgCl + Cl ⸩ –Si–CH$_2$MgCl →

Cl–Si–CH$_2$–Si–CH$_2$MgCl + MgCl$_2$

Lithium derivatives are reported to give better yields than the Grignard reagent, and methylpolysilmethylenes with 2, 3, 4, and 5 silicon atoms have been prepared.[74] Some physical constants of dodecamethylpenta-silmethylene, $CH_3[(CH_3)_2SiCH_2]_4Si(CH_3)_3$, are: bp 254°C (200 mm), 309°C (760 mm); $n^{20}D = 1.4640$; $d^{20} = 0.8408$. In place of methylene, larger groups, such as ethylene, phenylene, etc., may be inserted between the silicon atoms.[75] Polymers with the –Si–C–Si– bonding are heat resistant, water repellent, and inert to many reagents, but generally less so than the siloxanes.

**Organosiloxane Chains and Networks—Silicones.** When a dichloro-silane is hydrolyzed, a siloxane polymer usually results:

$$nH_2SiCl_2 + nH_2O \rightarrow (H_2SiO)_n + 2nHCl$$

Although the monomeric siloxane is occasionally known, $n$ usually varies

[73] J. T. Goodwin, Jr., W. E. Baldwin, and R. R. McGregor, *ibid.* 69, 2247 (1947).
[74] L. H. Sommer, F. A. Mitch, and G. M. Goldberg, *ibid.* 71, 2746 (1949).
[75] E. G. Rochow, **U.S. 2,352,974** (1944).

from six to a very large number. The product just mentioned is a closed chain of ($-H_2SiO-$) units, based on the monomer, $H_2SiO$, prosiloxane, which can exist momentarily. Among its liquid and solid polymers is a benzene-soluble hexamer, $(H_2SiO)_6$. Linear siloxanes of general formula, $H_3SiO(H_2SiO)_nSiH_3$, where $n$ can be zero (as in disiloxane, $H_3SiOSiH_3$) or small integers, can be prepared. The linear siloxanes resemble the silanes physically, but are decidedly different from them chemically. The siloxanes are not spontaneously flammable in air, nor are they cleaved by alkalies with the evolution of hydrogen, as are the silanes.

If monovalent organic groups completely replace the hydrogens of siloxanes, the repeat units become ($-R_2SiO-$), and an organosiloxane chain

$$\begin{array}{ccccc} & R & & R & & R \\ & | & & | & & | \\ -Si&-&O&-&Si&-&O&-&Si&-&O- \\ & | & & | & & | \\ & R & & R & & R \end{array}$$

results. Substances of this type are called silicones. The name was supplied by Kipping many years ago in the belief that, because of their composition, $R_2SiO$, they were similar to ketones $R_2CO$. However, they differ greatly from the ketones in that they do not contain doubly bound oxygen and are always polymers. Moreover, the silicones possess a thermal stability and general inertness to various reagents not generally found in organic polymers. Such properties are not unexpected in view of the stability of the silicon-oxygen chains in silica and the mineral silicates, and since the R–Si bonds of many silicon alkyls are highly resistant to oxidation. The specific properties of a silicone, of course, depend upon the length of the chain, the type of $R$ groups present, and other factors, such as the degree of cross-linking between chains.

The formation of a silicone polymer starts with choosing a suitable difunctional[76] compound, for instance, a dialkyldihalosilane, to yield the type of silicone desired. Addition of sufficient moisture hydrolyzes the halide to an organosilanediol, $R_2Si(OH)_2$, and the silicone chain grows by stepwise addition of the monomeric diol units or by condensing with

[76] *Functionality* in polymer chemistry refers to the number of groups in the molecule that can function in bonding it to other molecules. Monofunctional molecules alone are not useful in polymer technology because when two of them have reacted the product is nonfunctional and no chain longer than 2 units can form. Difunctional molecules, however, can react to form long chains, and tri- and tetrafunctional molecules make possible molecular networks.

other chains:

$$2R_2Si(OH)_2 \rightarrow HO-\underset{\underset{R}{|}}{\overset{\overset{R}{|}}{Si}}-O-\underset{\underset{R}{|}}{\overset{\overset{R}{|}}{Si}}-OH + H_2O$$

$$\downarrow + R_2Si(OH)_2$$

$$HO-\underset{\underset{R}{|}}{\overset{\overset{R}{|}}{Si}}-O-\underset{\underset{R}{|}}{\overset{\overset{R}{|}}{Si}}-O-\underset{\underset{R}{|}}{\overset{\overset{R}{|}}{Si}}-OH + H_2O \quad \text{etc.}$$

In such condensation reactions OH groups on the end of a chain are fully as reactive as on the monomer, and the process proceeds at a rate dependent upon the concentration of OH groups remaining in the mixture.[77] The condensation of dimethylsilanediol proceeds at great speed at 0°C, but diphenylsilanediol requires a temperature of 100°C to start the reaction. Usually, application of heat is necessary to increase the number of effective collisions toward the end of the process when the concentration of OH groups in the reaction mixture has greatly decreased. Dehydrating agents or catalysts may be useful to hasten the process.[78] Cyclic polymers are formed preferentially if a strong catalyst is used and if solvent is present; other procedures favor the formation of linear polymers.[79]

The silicone chains from the condensation of difunctional units are terminated by hydroxyl groups, which can condense further, although this condensation may be very sluggish for long chains. Such high polymers may be stabilized, or the condensation may be terminated at a given chain length, by the addition of monofunctional material, $R_3SiOH$. Each monofunctional unit on reacting blocks the end of the chain to which it is attached, and when present in the proper concentration terminates the chains at the desired length. The chains of linear polymers have no direct chemical bonds to one another. The action of heat, through thermal agitation, permits the chains to move about with some freedom and ultimately to flow. Such silicones are *thermoplastic*.

[77] P. O. Powers, *Synthetic Resins and Rubbers*, John Wiley and Sons, Inc., New York, 1943, pp. 25–33.

[78] E. G. Rochow, U.S. 2,371,068 (1945); W. Dilthey and F. Eduardoff, *Ber.* 37, 1139 (1904); W. Dilthey, *ibid.* 38, 4132 (1905); F. S. Kipping, *J. Chem. Soc.* 101, 2108, 2125 (1912); F. S. Kipping and R. Robison, *ibid.* 105, 484 (1914).

[79] R. R. McGregor, *Silicones and Their Uses*, McGraw-Hill Book Company, Inc., New York, 1954, pp. 270–279.

By cross-linking between chains a three-dimensional polymer network may be formed. The network polymer has a higher average molecular weight, decreased solubility, and increased rigidity. Cross-links may be inserted along the chain by introduction of certain proportions of trifunctional material, $RSiX_3$, into the condensation mixture. Hydrolysis and condensation of the third functional group of the molecule establishes an oxygen bridge between two chains:

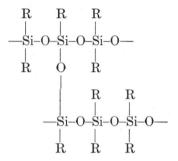

Care must be taken that the entire reaction does not take place too fast, in order that the product may be handled satisfactorily. Silicones of this

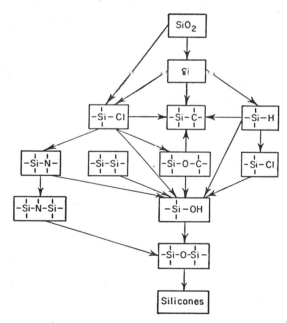

FIG. 3.1. Flow sheet of the production of silicones. (McGregor, *Silicones and Their Uses;* courtesy *McGraw-Hill Book Co.*)

type are infusible, insoluble, *thermosetting* resins.   Figure 3.1 presents in "flow sheet" form the various steps and possible alternative intermediate reaction stages in the production of silicones from the starting material, $SiO_2$.   The chlorine indicated in the diagram could usually be replaced by other halogens, but they are more expensive and have little if any advantage.   For further details on silicone polymerization technology the reader must be referred to the excellent monographs on the subject.[80]

**Molecular Structure of Siloxanes.**   Most of the quantitative structural details of the siloxanes have been obtained from X-ray and electron diffraction studies and the application of spectroscopic methods to the organosilicon intermediates and a few crystalline siloxane polymers. Other structural information has been deduced from the polymerization reactions and from such properties as molar refractivity, molar volume, density, heats of vaporization, and flow properties.   The electron microscope, too, has been useful in estimates of the molecular weights of elastomers.

In the halogen and alkyl substituted silanes, electron diffraction studies have revealed rather constant Si–C bonds of 1.90 ± 0.03 A and Si–Cl bonds of 2.01 ± 0.03 A.[81]   The bond angles in these compounds are very nearly tetrahedral.

Structural interest particularly centers around the Si–O–Si bond in the siloxanes.   An early preliminary study suggested that the cyclic dimethyl siloxanes, with the exception of the trimer, $[(CH_3)_2SiO]_3$, all contain puckered Si–O–Si rings, as observed for the octasilane, $[(CH_3)_2SiO]_8$,[82]   A complete analysis of the trimer established the planar configuration of its silicon-oxygen ring similar to that in the mineral benitoite.[83]   The two $(SiO)_3$ rings in octamethylspiro [5.5] pentasiloxane are planar and linked at 90° through a common silicon atom.[84]   In $[(CH_3)_2SiO]_4$, however, the $(SiO)_4$ ring is puckered.[85]   The average bond distances and bond angles for these compounds are listed in Table 3.3. The Si–C bond lengths are close to the sum of the covalent radii of silicon and carbon, 1.94 A, and indicate almost complete covalent character. The Si–O bond distance is almost the same as in quartz and the inorganic

[80] McGregor, *op. cit.*; Rochow, *op. cit.* ref. 14; Post, *op. cit.* ref. 11; *Chem. and Eng. News* **34**, 5060 (1956).

[81] See L. O. Brockway *et al.*, *J. Am. Chem. Soc.* **56**, 2373 (1934); **58**, 2036 (1936); **60**, 1836 (1938); **63**, 3287 (1941); **66**, 94 (1944); **68**, 719 (1946).

[82] L. K. Frevel and M. J. Hunter, *ibid.* **67**, 2275 (1945).

[83] G. Peyronel, *Atti accad. nazl. Lincei, Rend., Classe sci. fis., mat. e nat.* **15**, 402 (1953); **16**, 78, 231 (1954); *Chimica e industria (Milan)* **36**, 441 (1954).

[84] W. L. Roth and D. Harker, *Acta Cryst.* **1**, 34 (1948).

[85] H. Steinfink, B. Post, and I. Fankuchen, *ibid.* **8**, 420 (1955).

TABLE 3.3. BOND DISTANCES AND BOND ANGLES IN SILOXANES

| Compound* | Bond Distances in A | | Bond Angles, deg. | | |
|---|---|---|---|---|---|
| | Si–C | Si–O | Si–O–Si | O–Si–O | C–Si–C |
| $[(CH_3)_2SiO]_3$ | 1.93 | 1.61 | 136 | 104 | 106.6 |
| Octamethylspiro [5.5] pentasiloxane | $1.88 \pm 0.03$ | $1.64 \pm 0.03$ | $132 \pm 4$ | $107 \pm 4$ | $106 \pm 4$ |
| $[(CH_3)_2SiO]_4$ | 1.92 | 1.65 | 142.5 | 109 | 106 |

\* See footnotes 83, 84, and 85.

silicates. Values for the O–Si–O and C–Si–C bond angles represent only slight distortions from the tetrahedral angle (109°28′). To preserve planarity in the ring of the tetramer, $[(CH_3)_2SiO]_4$, the Si–O–Si bond would have had to increase to 160°. This evidently requires so much strain that a puckered configuration with an angle of 142.5° is adopted instead. Larger-ring compounds and linear siloxane chains have not been examined to date, but it seems likely that their Si–O–Si angles will be close to 143°.

An explanation of the low intermolecular attraction in the organosiloxanes has been sought from structural and other evidence. These compounds are characterized by unexpectedly low boiling points and low viscosity-temperature coefficients. The molar volumes of the methylpolysiloxanes seem high, indicating bulky molecules.[86] The limiting activation energy for viscous flow, although molecular-weight dependent, is only about 3.0 kcal for silicone oils of 500 molecular weight as against 5.0 kcal for equivalent hydrocarbons.[87] The rather large amount of ionic character, 37%[88] to 50%,[89] of the Si–O bond has been considered to contribute a certain looseness to the siloxane bond. In octamethylspiro [5.5] pentasiloxane, for instance, the $Si(CH_3)_2$ groups appear to oscillate, as though the silicon in O–Si–O were free to move as in a ball-and-socket joint.[84] From this bond looseness and the favorable steric geometry it was concluded that there should be relatively free rotation about the siloxane bonds in linear polymers. The low boiling points, temperature coefficients of viscosity, and similar properties can be attributed to such free rotation limiting the close approach of the chains

[86] C. B. Hurd, *J. Am. Chem. Soc.* **68**, 364 (1946).
[87] M. J. Hunter, E. L. Warrick, J. F. Hyde, and C. C. Currie, *ibid.* **68**, 2284 (1946).
[88] Based on N. B. Hannay and C. P. Smyth, *ibid.* **68**, 171 (1946).
[89] Based on Pauling, *op. cit.*, p. 74.

and, thereby, preventing strong intermolecular attractive forces.   Synthesis of a series of silmethylene compounds, which have $Si–CH_2–Si$ in place of $Si–O–Si$ of the siloxanes, has served to confirm the above conclusions about the siloxane link.   The silmethylenes always have a higher boiling point, higher viscosity, and higher viscosity change with temperature than the corresponding siloxanes.[90]

**Commercial Silicones.** Many commercial silicones are available, each with its special properties suited to special applications.  The silicone chain polymers and the network resinlike polymers are the starting materials for these numerous products.  As a group, these polymers are extraordinarily lacking in physiological response, thereby permitting their use in pharmacy, medicine, and food industries.   It is only possible here to describe briefly five general classes of these substances:[91]

*Silicone fluids.*   The various types of silicone fluids are usually either dimethyl silicone fluids or fluids with one or both of the methyl groups replaced with phenyl radicals.   The dimethyl silicone fluids are clear liquids with an oily feel and the chemical composition, $[–Si(CH_3)_2–O–]_n$. They are obtainable with viscosities in the range 0.65 centistokes to over 1,000,000 centistokes.   Other important properties are their stability at elevated temperatures, low freezing points, chemical inertness, and lack of toxicity.   They find uses as films on glassware, car and furniture polishes, release agents in molding operations, paint and rubber additives, antifoaming agents, damping and hydraulic fluids, lubricants, and dielectric liquids.

Phenyl substituted silicone fluids have better oxidation stability, improved lubricating properties, and, occasionally, spectacularly low freezing points.   Their low-temperature uses as damping fluids and circulating-bath liquids are well known.   Because of their oxidation stability and low volatility at high temperatures, they can be used in sterilizing and high-temperature baths to 250°C.   Other uses are as diffusion-pump fluids, water repellents on textiles, and in paper treatment.

*Silicone compounds.*   The addition of small amounts of very finely divided silica to dimethyl silicones yields petrolatum-like substances that do not flow on heating and that have good water repellency and dielectric properties.   Such compounds have applications as stopcock greases, mold releases, and moisture-proofing agents for electrical equipment.   A most amazing use is as a general-purpose antifoam, for which they are

[90] Sommer, Mitch, and Goldberg, *op. cit.* ref. 74.
[91] Based largely on the detailed discussion of commercial silicones by McGregor, *op. cit.* ref. 79; *Chem. and Eng. News* **33**, 4512 (1955).

frequently effective in the fantastically low concentration of 1 ppm, which corresponds roughly to one drop in 25 gallons.

*Silicone lubricants.* These are fluids or greases prepared by the addition of carbon black or soaps to silicone liquids. The greases, especially, are nonflowing, and suitable for use in "lifetime" sealed bearings, both at abnormally high or low temperatures. The fluid lubricants are all superior to petroleum oils in their viscosity characteristics. Low-phenyl oil, for instance, has a useful temperature span from $-75°$ to $200°C$ ($-103°$ to $392°F$), which is completely out of the range of petroleum lubricants. The lubricating greases are of several types, again with wide useful temperature ranges. Type E greases (methyl silicone + silica) are designed for use where movement is intermittent, as on plug and control valves. Type G greases (medium phenyl oil + lithium soap), on the other hand, are general-purpose greases, as for ball bearings operating at high speed and high temperature. At 1800 rpm and $150°C$ such a silicone grease has usually ten times the life of a petroleum grease.[92]

*Silicone resins.* Silicone resins have been "tailored" for many applications in the following categories: coating resins, laminating resins, release resins, water-repellent resins, molding resins, and electrical resins. They are generally characterized by heat stability, water repellency, good electrical properties, chemical inertness, and weather resistance. Solvents usually attack them, however, and abrasion resistance is not high. Most of them are supplied in solvent at 50% to 70% solids concentration; all require baking or heat treatment to develop their best properties. The superiority of silicone over organic coating resins is striking. Whereas the maximum temperature of usefulness is about $150°C$ for a pure organic resin, a pure silicon resin is good to around $250°C$, and coatings made up of silicone resin plus organic resin and aluminum can withstand temperatures to $500°C$ and above. A single treatment of baking pans with a release resin permits baking of 100 to 500 loaves of bread without the need for any greasing. Silicone electrical resins permit a 5-hp conventional motor to deliver 9 hp if insulated with class H components.

*Silicone rubbers.* Silicone rubbers have close similarity in their physical properties to organic rubbers, but little chemical similarity. Common to both are good stretch and retraction, bounce, and great flexibility. Tensile properties and abrasion resistance are poorer for the silicone rubbers, but they are useful to somewhat lower and higher temperatures than conventional rubbers. All silicone rubbers are flexible down to $-56°C$ ($-69°F$), and special formulations can be used below

---

[92] *Chem. and Eng. News* **35**, 72 (1957).

$-90°C$ ($-130°F$).   On the high-temperature side, silicone rubbers have virtually unlimited life at 150°C (302°F).   At 200° and 250°C these rubbers show aging effects that level off in about thirty days, after which the materials still have a long useful life.   Silicone rubbers withstanding 400°C (752°F) for 200 hours and 540°C (1004°F) for 90 hours have been prepared.   The resistance of silicone rubbers to many chemicals is better than the organic rubbers.

A dimethyl silicone polymer of approximately 10,000 units in the chain gives an elastomer.   The elastomer can be compounded to give a silicone rubber by milling into it an inorganic filler and a vulcanizer.   The fillers commonly used are $TiO_2$, $ZnO$, $Fe_2O_3$, and $SiO_2$, and the vulcanizing agent is usually a peroxide, such as benzoyl peroxide.

One methyl silicone polymer, when heated with about 5% of boric acid, forms a material known as "bouncing putty," a substance characterized by being plastic to slowly applied forces but elastic to rapidly applied forces.   It can be molded in the hand like soft putty, but a ball of it when dropped will rebound to 80% of the original elevation.   Under a sharp blow it actually is brittle and shatters.   "Bouncing putty," in spite of these unusual properties, has remained unimportant commercially.

# CHAPTER 4

## THE SILICATES

**Natural Silicates.** In Chapter 2 the *central role* of the element silicon in the inorganic world was stressed, and several of the important silicates found in nature were listed. The natural silicates are, indeed, very numerous and make up the largest chemical group among the minerals. Many of them are of considerable commercial value. Granite is an important building and ornamental stone. Garnet, topaz, beryl, and tourmaline are gem stones. Mica splits into thin sheets which are used as windows for stoves and for electrical insulation. Asbestos is a valuable material for heat insulation, and talc enters into face powders, polishing agents, and paper and leather manufacture. Kaolin from the weathering of feldspar forms the basis of clays from which brick, tile, earthenware, and china are made. This weathering, by the action of water and carbon dioxide, during which kaolinite and potassium carbonate are formed, is one of the primary reactions in the formation of soil from rocks:

$$2KAlSi_3O_8 + 2H_2O + CO_2 \rightarrow Al_2Si_2O_5(OH)_4 + 4SiO_2 + 2K^+ + CO_3^=$$

Many of the silicates are very complicated and only recently has it been possible to write their correct formulas. Purely analytical results were inadequate for determining true formulas for many of these substances, but X-ray analysis has met with more success in elucidating their structure.

The chemistry of the silicates is complicated by the almost universal occurrence of isomorphous replacement of one element by another in varying amounts. For example, olivine, $Mg_2SiO_4$, typically has part of the magnesium replaced by iron. The variety known as chrysolite has a composition represented approximately by the formula $6Mg_2SiO_4 \cdot Fe_2SiO_4$. Not only is isomorphous replacement of the metal cations common, but it is also a frequent occurrence for the silicon to be replaced to a certain extent by aluminum. Fluorine and OH readily replace each other. It is common practice to indicate such replacement by formulas of the type: troostite $(Zn, Mn)_2SiO_4$, chondrodite $Mg(F, OH)_2 \cdot 2Mg_2SiO_4$, vermiculite $(Mg, Fe)_3(Al, Si)_4O_{10} \cdot (OH)_2 \cdot 4H_2O$.

A second complicating feature in their structure analysis and systematization has been the departure from simple discrete anions in most

127

silicates.   Most elements show a variety of oxygen compounds by virtue of their having variable valences; but silicon presents the variety while acting only with the valence of four.   The formulas of the silicates suggest a great number of silicic acids, and, in fact, many such acids have been postulated, as derived from orthosilicic acid through the loss of one or more molecules of water as the following equations illustrate:

$$H_4SiO_4 - H_2O \rightarrow H_2SiO_3 \text{ metasilicic acid}$$
$$2H_4SiO_4 - H_2O \rightarrow H_6Si_2O_7 \text{ disilicic acid}$$
$$3H_4SiO_4 - 4H_2O \rightarrow H_4Si_3O_8 \text{ trisilicic acid}$$

These and many others have been suggested, but with very few exceptions they have never been prepared, and their existence is doubtful.   Poly-acids, as $H_6Si_2O_7$ and $H_4Si_3O_8$ are called, must generally be considered as having no reality, since X-ray determinations of structures of many silicates show that the assumption of acid radicals, in many cases, is meaningless.

X-ray analysis shows that the combining capacity of silicon in silicates results from the silicon atom always occupying the center of a tetrahedron of oxygen atoms (Fig. 4.1) and from the ability of these $SiO_4$ tetrahedra to link up with one another by sharing oxygen atoms in common.   Only a few of the simpler silicates have structures like ordinary inorganic com-pounds wherein metal ions and simple acid radicals pack together to build the structure.   Orthosilicates have discrete $SiO_4$ groups disposed through-out the structure, similar to $SO_4$ groups in sulfates.   In all other silicates some of the oxygen atoms form a part of two tetrahedra.

**The Framework of the Silicates.**   Bragg[1] and Pauling[2] found the key to these structures in the following simple concepts.   Silicates have a framework determined essentially by the packing of the large ions, the oxygens, which frequently approximates close-packing of these ions.   The small ions, silicons and metal cations, are tucked into the interstices of the framework so that each one is equidistant from four or six large ions. The composition and the principles of isomorphous replacement are taken into account in the consideration or prediction of a structure for a given mineral.

Pauling[2] formulated his ideas in a set of basic principles which govern the structure of all ionic crystals, but which have been especially useful in the analysis of the complex silicates.   The anions in such crystals form coordinated polyhedra around each cation, with distances determined by

[1] W. L. Bragg, *Trans. Faraday Soc.* 25, 291 (1929).
[2] L. Pauling, *J. Am. Chem. Soc.* 51, 1010 (1929).

the sums of the ionic radii and the coordination about the cation by the radius ratio. In silicates, therefore, the $Si^{+4}$ cations are always tetrahedrally surrounded by $4O^{-2}$ ions at an Si–O distance of $1.60 \pm 0.01$ A.[3] Other cations ($Al^{+3}$, $Mg^{++}$, $Na^{+}$, etc.) in the structure lie at the centers of anion polyhedra whose anions are usually the $O^{=}$ ions of neighboring

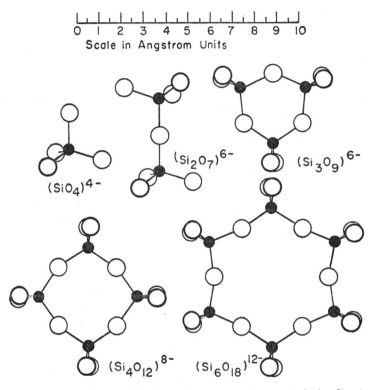

FIG. 4.1. Tetrahedral coordination of oxygen (open circles) about silicon (black) in the silicates. Forms of discrete silicate radicals. (Bragg, *Atomic Structure of Minerals;* courtesy *Cornell University Press.*)

$SiO_4$ tetrahedra. The electric charge of each cation is shared by the surrounding anions, the strength of each electrostatic valence bond being equal to the charge on the cation divided by the number of surrounding anions. In the $SiO_4$ tetrahedra each Si–O bond has an electrostatic bond strength of 1. In a stable structure the total strength of the electrostatic bonds to an anion should add up closely to the charge on the anion.

[3] J. V. Smith, *Acta Cryst.* **7**, 479 (1954).

This relationship (electrostatic valence principle) determines the number of polyhedra sharing a given anion at a common corner. In topaz, $(AlF)_2SiO_4$, for instance, each $Al^{+3}$ ion is surrounded by $4O^=$ ions and $2F^-$ ions, and the electrostatic valence bonds have a strength of $\frac{1}{2}$. The $F^-$ ions are thus common to two aluminum octahedra, and each $O^=$ ion is attached to one silicon tetrahedron and two aluminum octahedra.

The electrostatic valence principle indicates the number of polyhedra with a common corner, but it tells nothing about the number of corners common to two polyhedra. Whether they share one corner only, two corners defining an edge, or three or more corners defining a face must be determined otherwise. The presence of shared edges, and particularly of shared faces, decreases the stability of a coordinated structure, because of the closer approach of the cations of the two polyhedra. When two tetrahedra share an edge, the two cations are brought to 0.58 of their former distance (sharing corners). Thus $SiO_4$ tetrahedra usually share only corners. The effect is not so large for octahedra, and $TiO_6$ octahedra may share edges, and $AlO_6$ octahedra may share a common face. Some compensating deformation of the polyhedra always occurs. Cations with high electric charge and small coordination number tend to distribute themselves as far apart from each other as possible, in order to reduce their contribution to the coulomb energy of the crystal. Then, finally, the number of different kinds of constituents in a crystal tends to be small (rule of parsimony).

Pauling's concepts made it possible to predict probable structures for a mineral for comparison with the X-ray data. Once a structure can be predicted for comparison with the X-ray data, the crystal analyst has a direct means for proving whether or not it is the structure of the compound being investigated. With these simple rules the most complicated silicates have been structurally analyzed, and all known crystalline silicates can now be classified into a few groups, based upon the manner of linking of the $SiO_4$ tetrahedra. The principal structural groups are:[4]

1. *Discrete silicate radicals.* There are five types in this class:

a. Single tetrahedra as $SiO_4^{-4}$ groups or the orthosilicates as zircon, $ZrSiO_4$; phenacite, $Be_2SiO_4$; olivine, $Mg_2SiO_4$. Fig. 4.1.

b. Two tetrahedra as $Si_2O_7^{-6}$ groups or pyrosilicates as in thortveitite, $Sc_2Si_2O_7$; hardystonite, $Ca_2ZnSi_2O_7$. Fig. 4.1.

[4] This structural classification is essentially that of W. L. Bragg, *Z. Krist.* **74**, 237 (1930), a scheme that has well stood the test of time. For other proposals and discussions on structural classification, see H. Strunz, *ibid.* **98**, 60 (1937); H. Berman, *Am. Mineral.* **22**, 342 (1937); C. K. Swartz, *ibid.* **22**, 1073 (1937); J. W. Gruner, *ibid.* **33**, 679 (1948).

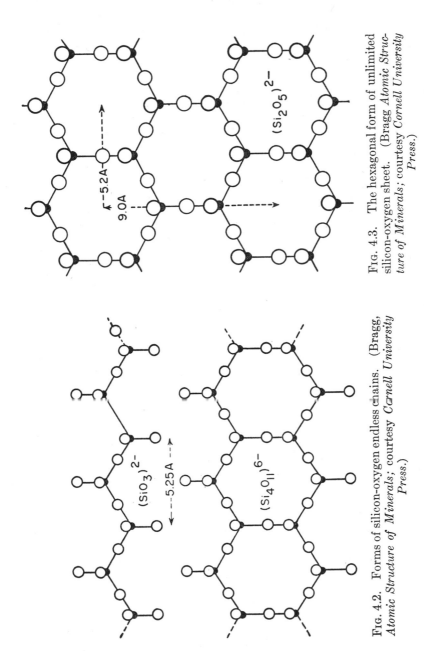

Fig. 4.3.   The hexagonal form of unlimited silicon-oxygen sheet.   (Bragg *Atomic Structure of Minerals*; courtesy *Cornell University Press*.)

$(Si_2O_5)^{2-}$

5.2A

9.0A

Fig. 4.2.   Forms of silicon-oxygen endless chains.   (Bragg, *Atomic Structure of Minerals*; courtesy *Cornell University Press*.)

$(SiO_3)^{2-}$

5.25A

$(Si_4O_{11})^{6-}$

c. Three tetrahedra as $Si_3O_9^{-6}$ groups forming a three-membered ring as in benitoite, $BaTiSi_3O_9$. Fig. 4.1.

d. Four tetrahedra as $Si_4O_{12}^{-8}$ groups forming a four-sided ring as in axinite, $(Fe, Mn)Ca_2Al_2BO_3Si_4O_{12}(OH)$. Fig. 4.1.

e. Six tetrahedra as $Si_6O_{18}^{-12}$ groups forming a hexagonal ring as in beryl, $Be_3Al_2Si_6O_{18}$. Fig. 4.1.

2. *Silicon-oxygen endless chains.*   This class consists of two types:

a. Single chains having a radical composition represented by the empirical formula $SiO_3^{-2}$. There are, however, no $SiO_3$ groups as such in these compounds. They are metasilicates as diopside, $CaMg(SiO_3)_2$, and the pyroxenes. Fig. 4.2.

b. Double chains having a radical composition represented by the empirical formula $Si_4O_{11}^{-6}$. These, too, have been considered as metasilicates to which tremolite, $Ca_2Mg_5(Si_4O_{11})_2(OH)_2$, and the amphiboles belong. Fig. 4.2.

3. *Silicon-oxygen sheets.*   By a continuation of the process of forming double chains, an unlimited sheet of linked $SiO_4$ tetrahedra is formed (Fig. 4.3) having an empirical radical composition of $Si_2O_5^{-2}$. These are the flaky or platy minerals as talc, $Mg_3(Si_2O_5)_2(OH)_2$, and muscovite mica, $KAl_2(AlSi_3O_{10})(OH, F)_2$. In the mica sheet one silicon out of four has been replaced by a trivalent aluminum atom which alters the composition of the radical to $AlSi_3O_{10}^{-5}$.

4. *Three-dimensional silicon-oxygen networks.*   Extension of the silicon-oxygen sheets to three dimensions forms a continuous framework of linked $SiO_4$ tetrahedra as in quartz, tridymite, and cristobalite. Such a framework is neutral; but, if a certain proportion of the tetravalent silicon is replaced by trivalent aluminum, the network becomes negatively charged and must be neutralized by distributing cations throughout the structure. The general formula of the silicate radical produced is $(Si, Al)_nO_{2n}$, as exemplified by feldspar, $K(AlSi_3O_8)$, the zeolites, such as $Na_2(Al_2Si_3O_{10})\cdot 2H_2O$, and the ultramarine network, $(Al_6Si_6O_{24})^{-6}$. Fig. 4.4.

The X-ray results[5] demonstrate the general soundness of earlier mineralogical classification[6] in laying more stress on similarity of physical

---

[5] An excellent discussion of the earlier X-ray results is presented in W. L. Bragg, *The Atomic Structure of Minerals*, Cornell University Press, Ithaca, New York, 1937, pp. 139–272.

[6] A standard reference on the mineralogical classification of the silicates is E. S. Dana and W. E. Ford, *A Textbook of Mineralogy*, John Wiley and Sons, Inc., New York, 4th Edition, 1932.

properties than on chemical composition. X-ray examination, however, has also revealed hitherto unsuspected relationships and has disproved formerly well-established ones. The classifications in the succeeding sections are based, as far as possible, on the findings of X-ray analysis. All formulas are presented in such a way as to distinguish between the aluminum that enters into the structure of tetrahedra and plays the same role as silicon, and the aluminum that is in sixfold coordination and plays the same role as the cations of calcium, magnesium, or iron. The brief

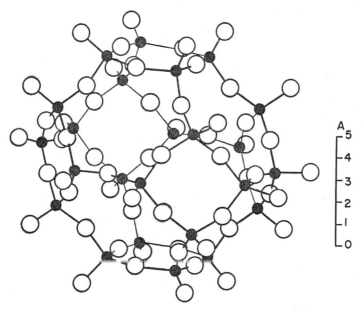

Fig. 4.4. A portion of the three-dimensional silicon-oxygen framework of ultramarine. (Bragg, *Atomic Structure of Minerals;* courtesy *Cornell University Press.*)

discussions in the following sections have been limited to examples of the important structural concepts and to the commercially prominent natural silicates.[7]

**Orthosilicates.** The orthosilicates are characterized by the presence of individual tetrahedral $SiO_4^{-4}$ groups. Metallic cations (and occasionally other anions) are distributed between the $SiO_4$ groups so that the whole crystal is a stable structure electrically. Table 4.1 lists many of

[7] For a detailed general treatment of the physical chemistry of the silicates the reader is urged to consult the monumental work: W. Eitel, *The Physical Chemistry of the Silicates*, The University of Chicago Press, Chicago, Ill., 1954, 1600 pp.

TABLE 4.1. NATURAL ORTHOSILICATES

| Mineral | Composition | Crystal Symmetry | Hardness | Specific Gravity | Structure Reference |
|---|---|---|---|---|---|
| *Chrysolite Group* | | | | | |
| Forsterite............. | $Mg_2SiO_4$ | Orthorhombic | 6–7 | 3.21–3.33 | (1) |
| Olivine (Chrysolite)... | $(Mg, Fe)_2SiO_4$ | Orthorhombic | 6.5–7 | 3.27–3.37 | (1)(2) |
| Fayalite............. | $Fe_2SiO_4$ | Orthorhombic | 6.5 | 4.1 | (1) |
| Tephroite............. | $Mn_2SiO_4$ | Orthorhombic | 6 | 4.1 | (3)(4) |
| Monticellite.......... | $MgCaSiO_4$ | Orthorhombic | 5 | 3.2 | (5) |
| Larsenite............ | $PbZnSiO_4$ | Orthorhombic | ··· | 5.9 | ··· |
| | | | | | |
| *Chondrodite Group* | | | | | |
| Norbergite.......... | $Mg(F, OH)_2 \cdot Mg_2SiO_4$ | Orthorhombic | 6–6.5 | 3.1–3.2 | (6) |
| Chondrodite........ | $Mg(F, OH)_2 \cdot 2Mg_2SiO_4$ | Monoclinic | 6–6.5 | 3.1–3.2 | (6) |
| Humite.............. | $Mg(F, OH)_2 \cdot 3Mg_2SiO_4$ | Orthorhombic | 6–6.5 | 3.1–3.2 | (6) |
| Clinohumite......... | $Mg(F, OH)_2 \cdot 4Mg_2SiO_4$ | Monoclinic | 6–6.5 | 3.1–3.2 | (6) |
| | | | | | |
| *Datolite Group* | | | | | |
| Datolite............. | $Ca(BOH)SiO_4$ | Monoclinic | 5–5.5 | 2.9–3.0 | (7) |
| Homilite............. | $Ca_2Fe(BO)_2(SiO_4)_2$ | Monoclinic | 5 | 3.38 | ··· |
| Euclase............. | $Be(AlOH)SiO_4$ | Monoclinic | 7.5 | 3.05–3.10 | (8) |
| Gadolinite.......... | $Be_2Fe(YO)_2(SiO_4)_2$ | Monoclinic | 6.5–7 | 4.0–4.5 | (7) |
| | | | | | |
| *Garnet Group* | | | | | |
| Grossularite........ | $Ca_3Al_2(SiO_4)_3$ | Cubic | 6.5–7.5 | 3.53 | (9) |
| Pyrope.............. | $(Mg, Fe)_3Al_2(SiO_4)_3$ | Cubic | 6.5–7.5 | 3.51 | (9) |
| Almadite............ | $Fe_3Al_2(SiO_4)_3$ | Cubic | 6.5–7.5 | 4.25 | (9) |
| Spessartite.......... | $Mn_3Al_2(SiO_4)_3$ | Cubic | 6.5–7.5 | 4.18 | (9) |
| Andradite........... | $Ca_3Fe_2(SiO_4)_3$ | Cubic | 6.5–7.5 | 3.75 | (9) |
| Uvarovite........... | $Ca_3Cr_2(SiO_4)_3$ | Cubic | 7.5 | 3.41–3.52 | (9) |
| | | | | | |
| *Phenacite Group* | | | | | |
| Phenacite........... | $Be_2SiO_4$ | Rhombohedral | 7.5–8 | 2.97–3.00 | (10) |
| Willemite............ | $Zn_2SiO_4$ | Rhombohedral | 5.5 | 3.89–4.18 | (10) |
| Troostite............ | $(Zn, Mn)_2SiO_4$ | Rhombohedral | ··· | ··· | ··· |
| | | | | | |
| *Zircon Group* | | | | | |
| Zircon............... | $ZrSiO_4$ | Tetragonal | 7.5 | 4.68–4.70 | (11) |
| Thorite.............. | $ThSiO_4$ | Tetragonal | 4.5–5 | 5.3 | (12) |
| Coffinite............ | $USiO_4$ | Tetragonal | ··· | 5.1 | (13) |
| | | | | | |
| *Miscellaneous* | | | | | |
| Titanite............. | $(TiO)CaSiO_4$ | Tetragonal | 5–5.5 | 3.4–3.56 | (14) |
| Eucryptite.......... | $\alpha\text{-}LiAlSiO_4$ | Rhombohedral | ··· | 2.63 | (15) |
| Kyanite............. | $(AlO)AlSiO_4$ | Triclinic | 5–7.25 | 3.56–3.67 | (16) |
| Sillimanite.......... | $(AlO)AlSiO_4$ | Orthorhombic | 6–7 | 3.23–3.24 | (17) |
| Andalusite.......... | $(AlO)AlSiO_4$ | Orthorhombic | 7.5 | 3.16–3.20 | (17) |
| Staurolite........... | $Fe(OH)_2 \cdot 2(AlO)AlSiO_4$ | Orthorhombic | 7–7.5 | 3.65–3.77 | (18) |
| Topaz............... | $(AlF)_2SiO_4$ | Orthorhombic | 8 | 3.4–3.6 | (19) |
| Larnite.............. | $\beta\text{-}Ca_2SiO_4$ | Monoclinic | ··· | 3.28–3.31 | (20) |
| Ilvaite.............. | $CaFe_2^{II}Fe^{III}(OH)(SiO_4)_2$ | Orthorhombic | 5.5–6 | 3.99–4.05 | (21) |
| Eulytite............. | $Bi_4(SiO_4)_3$ | Cubic | 4.5 | 6.1 | (22) |
| Agricolite........... | $Bi_4(SiO_4)_3$ | Monoclinic | ··· | ··· | (23) |

(1) F. Rinne, *Z. Krist.* **59**, 230 (1923); F. Rinne, J. Leonhardt, and H. Hentschel, *ibid.* **59**, 548 (1924).
(2) W. L. Bragg and G. B. Brown, *ibid.* **63**, 538 (1926).
(3) W. L. C. Greer, *Am. Mineral.* **17**, 135 (1932).
(4) H. O'Daniel and L. Tscheischwili, *Z. Krist.* **105**, 273 (1943).
(5) G. B. Brown and J. West, *ibid.* **66**, 154 (1927).
(6) W. H. Taylor and J. West, *Proc. Roy. Soc.* (*London*) **A117**, 517 (1928).
(7) T. Ito and H. Mori, *Acta Cryst.* **6**, 24 (1953).
(8) J. Biscoe and B. E. Warren, *Z. Krist.* **86**, 292 (1933).
(9) G. Menzer, *ibid.* **69**, 300 (1928).
(10) W. L. Bragg and W. H. Zachariasen, *ibid.* **72**, 518 (1930).
(11) L. Vegard, *Skr. Norske Vid. Akad.*, No. 11 (1925); *Phil. Mag.* **1**, 1151 (1926); O. Hassel, *Z. Krist.* **63**, 247 (1926); W. Binks, *Mineralog. Mag.* **21**, 176 (1926); R. W. G. Wyckoff and S. B. Hendricks, *Z. Krist.* **66**, 73 (1927).

the better known orthosilicates. A number of mineral groups, such as the nephelite, sodalite, helvite, and scapolite groups, formerly thought to be orthosilicates, have now been demonstrated to have more complicated Si–O groupings and are listed under their new classifications.

The packing and structural relations in a simple orthosilicate are readily visualized by consideration of the mineral olivine, $(Mg, Fe)SiO_4$.[8] In Fig. 4.5 the atoms making up the $SiO_4$ groups have been connected. The oxygen atoms lie in approximately hexagonal close-packed sheets parallel to the (100) face. Those of one layer are shown as shaded circles,

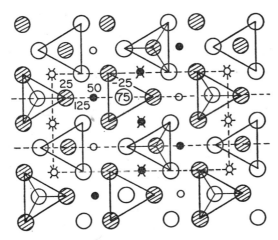

Fig. 4.5. The structure of olivine projected upon the (100) face. Large circles represent oxygen; small circles are magnesium; silicon atoms not shown. (Bragg, *Atomic Structure of Minerals;* courtesy *Cornell University Press.*)

(12) A. Pabst, *Bull. Geol. Soc. Am.* **61**, 1492 (1950); S. Bonatti and P. Gallitelli, *Atti soc. Toscana sci. nat. (Pisa), Mem. Ser. A* **57**, 182 (1950).
(13) H. R. Hoekstra and L. H. Fuchs, *Science* **123**, 105 (1956).
(14) W. H. Zachariasen, *Z. Krist.* **73**, 7 (1930).
(15) H. G. F. Winkler, *Acta Cryst.* **6**, 99 (1953).
(16) St. Náray-Szabó, W. H. Taylor, and W. W. Jackson, *Z. Krist.* **71**, 117 (1929).
(17) W. H. Taylor, *ibid.* **68**, 503 (1928); **71**, 205 (1929); J. S. Hey and W. H. Taylor, *ibid.* **80**, 428 (1931).
(18) St. Náray-Szabó, *ibid.* **71**, 103 (1929).
(19) L. Pauling, *Proc. Nat. Acad. Sci.* **14**, 603 (1928); N. A. Alston and J. West, *Z. Krist.* **69**, 149 (1928).
(20) C. M. Midgley, *Acta Cryst.* **5**, 307 (1955).
(21) T. Ito, *X-Ray Studies on Polymorphism*, Maruzen, Tokyo, 1950, pp. 151–159.
(22) G. Menzer, *Z. Krist.* **78**, 136 (1931).
(23) G. Menzer, *ibid.* **106**, 34 (1945).

[8] W. L. Bragg and G. B. Brown, *Z. Krist.* **63**, 538 (1926).

while those of the neighboring layer are plain circles.   In accordance with the full orthorhombic symmetry, the $SiO_4$ tetrahedra point alternately either way along the $b$ axis and either way along the $a$ axis.   Each $Mg^{++}$ (or $Fe^{++}$) ion is surrounded octahedrally by six oxygens, three plain and three shaded atoms in Fig. 4.5.   The positively charged $Mg^{++}$ or $Fe^{++}$ are seen to be uniformly distributed throughout the structure and serve to bind the negative $SiO_4^{-4}$ radicals together.   With silicon coordinating four oxygen atoms, the effective valence of each Si–O bond must be 1; similarly, magnesium (or iron) with six surrounding oxygen atoms results in the effective valence of the Mg–O bond being one third.   Examination of the structure reveals that each oxygen atom has as nearest neighbors one silicon and three magnesium atoms.   The electrostatic valence rule is thus satisfied, since the total bonding power of the oxygen's four neighbors is $1 + \frac{1}{3} + \frac{1}{3} + \frac{1}{3} = 2$.

Monticellite, $CaMgSiO_4$, has a structure[9] closely analogous to that of olivine.   Ideally, one half of the magnesium atoms of olivine are replaced by calcium atoms, indicated by the unstarred atoms in Fig. 4.5.   Thus monticellite is a definite compound, although usually some iron and manganese have isomorphously replaced a portion of the magnesium. The compounds forsterite, $Mg_2SiO_4$, fayalite, $Fe_2SiO_4$, and tephroite, $Mn_2SiO_4$, belong to the olivine group and have similar structures.

The chondrodite group[10] is interesting because of the increasing $Mg_2SiO_4$ content from one end of the series to the other.   X-ray analysis has shown that these minerals consist of alternate slabs of the olivine structure and of magnesium hydroxide.   Denoting the two types of olivine layer by $A$ and $B$, and the two types of magnesium hydroxide layer by $R$ and $L$, the sequence of layers in these minerals is as follows (reading upward from bottom of unit cell):

|  |  | *No. of Sheets of Oxygen Atoms in Unit Cell Parallel to (001)* |
| --- | --- | --- |
| Olivine | *AB.AB.AB* | 4 |
| Norbergite | *ALBR.ALBR* | 6 |
| Chondrodite | *BRA.BRA* | 5 |
| Humite | *BABRABAL.BABRABAL* | 14 |
| Clinohumite | *ABRAB.ABRAB* | 9 |

The $a$ and $b$ axes of their cells are almost identical with those of olivine, but the $c$ direction is determined in each case by the number of sheets of

[9] G. B. Brown and J. West, *ibid.* 66, 154 (1927).
[10] W. H. Taylor and J. West, *Proc. Roy. Soc.* (*London*) A117, 517 (1928).

oxygen atoms (each about 1.49 A thick) parallel to (001). Identification by X-ray analysis is simple and certain because of the very strong spectrum from (001) which differs for each mineral.

Members of the phenacite group[11] are characterized by large unit cells, although the cations, $Si^{+4}$, $Be^{++}$, and $Zn^{++}$, are all tetrahedrally coordinated by $O^=$ ions in a simple manner.

The garnet minerals[12] possess large cubic cells containing 8 molecules of composition $R_3^{II}R_2^{III}(SiO_4)_3$ and are notable for belonging to space group $O_h^{10} - Ia3d$, the last in the list of the 230 space groups. $R^{III}$ atoms, such as aluminum, are octahedrally coordinated by oxygen atoms, and $R^{II}$ atoms, such as calcium, have eight oxygen neighbors. Scientists at the General Electric Company[13] have synthesized garnets from dark-green hornblende by dehydration at pressures exceeding 375,000 psi and at temperatures of about 2200°F in the presence of a suitable dehydrator. The change can be reversed at a slightly lower pressure. These results give a glimpse of how garnets may have originally been formed in nature and suggest that the initial formation occurred some 60 miles below the earth's surface.

Kyanite, sillimanite, and andalusite[14,15] present an interesting case of polymorphism. All possess chains of $AlO_6$ groups linked by the independent $SiO_4$ groups and the remaining aluminum atoms. The chief structural difference between the three minerals arises from the coordination around these remaining aluminum atoms, which is four in sillimanite, five in andalusite, and six in kyanite. The mineral mullite, $3Al_2O_3 \cdot 2SiO_2$, is remarkably similar to sillimanite ($Al_2O_3 \cdot SiO_2$) in many of its physical properties despite the large difference in their chemical composition. The structure of mullite is best explained on the basis of a quadrupled sillimanite cell containing $16Al_2SiO_5$, or $Al_{32}Si_{16}O_{80}$. If four of the sixteen silicon cations of this cell are statistically replaced by $Al^{+3}$ cations and two oxygen anions are simultaneously removed from the cell, electrical neutrality is preserved and the mullite composition is attained, $6(3Al_2O_3 \cdot 2SiO_2) = Al_{36}Si_{12}O_{78}$.[15,16,17] Such a structure, since it contains two less than the requisite number of oxygen atoms for a complete frame-

[11] W. L. Bragg and W. H. Zachariasen, *Z. Krist.* **72**, 518 (1930).

[12] G. Menzer, *ibid.* **69**, 300 (1928).

[13] Anonymous, *Chem. Eng. News* **33**, 1778 (1955).

[14] St. Náray-Szabó, W. H. Taylor, and W. W. Jackson, *Z. Krist.* **71**, 117 (1929).

[15] W. H. Taylor, *ibid.* **68**, 503 (1928); **71**, 205 (1929); J. S. Hey and W. H. Taylor, *ibid.* **80**, 428 (1931).

[16] W. H. Taylor, *J. Soc. Glass Tech.* **16**, 111 (1932).

[17] B. E. Warren, *J. Am. Ceram. Soc.* **16**, 412 (1933).

work, is termed a *defective structure*.[18]   The structure of staurolite is closely related to that of kyanite.

Coffinite, $USiO_4$, is a new uranium mineral of major importance found on the Colorado Plateau.[19]   It is reported to be isomorphous in structure with uranothorite, $(Th, U)SiO_4$, thorite, and zircon.

The rare mineral afwillite (empirically $3CaO \cdot 2SiO_2 \cdot 3H_2O$) is of practical interest in connection with the hydration of Portland cement clinker.   It also proves to be the first demonstrated instance of a direct linkage of OH to silicon in a well-crystallized material.[20]   The formula should be written $Ca_3(SiO_3OH)_2 \cdot 2H_2O$.   It thus deviates from a true orthosilicate since one corner of each isolated Si tetrahedron has an OH instead of O.   Dehydration studies[21] have demonstrated that afwillite decomposes into $\gamma$-$Ca_2SiO_4$, amorphous $SiO_2$, and water at temperatures between 350°C and 850°C.

Many insoluble orthosilicates have been synthesized in the laboratory. Dicalcium silicate, an important constituent of Portland cement and various slags, exhibits an unusual case of polymorphism (Table 4.2):[22]

TABLE 4.2.   POLYMORPHISM OF DICALCIUM SILICATE

|  | Stability Range | Crystal Symmetry | Structure Type |
|---|---|---|---|
| $\alpha$-$Ca_2SiO_4$ | 1450°C to mp = 2130°C | Hexagonal | $\alpha$-$K_2SO_4$ |
| $\alpha'$-$Ca_2SiO_4$ | 850°C to 1450°C | Orthorhombic | $\beta$-$K_2SO_4$ |
| $\gamma$-$Ca_2SiO_4$ | Below 850°C | Orthorhombic | Olivine |
| $\beta$-$Ca_2SiO_4$ | Metastable below 675°C | Monoclinic | Larnite |

In addition to larnite, $\beta$-$Ca_2SiO_4$, both $\alpha'$- and $\gamma$-$Ca_2SiO_4$ have been reported to exist as natural minerals.[23]   The structures of $Ba_2SiO_4$ and $Sr_2SiO_4$ are isotypic with $K_2SO_4$, and the two silicates form a complete series of solid solutions.[24]   In the system $CoO$–$SiO_2$, only the orthosilicate, $Co_2SiO_4$, can be obtained by heating.   Its lattice constants and type are close to those of $Fe_2SiO_4$.[25]

**Polysilicates.**   The polysilicates (Table 4.3) contain separate Si—O complexes made up of 2, 3, 4, 5, 6, and occasionally 12 $SiO_4$ tetrahedra

[18] G. Hägg, *Z. Krist.* **91**, 114 (1935); L. W. Strock, *ibid.* **93**, 285 (1936).
[19] H. R. Hoekstra and L. H. Fuchs, *Science* **123**, 105 (1956).
[20] H. D. Megaw, *Acta Cryst.* **5**, 477 (1952).
[21] H. F. W. Taylor, *ibid.* **8**, 440 (1955).
[22] M. Bredig, *J. Am. Ceram. Soc.* **33**, 188 (1950).
[23] C. M. Midgley, *Acta Cryst.* **5**, 307 (1955).
[24] H. O'Daniel and L. Tscheischwili, *Z. Krist.* **104**, 348 (1942).
[25] N. P. Diev and V. V. Gribovskii, *J. Applied Chem. U.S.S.R.* **18**, 181 (1945).

sharing certain oxygen atoms.    Disilicates with $Si_2O_7^{-6}$ groups (Fig. 4.1) are the most numerous and are observed especially among the rare-earth silicates, e.g., thortveitite, $Sc_2Si_2O_7$, and thalenite, $Y_2Si_2O_7$.    In thortveitite the $Si_2O_7$ groups are linked together through octahedral $ScO_6$ groups, but in hemimorphite, $(OH)_2Zn_4Si_2O_7 \cdot H_2O$, they are joined through $ZnO_3 \cdot OH$ tetrahedra.    The electrostatic valence rule is strictly satisfied in both compounds.    Dehydration phenomena for hemimorphite are simply interpreted on the basis of its chemical formula as derived from the structure.    On heating hemimorphite crystals to 500°C water is lost

TABLE 4.3.    NATURAL POLYSILICATES

| Mineral | Composition | Crystal Symmetry | Hardness | Specific Gravity | Structure Reference |
|---|---|---|---|---|---|
| Hemimorphite | $(OH)_2Zn_4Si_2O_7 \cdot H_2O$ | Orthorhombic | 4.5–5 | 3.40–3.50 | (1) |
| Thortveitite | $Sc_2Si_2O_7$ | Monoclinic | 6–7 | 3.57 | (2) |
| Melilite | $(Ca, Na)_2(Mg, Al)_1(Si, Al)_2O_7$ | Tetragonal | 5 | 2.9–3.10 | (3) |
| Hardystonite | $Ca_2ZnSi_2O_7$ | Tetragonal | 3–4 | 3.4 | (4) |
| Vesuvianite | $Ca_{10}Al_4(Mg, Fe)_2(Si_2O_7)_2(SiO_4)_5(OH)_4$ | Tetragonal | 6.5 | 3.35–3.45 | (5) |
| Epidote | $Ca_2(Al, Fe)Al_2O(Si_2O_7)(SiO_4)OH$ | Monoclinic | 6–7 | 3.25–3.5 | (6) |
| Lawsonite | $CaAl_2(Si_2O_7)(OH)_2 \cdot H_2O$ | Orthorhombic | 7–8 | 3.09 | (7) |
| Tilleyite | $Ca_5Si_2O_7(CO_3)_2$ | Monoclinic | . . . | 2.82–2.88 | (8) |
| Danburite | $CaB_2OSi_2O_7$ | Orthorhombic | 7–7.25 | 2.97–3.02 | (9) |
| Benitoite | $BaTiSi_3O_9$ | Rhombohedral | 6.2–6.5 | 3.6 | (10) |
| Axinite | $(Fe, Mn)Ca_2Al_2BO_3(Si_4O_{12})OH$ | Triclinic | 6.5–7 | 3.31–3.33 | (11) |
| Zunyite | $Al_{13}O_4(Si_5O_{16})(OH, F)_{18}Cl$ | Cubic | 7 | 2.87–2.90 | (12) |
| Beryl | $Be_3Al_2Si_6O_{18}$ | Hexagonal | 7.5–8 | 2.63–2.80 | (13) |
| Cordierite | $Al_3Mg_2Si_5AlO_{18}$ | Orthorhombic | 7–7.5 | 2.60–2.66 | (14) |
| Dioptase | $Cu_6Si_6O_{19} \cdot 6H_2O$ | Rhombohedral | 5 | 3.28–3.35 | (15) |
| Tourmaline | $(Na, Ca)(Mg, Fe)_2Al_6(OH)_4(BO_3)_3-Si_6O_{18}$ | Rhombohedral | 7–7.5 | 2.98–3.20 | (16) |
| Milarite | $K_2Ca_4Be_{1.6}Al_2Si_{2.4}-[(Be_{0.10}Si_{0.90})_{12}O_{30}]_2 \cdot H_2O$ | Hexagonal | 5.5–6 | 2.46–2.50 | (17) |

(1)  T. Ito and J. West, *Z. Krist.* **83**, 1 (1932).
(2)  W. H. Zachariasen, *ibid.* **73**, 1 (1930).
(3)  B. E. Warren, *ibid.* **74**, 131 (1930).
(4)  B. E. Warren and O. R. Trautz, *ibid.* **75**, 525 (1930).
(5)  B. E. Warren and D. I. Modell, *ibid.* **78**, 422 (1931).
(6)  T. Ito, N. Morimoto, and R. Sadanaga, *Acta Cryst.* **7**, 53 (1954).
(7)  F. E. Wickman, *Arkiv Kemi Mineral. Geol.* **25A**, No. 2, 7 pp. (1947).
(8)  J. V. Smith, *Acta Cryst.* **6**, 9 (1953).
(9)  C. Dunbar and F. Machatschki, *Z. Krist.* **76**, 133 (1930).
(10)  W. H. Zachariasen, *ibid.* **74**, 139 (1930).
(11)  T. Ito and Y. Takéuchi, *Acta Cryst.* **5**, 202 (1952).
(12)  L. Pauling, *Z. Krist.* **84**, 442 (1933).
(13)  W. L. Bragg and J. West, *Proc. Roy. Soc. (London)* **A111**, 691 (1926).
(14)  Bragg, *The Atomic Structure of Minerals*, Cornell University Press, Ithaca, New York, 1937, p. 183.
(15)  H. G. Heide, K. Boll-Dornberger, E. Thilo, and E. M. Thilo, *Acta Cryst.* **8**, 425 (1955).
(16)  G. Donnay and M. J. Buerger, *ibid.* **3**, 379 (1950); T. Ito and R. Sadanaga, *ibid.* **4**, 385 (1951).
(17)  T. Ito, N. Morimoto, and R. Sadanaga, *ibid.* **5**, 209 (1952).

continuously without the crystal losing its shape or transparency, and in amount corresponding to one molecule of water of crystallization. This water exists as isolated water molecules in the structure. At a much higher temperature additional water comes off with destruction of the crystal, its source being the OH groups of the zinc tetrahedra. The minerals vesuvianite and epidote (Table 4.3) contain separate $SiO_4^{-4}$ groups as well as $Si_2O_7^{-6}$ groups, and are both orthosilicates and disilicates. Tilleyite contains carbonate groups, $CO_3^=$, and is the first carbonate silicate mineral to have its structure determined.[26] Danburite, $CaB_2OSi_2O_7$, has tetrahedral $BO_4$ groups linking the $Si_2O_7$ groups so that the whole structure resembles in some respects the linked Si–Al tetrahedral frameworks of the feldspars.[27]

Polysilicates with complexes made up of 3, 4, or 5 $SiO_4$ tetrahedra are rare. Benitoite, $BaTiSi_3O_9$, is the only established example of the $Si_3O_9^{-6}$ group (Fig. 4.1). It is unique also as the only known example of the $D_{3h} - \bar{6}m2$ symmetry class among mineral structures.[28,29] The complex triclinic mineral axinite (Table 4.3) contains separate $Si_4O_{12}^{-8}$ and $BO_3^{-3}$ groups bound together by the Fe, Al, and Ca atoms.[30] Except for this instance, such four-membered rings have previously been observed only in zeolites and similar compounds where they are part of a more extended structure. Finally, the $Si_5O_{16}^{-12}$ group of zunyite[31] has the remarkable arrangement of five $SiO_4$ tetrahedra pictured in Fig. 4.6. Groups of twelve $AlO_6$ octahedra form a second structural unit in zunyite, and these pack together in a ZnS-type arrangement with the extra Al atom and the $Cl^-$ ion in cavities in the structure.

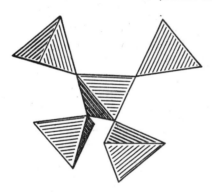

FIG. 4.6. Group of five silicon tetrahedra, $Si_5O_{16}$, found in zunyite. (Pauling, *Z. Krist.* **84**, 442 (1933)).

The structure of beryl, $Be_3Al_2Si_6O_{18}$, is one of the most elegant of the silicate structures (Fig. 4.7).[32] The hexagonal $Si_6O_{18}^{-12}$ rings lie on the

[26] J. V. Smith, *Acta Cryst.* **6**, 9 (1953).

[27] C. Dunbar and F. Machatschki, *Z. Krist.* **76**, 133 (1930).

[28] J. D. H. Donnay and W. Nowacki, *Crystal Data*, Geological Society of America Memoir 60, Geological Society of America, New York, 1954, pp. 63, 64.

[29] A structure for β-wollastonite, $CaSiO_3$, involving $Si_3O_9$ rings now appears to be disproved: K. Dornberger-Schiff, F. Liebau, and E. Thilo, *Acta Cryst.* **8**, 752 (1955).

[30] T. Ito and Y. Takéuchi, *Acta Cryst.* **5**, 202 (1952).

[31] L. Pauling, *Z. Krist.* **84**, 442 (1933).

[32] W. L. Bragg and J. West, *Proc. Roy. Soc.* (*London*) **A111**, 691 (1926).

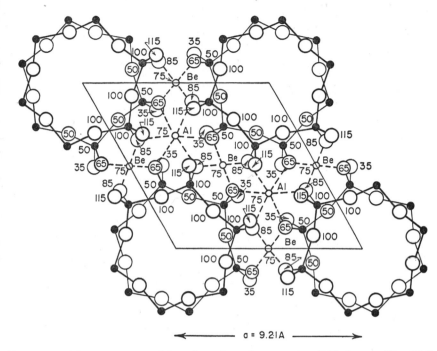

Fɪɢ. 4.7. The structure of beryl projected upon the (00*l*) face. The $Si_6O_{18}$ rings are at the corners. Superimposed oxygen atoms are symmetrically displaced. (Bragg, *Atomic Structure of Minerals;* courtesy *Cornell University Press.*)

reflection planes parallel to (00*l*) with the silicon atoms and the shared oxygen atoms on these planes. The remaining oxygen atoms of the group are in mirror-image positions above and below the plane. Binding of the rings laterally and vertically in the structure is through the aluminum and beryllium atoms which are sixfold and fourfold coordinated, respectively. Rather large open channels are present along the hexagonal axes of the structure. Gigantic beryl crystals found in Maine and New Hampshire are among the largest single crystals ever found. One crystal was 18 ft in length, 4 ft in diameter, and weighed 18 tons.

The $Si_6O_{18}$ rings in dioptase[33] have only $\bar{3}$ symmetry with alternate tetrahedra pointing in opposite directions, and their packing is different from that in beryl. Although channels similar to those in beryl are present, the water of crystallization is not readily expelled from the structure. Two determinations of the structure of tourmaline lead to

[33] H. G. Heide, K. Boll-Dornberger, E. Thilo, and E. M. Thilo, *Acta Cryst.* **8**, 425 (1955).

TABLE 4.4.  GENERAL SURVEY OF PYROXENE AND AMPHIBOLE MINERALS

| Pyroxene Group | | Structure Reference | Amphibole Group | | Structure Reference |
|---|---|---|---|---|---|
| **ORTHORHOMBIC SYMMETRY** | | | | | |
| Enstatite | $MgSiO_3$ | (1)(2) | Anthophyllite | $(OH)_2(Mg, Fe)_7Si_8O_{22}$ | (5)(6) |
| Hypersthene | $(Mg, Fe)SiO_3$ | (1) | | | |
| **MONOCLINIC SYMMETRY** | | | | | |
| Clinoenstatite | $MgSiO_3$ | (3) | Tremolite | $(OH)_2Ca_2Mg_5Si_8O_{22}$ | (7) |
| Diopside | $CaMg(SiO_3)_2$ | (4) | Soda-tremolite | $(OH)_2CaNa_2Mg_5Si_8O_{22}$ | (7) |
| Hedenbergite | $CaFe(SiO_3)_2$ | (3) | Actinolite | $(OH)_2Ca_2(MgFe^{II})_5Si_8O_{22}$ | (7) |
| Augite | $(Ca, Mg)(Mg, Fe^{II})(SiO_3)_2$ with $(Mg, Fe^{II})Si$ partly replaced by $(Al, Fe^{III})Al$ | (3) | Arfvedsonite | $(OH)_2Na_3Mg_4AlSi_8O_{22}$ | (7) |
| | | | Kupferrite | $(OH)_2Mg_7Si_8O_{22}$ | |
| | | | Cummingtonite | $(OH)_2(Mg, Fe)_7Si_8O_{22}$ | |
| Acmite | $NaFe^{III}(SiO_3)_2$ | (3) | Grinerite | $(OH)_2Fe_7Si_8O_{22}$ | |
| Jadeite | $NaAl(SiO_3)_2$ | (3) | Riebeckite | $(OH)_2Na_2Fe_2{}^{II}Fe_2{}^{III}Si_8O_{22}$ | (7) |
| Spodumene | $LiAl(SiO_3)_2$ | (3) | Glaucophane | $(OH)_2Na_2(Mg, Fe^{II})_3(Al, Fe^{III})_2Si_8O_{22}$ | (7) |
| | | | Hornblende | $(OH)_2Na_2(Ca, Na, K)_{2-3}(Mg, Fe, Al)_5$ $(Si, Al)_2Si_6O_{22}$ | |
| **TRICLINIC SYMMETRY** | | | | | |
| Rhodonite | $MnSiO_3$ | (8) | Aenigmatite | A titano-silicate of iron, sodium, and aluminum of similar composition to an amphibole | |
| Babingtonite | $(Ca, Fe, Mn)SiO_3 \cdot Fe_2(SiO_3)_3$ | | | | |

(1) B. E. Warren and D. I. Modell, Z. Krist. 75, 1 (1930).
(2) T. Ito, X-Ray Studies on Polymorphism, Maruzen, Tokyo, 1950, pp. 30–41.
(3) B. E. Warren and J. Biscoe, Z. Krist. 80, 391 (1931).
(4) B. E. Warren and W. L. Bragg, ibid. 69, 168 (1928).
(5) B. E. Warren and D. I. Modell, ibid. 75, 161 (1930).
(6) Ito, op. cit., pp. 42–49.
(7) B. E. Warren, ibid. 72, 42 (1929).
(8) M. Perutz, Mineralog. Mag. 24, 573 (1937).

structures that are essentially the same.[34]   Both have ring-shaped $Si_6O_{18}$ and triangular $BO_3$ groups, but differ in the precise configuration of the $Si_6O_{18}$ groups.   Milarite's outstanding structural feature is the double hexagonal ring, $(Be, Si)_{12}O_{30}$, made up of twelve tetrahedra.[35]

**The Pyroxenes and the Amphiboles.**   The pyroxenes and the amphiboles are well-defined groups of minerals widely known in the past as *metasilicates*.   Although they show a wide variety of compositions, mineralogists formerly referred all of them to general formulas of the type $RSiO_3$, in which R is a divalent metal.   In some pyroxenes there may be a partial substitution of $RSiO_3$ by $Al_2O_3$ or $Fe_2O_3$.   In the amphiboles, chemical analysis reveals a small proportion of water, up to 2.2%.   This water is actually present as OH groups which may be partially replaced by $F^-$ ions.   Thus the ideal formula of tremolite, sometimes given as $CaMg_3(SiO_3)_4$, is actually $(OH)_2Ca_2Mg_5(Si_4O_{11})_2$.   The angle between the cleavage cracks, 93° in pyroxenes and 56° in amphiboles, is a characteristic difference.   Table 4.4 gives a general survey of the minerals of the pyroxene and amphibole groups together with structure references.

The silicon-oxygen chains are the essential feature of these minerals. The pyroxenes are based on single chains of linked $SiO_4$ tetrahedra with

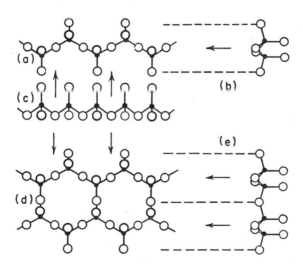

FIG. 4.8.   Plan (a), elevation (c), and end-on view (b) of the pyroxene chain. The same three aspects (d), (c), (e), for the amphibole chain.   (Bragg, *Atomic Structure of Minerals;* courtesy *Cornell University Press.*)

[34] G. Donnay and M. J. Buerger, *ibid.* **3**, 379 (1950); T. Ito and R. Sadanaga, *ibid.* **4**, 385 (1951).

[35] T. Ito, N. Morimoto, and R. Sadanaga, *ibid.* **5**, 209 (1952).

the repeating unit of composition $SiO_3^=$, while the amphiboles have double chains whose repeating unit is $Si_4O_{11}^{-6}$. Various aspects of these chains are shown in Fig. 4.8. A typical pyroxene, such as the monoclinic mineral diopside, $CaMg(SiO_3)_2$, has these single chains running through the structure parallel to the *c* axis.[36] The chains are then bound together by the calcium and magnesium ions which are arranged alternately along the *c* axis in such a way that each is surrounded by six active oxygens of the chain. These oxygens are bound to silicon by a bond of strength one and have their remaining unit of electrostatic valence satisfied by one calcium and one magnesium atom. Two inactive oxygens in the chains are also near neighbors of each calcium ion to make its coordination number eight. The silicate chains and the general packing of the ions in diopside are shown in Fig. 4.9.

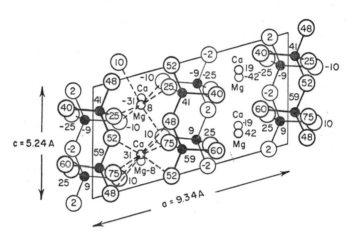

Fɪɢ. 4.9. The structure of diopside projected upon the (010) face. Ca and Mg atoms which should project superimposed are shifted slightly. (Bragg, *Structure of Minerals;* courtesy *Cornell University Press.*)

The double chains in the amphiboles are really two pyroxene chains bound together by sharing certain oxygen atoms. The amphiboles, as a result, have structures closely similar to the pyroxenes. For instance, tremolite, $(OH)_2Ca_2Mg_5(Si_4O_{11})_2$, is monoclinic with a unit cell and atomic arrangement very similar to diopside except that its *b* axis is twice the length of that of diopside, because the chain is twice as wide.[37] The relation between the two structures is shown in Fig. 4.10. The double

[36] B. E. Warren and W. L. Bragg, *Z. Krist.* **69**, 168 (1928).
[37] B. E. Warren, *ibid.* **72**, 42 (1929).

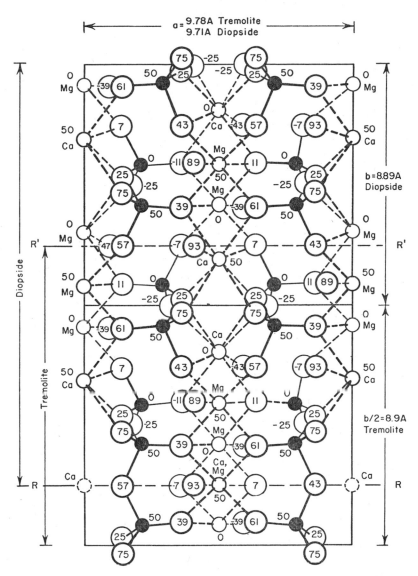

Fig. 4.10. Projection parallel to *c* depicting the relation between tremolite and diopside. Extents of the two structures, and region common to both, are indicated on the left. Superimposed oxygens have been shifted. (Bragg, *Atomic Structure of Minerals;* courtesy *Cornell University Press.*)

chains are parallel to the $c$ axis and again the metal ions form the links between the chains. Because of the chains these minerals show elongated growth along the $c$ axis or chain axis. The binding force between the chains is ionic and not as strong as the Si–O bonds along the chains. This kind of binding gives rise to the well-known fibrous nature of the amphiboles, the bonds in the double chains being much stronger than in other directions.

The material jade, highly prized from antiquity for carved ornaments and utensils, properly includes two species only from this group of minerals. The more common is the amphibole nephrite, a tough, compact, fine-grained tremolite (or actinolite). Less common is jadeite of the pyroxene group. Several amphiboles are of minor importance as asbestos minerals (Table 4.5). Fibrous varieties of anthophyllite, tremolite, and actinolite are sources of asbestos. Amosite is a long-fibered, gray or greenish asbestos having the composition of an iron-rich anthophyllite. Also of importance is crocidolite (blue asbestos), a fibrous variety of riebeckite. Both amosite and crocidolite have been found to have similar structures resembling that of tremolite.[38]

The clay mineral attapulgite, $Mg_5Si_8O_{20}(OH)_2 \cdot 8H_2O$, has a double chain structure related to the amphiboles. The water molecules are said to occupy large spaces between the chains.[39] Infinite threefold chains[40] with a repeat unit of $Si_3O_8^{-4}$ are found in the minerals eudidymite (monoclinic) and epididymite (orthorhombic),[41] both of composition $HNaBeSi_3O_8$. By lateral junctions in a common oxygen atom, the chains form infinite sheets $(Si_3O_7)_\infty$. The sodium atoms pack between the chains, and the $Be^{++}$ and $OH^-$ lie on the outside of the network, making a structure of composition $BeOH \cdot NaSi_3O_7$. These sheets are stacked parallel to (001) with only van der Waals forces between the layers. In agreement with this structure, both minerals show excellent basal cleavage. Similar $Si_3O_8$ chains are reported in sanbornite, $Ba_2Si_4O_{10}$.[42]

Wollastonite, $CaSiO_3$, resembles the pyroxenes in composition but differs from them crystallographically, structurally, and optically.[43] It exists in two low-temperature forms: $\beta$-$CaSiO_3$, triclinic, and parawollastonite, monoclinic. Above 1126°C the high-temperature pseudowollastonite, $\alpha$-$CaSiO_3$, with triclinic symmetry is the stable form. Al-

[38] E. J. W. Whittaker, *Acta Cryst.* **2**, 312 (1949); R. I. Garrod and C. S. Rann, *ibid.* **5**, 285 (1952).

[39] W. F. Bradley, *Am. Mineral.* **25**, 405 (1940).

[40] T. Ito, *Proc. Imp. Acad. (Tokyo)* **9**, 53 (1933).

[41] T. Ito, *Am. Mineral.* **32**, 442 (1947).

[42] S. B. Hendricks, *J. Wash. Acad. Sci.* **34**, 241 (1944).

[43] Warren and Biscoe, *op. cit.*; M. A. Peacock, *Am. J. Sci.* **30**, 495 (1935).

though early X-ray investigations proposed a structure for $\beta$-CaSiO$_3$ containing separate Si$_3$O$_9$ groups, more recent studies[44] suggest the presence of infinite silicate chains, which, in turn, more adequately explain the fibrous habit of the mineral.

**Asbestos.** Most commercial asbestos is the mineral chrysotile, although, as mentioned above, some types of asbestos are amphiboles. Chrysotile is fibrous serpentine and has the formula Mg$_6$Si$_4$O$_{10}$·(OH)$_8$. It occurs as bundles of parallel fibers, each made up of crystals with the $c$ axis parallel to the fiber axis. The individual crystals in the fiber have their remaining two axes randomly oriented with respect to the fiber axis. As a result, the X-ray pattern of a bundle of the fibers is similar to a complete rotation pattern for a single crystal. Such bundles are not single crystals but are excellent examples of fibering, a rather common phenomenon among the long-chain organic compounds and polymers. The necessity of working with such fiber diagrams, rather than single crystal patterns, has complicated greatly the structural study of chrysotile.

From an early study chrysotile appeared to be based on the Si$_4$O$_{11}$ amphibole chain,[45] despite the fact that it contains a much greater proportion of magnesium and hydroxide than an amphibole. A ribbon structure involving long but narrow Si$_4$O$_{10}$ sheets now seems more probable than that based on the chains.[46] Indeed, it was largely the fibrous nature of the material that originally suggested a chain structure. The layers are built up in the sequence 3O, 2Si, 2OOH, 3Mg, 3OH. The presence of smeared but *0kl*-type reflections indicates some randomness in the stacking of successive layers. The layers would resemble closely those of kaolinite except for the presence of Mg in place of Al in chrysotile which causes severe strain and prevents layer growth beyond a ribbonlike fiber stage 30 to 100 A wide. From electron micrographs of both natural and synthetic chrysotile, the fibers appear to have a hollow, tubular structure which is ascribed to the dimensional differences of the Si–O and Mg–OH bonds in the sheets.[47] Density data, on the other hand, seem to indicate that the fibers do not contain the void space required by a hollow-tube structure.[48] Although a triclinic unit cell was proposed by one investigator,[49] the monoclinic cell with $a = 14.65$, $b = 9.24$, $c = 5.33$ A, and $\beta = 93°16'$ appears firmly established.[46,50]

[44] Dornberger-Schiff *et al.*, *loc. cit.* ref. 29.
[45] B. E. Warren and W. L. Bragg, *Z. Krist.* **76**, 201 (1930).
[46] B. E. Warren, *Am. Mineral.* **27**, 235 (1942).
[47] T. F. Bates, L. B. Sand, and J. F. Mink, *Science* **111**, 512 (1950); W. Noll and H. Kircher, *Naturwiss.* **37**, 540 (1950).
[48] F. L. Pundsack, *J. Phys. Chem.* **60**, 361 (1956).
[49] N. N. Padurow, *Acta Cryst.* **3**, 204 (1950).
[50] E. J. W. Whittaker, *ibid.* **5**, 143 (1952).

Examination of specimens of chrysotile from a variety of sources has disclosed that their diffraction patterns often differ extensively. This difference arises from the specimens being mixtures, in different proportions, of the well-known monoclinic variety and a new orthorhombic variety with substantially the same cell dimensions.[51] The kaolin-type layers present in the two varieties are identical except for the positions of the Mg atoms which may occupy either of two alternative sets of positions. If these layers are denoted as *A*-type when the Mg atoms are in one position and *B*-type when they are in the alternative positions, the structures of the two chrysotile varieties are represented by the sequences:

monoclinic chrysotile, *A A A A A A* $\cdots$

orthorhombic chrysotile, *A B A B A B* $\cdots$

This arrangement suggests the possibility of further types of polymorphism in chrysotile arising from still more elaborate sequences of the two types of layers.

The lamellar form of serpentine, antigorite, has the same composition as chrysotile, and is probably also a kaolin-type layer structure.[52]

On dehydration at temperatures between 550°–1000°C serpentine passes directly to forsterite without the formation of an amorphous phase (except for the excess $SiO_2$):[53]

$$Mg_6Si_4O_{10}\cdot(OH)_8 \rightarrow 3Mg_2SiO_4 + SiO_2 + 4H_2O \quad (550°\text{--}1000°C)$$

serpentine                     forsterite       amorphous

The formation of forsterite with separate $SiO_4$ groups is rather unexpected here. Instead, enstatite whose single-chain structure is more closely related to serpentine might have been predicted. The forsterite, moreover, is oriented with its *c* axis parallel to the original fiber axis and gives a fairly well-defined rotation photograph. In terms of the bond destruction during dehydration, this is interpreted to mean that the $SiO_4$ tetrahedra separate in the process, but that the $MgO_6$ octahedra retain their linkages. On heating above 1100°–1200°C an enstatite phase does appear as an additional compound:

$$3Mg_2SiO_4 + SiO_2 \rightarrow 2Mg_2SiO_4 + 2MgSiO_3 \quad (>1100°C)$$

forsterite      amorphous       forsterite       enstatite

[51] E. J. W. Whittaker, *ibid.* **4**, 187 (1951); **6**, 747 (1953).

[52] T. Ito, *X-Ray Studies on Polymorphism*, Maruzen, Tokyo, 1950, p. 160; J. Zussman, *Am. Mineral.* **41**, 148 (1956).

[53] J. W. Gruner, *Am. Mineral.* **33**, 679 (1948).

TABLE 4.5. WORLD OUTPUT OF ASBESTOS MINERALS FOR 1952*

| Country | Class of Asbestos | Metric Tons |
|---|---|---|
| Canada | Chrysotile | 843,078 |
| South Africa | Chrysotile, Amosite and Crocidolite | 121,416 |
| South Rhodesia | Chrysotile | 76,960 |
| U. S. America | Chrysotile, Anthophyllite | 48,864 |
| Europe | Chrysotile, Anthophyllite | 38,570 |
| Swaziland | Chrysotile | 32,420 |
| Cyprus | Chrysotile | 18,479 |
| Australia | Chrysotile, Crocidolite and Anthophyllize | 4,124 |
| Asia | Chrysotile, Anthophyllite | 3,588 |
| North Africa | Chrysotile, Anthophyllite | 933 |
| South America | Chrysotile, Crocidolite and Anthophyllite | 860 |
| | Approximate Total of all Classes | 1,425,000 |

* Not included is an unknown but probably large output in the U.S.S.R. World resources of asbestos,[54] principally chrysotile, are estimated at about 92,000,000 short tons located chiefly in Canada, U.S.S.R., and Africa. Asbestos finds use in a variety of manufactured products, including asbestos textiles and paper, brake linings, gaskets, insulation, and asbestos cement pipes and sheets.

The importance of the asbestos minerals as a commercial product is evidenced by data on the world output of asbestos in 1952 (Table 4.5).[54]

**Micas and Related Minerals.** The silicates to be considered in this section are based on infinite anion radicals of the hexagonal type silicon-oxygen sheet (Fig. 4.3) with a repeating unit of composition of $Si_2O_5^=$ (or $Si_4O_{10}^{-4}$ in the double sheet). These infinite sheets are held together by metallic cations placed between them or by residual valence forces when the composition leads to electrically neutral sheets. The hexagonal nature of the sheets confers pseudohexagonal symmetry on the minerals, and the sheets lead to flaky or platy habits and easy cleavage. Structural similarities thus make it logical to consider not only the micas, but talc, pyrophyllite, the clintonite group, and the chlorites, as well, in the same grouping. Because of their special industrial importance, the clay minerals (also based on these same Si–O sheets) are considered separately. Table 4.6 lists formulas and other data for the micas and related minerals.

Pauling, applying his set of principles governing the structures of complex ionic crystals,[55] laid the foundation for investigating these minerals by formulated structures for talc, pyrophyllite, the micas, and the brittle micas.[56] X-ray study had provided the dimensions of the mono-

[54] From W. E. Sinclair, *Asbestos* 37, p. 2 (Sept., 1955).
[55] Pauling, *op. cit.* ref. 2.
[56] L. Pauling, *Proc. Nat. Acad. Sci.* 16, 123 (1930).

TABLE 4.6. MICAS AND RELATED MINERALS

(The symmetry is normally monoclinic in all cases)

| Mineral | Composition* | Hardness | Specific Gravity | Structure Reference |
|---|---|---|---|---|
| Pyrophyllite | $Al_2(Si_4O_{10})(OH)_2$ | 1–2 | 2.8–2.9 | (1) |
| Talc | $Mg_3(Si_4O_{10})(OH)_2$ | 1–1.5 | 2.7–2.8 | (1) |
| *Mica Group* | | | | |
| Muscovite | $KAl_2(AlSi_3O_{10})(OH)_2$ | 2–2.5 | 2.76–3 | (2) |
| Paragonite | $NaAl_2(AlSi_3O_{10})(OH)_2$ | | 2.78–2.90 | |
| Lepidolite | $KLi_2Al(Si_4O_{10})(OH)_2$ | 2.5–4 | 2.8–3.3 | (3) |
| Zinnwaldite | $KLiFeAl(AlSi_3O_{10})(OH)_2$ | | | (3) |
| Biotite | $K(Mg, Fe)_3(AlSi_3O_{10})(OH)_2$ | 2.5–3 | 2.7–3.1 | (3) |
| Phlogopite | $KMg_3(AlSi_3O_{10})(OH)_2$ | 2.5–3 | 2.78–2.85 | (3) |
| *Clintonite Group* | | | | |
| Margarite | $CaAl_2(Al_2Si_2O_{10})(OH)_2$ | 3.5–4.5 | 2.99–3.08 | (3) |
| Chloritoid | $(Fe, Mg)_2Al_2(Al_2Si_2O_{10})(OH)_4$ | 6.5 | 3.52–3.57 | (4) |
| Clintonite | Fe and Mg partly replace Ca and Al of margarite | 4–5 | 3–3.1 | |
| *Chlorite Group* | | | | |
| Penninite | $Mg_5(Al, Fe)(Al, Si)_4O_{10}(OH)_8$ | 2–2.5 | 2.6–2.85 | (5) |
| Clinochlore | $Mg_5Al(AlSi_3O_{10})(OH)_8$ | 2–2.5 | 2.65–2.78 | (5) |
| Prochlorite | Lower in Si and higher in $Fe^{II}$ than clinochlore | 1–2 | 2.78–2.96 | (5) |
| Illitic Minerals | Hydrous micas | | | (6) |
| Vermiculites | $(Mg, Fe)_3(Si, Al)_4O_{10}(OH)_2 \cdot 4H_2O$ | 1.5 | 2.2–2.5 | (7) |

* Formulas are largely simplified to an ideal type, since most actual compositions are very complex owing to isomorphous substitution.

(1) J. W. Gruner, *Z. Krist.* **88**, 412 (1934); S. B. Hendricks, *ibid.* **99**, 264 (1938).
(2) W. W. Jackson and J. West, *ibid.* **76**, 211 (1931); **85**, 160 (1933).
(3) C. Mauguin, *Compt. rend.* **186**, 879, 1131 (1928).
(4) F. Machatschki and F. Mussgnug, *Naturwiss.* **30**, 106 (1942).
(5) R. C. McMurchy, *Z. Krist.* **88**, 420 (1934).
(6) G. W. Brindley, *X-Ray Identification and Crystal Structures of Clay Minerals*, The Mineralogical Society, London, 1951, Chap. V.
(7) J. W. Gruner, *Am. Mineral.* **19**, 557 (1934); S. B. Hendricks and M. E. Jefferson, *ibid.* **23**, 851 (1938).

clinic (pseudohexagonal) cell of muscovite mica, $KAl_2(AlSi_3O_{10})(OH)_2$:[57]

$$a = 5.17 \quad b = 8.94 \quad c = 20.01 \text{ A} \quad \beta = 96°$$

The dimensions of this unit in the basal plane closely approximate those of the similarly pseudohexagonal crystal hydrargillite, $Al(OH)_3$, also those

[57] C. Mauguin, *Compt. rend* **185**, 288 (1927).

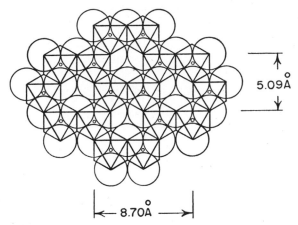

FIG. 4.11. A hydrargillite layer of octahedra. (Pauling, *Proc. Nat. Acad. Sci.* **16**, 123.)

of the hexagonal layers found in β-tridymite and β-cristobalite. The hydrargillite layers are built up of octahedra consisting of an $Al^{+3}$ ion surrounded by $6OH^-$ ions. Figure 4.11 illustrates such a layer, whose dimensions are $5.09 \times 8.70$ A. The electrostatic valences are all satisfied, each $OH^-$ ion being held by two bonds of strength one half. The hydrargillite crystal is made up of these layers superimposed but sharing no octahedral elements with each other.

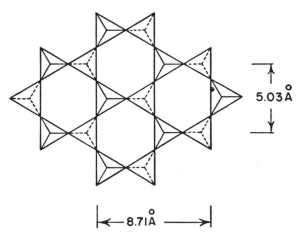

FIG. 4.12. The Si–O tetrahedral layer from β-cristobalite or β-tridymite. (Pauling, *Proc. Nat. Acad. Sci.* **16**, 123.)

Tetrahedral layers with repeat dimensions of 5.03 × 8.71 A, Fig. 4.12, extend through the structures of β-tridymite and β-cristobalite. A layer of the same dimensions, but different in type, can be formed by orienting all tetrahedra to point in the same direction, Fig. 4.13. In such a layer

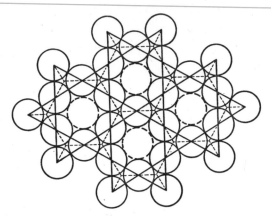

FIG. 4.13.   A tetrahedral layer with all tetrahedra pointing in the same direction.   (Pauling, *Proc. Nat. Acad. Sci.* **16**, 123.)

the oxygens in the bases of the tetrahedra have their valences satisfied, but those on the unshared corners still have a valence of 1 unsatisfied and must be joined to other atoms.

A superposition of the latter tetrahedral layer on a hydrargillite layer is possible.   The unshared tetrahedral corners will be coincident with two

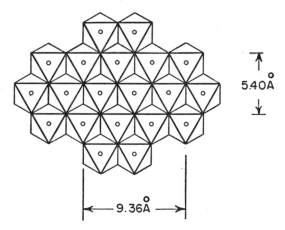

FIG. 4.14.   The complete octahedral layer found in brucite.   (Pauling, *Proc. Nat. Acad. Aci.* **16**, 123.)

thirds of the shared octahedron corners, and the OH⁻ ions at these points must be replaced with O⁼ ions. A similar layer attached to the underside of the octahedral layer gives an electrically neutral layer structure about 10 A in thickness. The composition of these layers is $Al_2Si_4O_{10}(OH)_2$. The mineral pyrophyllite, with this composition, was predicted by Pauling[56] to have a structure built up by the superposition of such layers, and the prediction was later completely verified.[58]

Another mineral built up of complete octahedral layers is brucite, $Mg(OH)_2$, Fig. 4.14. Its dimensions are 5.40 × 9.36 A, slightly larger than hydrargillite. A similar layer structure can be formed by sandwiching a brucite layer between two tetrahedral silica layers. The composition of such layers is that of talc, $Mg_3Si_4O_{10}(OH)_2$, and again Pauling's prediction was completely confirmed.[58]

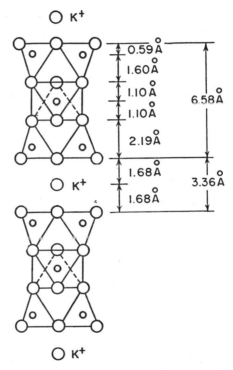

Mica

Isomorphous replacement of silicon by aluminum is fairly common in the silicates. If one fourth of the $Si^{+4}$ ions in a pyrophyllite layer are replaced by $Al^{+3}$ ions with the same coordination, the layers are no longer neutral but bear a negative charge. Neutrality in a structure made up of such layers could be regained by inserting positive ions, such as $Na^+$ or $K^+$, between the layers. There is ample space for these ions in the pockets formed by the hexagonal rings of oxygens opposing each other in the layers. The composition of a crystal built up of such layers and $K^+$ ions, Fig. 4.15, is $KAl_2(AlSi_3O_{10})(OH)_2$, which is the composition of muscovite mica. If talc layers are used, the composition is

FIG. 4.15. The structure of mica, showing the sequence of atomic layers normal to the cleavage planes (001). (Pauling, *Proc. Nat. Acad. Sci.* **16**, 578.)

$KMg_3(AlSi_3O_{10})(OH)_2$, which is the mica biotite. Pauling verified this structure for muscovite, and it was later the subject of a complete anal-

[58] J. W. Gruner, *Z. Krist.* **88**, 412 (1934); S. B. Hendricks, *ibid.* **99**, 264 (1938).

ysis.[59]  $Ca^{++}$  ions take the place of the  $K^+$  ions between the layers in the brittle micas (margarite), whose layers have twice the electrical charge of those in the micas.

An extensive study of natural micas has revealed a considerable amount of polymorphism.[60]  By a slight shifting of the layers in the *a* or *b* directions, a multiplicity of additional mica structures is obtained in which the structure repeats after the second, third, sixth, or a higher number of layers. Some of these more complex structures have rhombohedral and triclinic symmetries. Such polymorphism is common among the biotites. Mixed structures also exist.

Crystal chemistry teaches that *the properties of crystalline solids are related to their structures*, a relationship that is strikingly demonstrated in the case of these minerals. Because of the strong Si–O and Al–O bonds, the pseudohexagonal layers are tough. The weaker forces between the layers, however, permit them to be separated readily, giving rise to the pronounced cleavage common to these minerals. The layers in hydrargillite, brucite, pyrophyllite and talc are electrically neutral and are held together by weak secondary forces. Hence all of them are very soft. Talc and pyrophyllite have a hardness of 1 to 2 on the Mohs scale. In the case of micas it is necessary to break the univalent  $K^+$  ion bonds to separate the layers. They are thus harder, 2.5 to 4 on the Mohs scale, and somewhat elastic. Still stronger bonds must be broken in the brittle micas, hardness 3.5 to 6, and they are brittle instead of elastic. All show eminent or perfect basal cleavage.

The chlorites are silicates of magnesium and iron with properties and structures closely similar to the micas. Again, it was Pauling who gave the first insight into their structure.[61] The chlorites are built of alternate mica and brucite layers, Fig. 4.16. The symmetrical layers are charged. The mica layers are negative as a result of substitution of  $Al^{+3}$  for  $Si^{+4}$ , while the brucite layers compensate with a positive charge resulting from replacement of  $Mg^{++}$  by  $Al^{+3}$ .[62] The chlorites are not as soft as talc and pyrophyllite because of the alternate charges on the layers, and they are not as elastic as the micas because the keying effect of the potassium ions between adjacent layers is missing. As in the case of the micas, the chlorites also show a complex polymorphism.[63] Dehydration of chlorites proceeds in stages, the first (on heating to 600°C) involving the removal

[59] W. W. Jackson and J. West, *ibid.* **76**, 211 (1931); **85**, 160 (1933).
[60] S. B. Hendricks and M. E. Jefferson, *Am. Mineral.* **24**, 729 (1939).
[61] L. Pauling, *Proc. Nat. Acad. Sci.* **16**, 578 (1930).
[62] R. C. McMurchy, *Z. Krist.* **88**, 420 (1934).
[63] G. W. Brindley, B. M. Oughton, and K. Robinson, *Acta Cryst.* **3**, 408 (1950).

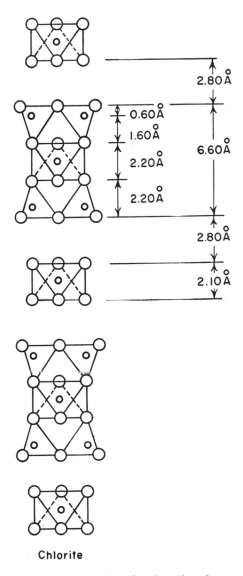

**Chlorite**

FIG. 4.16. The structure of chlorite, showing the alternate arrangement of mica and brucite layers. (Pauling, *Proc. Nat. Acad. Sci.* **16**, 578.)

of water from the brucite layers only of the structure.   The second stage continues at higher temperatures (700°–800°C) with the expulsion of water from the mica layers and is followed by the formation of olivine, $Mg_2SiO_4$.[64]

*Illite* is not a specific mineral name, but is the term applied to a group of hydrous mica minerals found in clays.   The illites are chemically distinguished from the normal well-crystallized micas by containing less potassium and more water.   They are also characterized by little change of the 10-A reflection under the action of chemicals or mild heat.   Diagnostic criteria for the micas and the illites have been proposed.[65]

The vermiculites are secondary minerals, usually golden yellow or brown in color, produced by the decomposition of mica.   Their crystals form soft pliable inelastic lamellae.   Heat drives off a considerable amount of water, and exfoliation of the sheets causes the lamellae to open out into wormlike forms.   Flakes may expand to 20 to 30 times their original length normal to the talclike layers.   Expanded or exfoliated vermiculite is an important thermal and sound insulation because of its low density and thermal conductivity.   It is also highly refractory and rot-resistant.

The talclike layers of vermiculite are separated by double layers of water molecules.   Almost half of this water is lost at 110°C without exfoliation, the water producing exfoliation being apparently more tightly bound and related to the pronounced base-exchange capacity of vermiculite.   The exchangeable ions in natural vermiculite are usually Mg (present to the extent of about 1.17 ion per unit cell), and the process is reversible as between Na, Ca, Mg, and K ions, but not completely as between K, $NH_4$, Rb, and Cs ions.[66]   The water layers appear to be best explained as being made up of a hydration shell of six water molecules around each exchange Mg ion (the "bound" water) and about eight relatively loosely bound water molecules per Mg ion (the "unbound" water).   These proportions account for the maximum of sixteen water molecules per unit cell.[67]   Glycerol and several amines form complexes with vermiculite by entering the structure between the layers.   The basal reflection, in turn, is displaced from about 10 A to 14 A.[68]

**The Clay Minerals.**   The clay minerals are sometimes classified in four main groups:[69]   (1) the kaolin group, (2) the montmorillonite-

[64] G. W. Brindley and S. Z. Ali, *ibid.* **3**, 25 (1950).
[65] G. W. Brindley, *X-Ray Identification and Crystal Structures of Clay Minerals*, The Mineralogical Society, London, 1951, Chap. V.
[66] I. Barshad, *Am. Mineral.* **33**, 655 (1948).
[67] G. F. Walker, *Nature* **163**, 726 (1949).
[68] G. F. Walker, *ibid.* **166**, 695 (1950).
[69] C. S. Ross and P. F. Kerr, *J. Sed. Pet.* **1**, 55 (1931).

beidellite group, (3) the potash-bearing clays, and (4) a group found in shales. The kaolin minerals, kaolinite, dickite, nacrite, and halloysite are characteristic clay minerals but are not the dominant constituents of most clays, shales, and soils. The montmorillonites are characteristic clay constituents of many sedimentary rocks and are prominent constituents of fuller's earth. They contain a higher ratio of silica to alumina than in kaolinite, and also such other bases as $Fe_2O_3$, MgO, and CaO. The potassium-bearing clays are micaceous in nature. Further study of all the clay minerals is extremely important because of the part they play in soil chemistry.

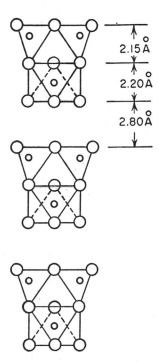

The naturally occurring clays vary widely in composition and in their clay-mineral content. *China clay*, used for the production of porcelain, may be almost pure kaolinite. Most clays, however, contain finely divided quartz, feldspar, mica, and other minerals. Clays used for the manufacture of common pottery and terra cotta are rich in iron oxide and turn brown or red when they are ignited ("fired"). Clay containing considerable sand, as well as iron oxide, is called *loam*. It is chiefly used for the fabrication of bricks and tiles. When contaminated with much calcium and magnesium carbonate, the clays are known as *marls*. These have no value in the ceramic field, but find use in the cement industry.

Kaolinite

Fig. 4.17. The structure and stacking of the unsymmetrical layers in kaolinite. (Pauling, *Proc. Nat. Acad. Sci.* **16**, 578.)

Kaolinite, dickite, nacrite, and dehdyrated halloysite all have the formula $Al_2(Si_2O_5)(OH)_4$, and are built up from the basic "kaolin layer" whose structure was first proposed by Pauling.[70] If a tetrahedral Si–O layer is imposed on only one side of an octahedral hydrargillite, $Al(OH)_3$, layer, an unsymmetrical neutral layer results. The composition is that of kaolinite and these layers pack together to give the crystal of kaolinite with a $d_{001}$ spacing of 7.1 A (Fig. 4.17). Usually the layers of a layer crystal must be symmetrical, for if the two faces of the layer are not equivalent there would be a tendency for the layer to curve, one face becoming concave and

[70] Pauling, *op. cit.* ref. 61.

one convex.   The forces between adjacent layers would not in general be strong enough to overcome this curving.   The layers in the micas, brucite, hydrargillite, and in most other layer structures are symmetrical.   In the case of kaolinite the dimensions of the two layers are so nearly the same, $Al(OH)_3$, 5.07 $\times$ 8.65 A, and Si–O layer, 5.03 $\times$ 8.71 A, that the tendency to curve is probably slight.   Kaolinite, and also dickite and nacrite, minerals with the same composition but differing in the orientation of the superimposed layers, all form very small crystals with perfect cleavage.   It has been suggested that the nonexistence of large crystals among them may result from a slight tendency to curvature of the layers, which the weak forces between the layers are unable to overcome.

No magnesium analogue of kaolinite is known.   This fact may be attributed to the larger values of the fundamental translations in the brucite layer, 5.40 $\times$ 9.36 A, which would lead to considerable curvature of the unsymmetrical layers.

The essential correctness of Pauling's kaolin layer was soon demonstrated, and a two-layer monoclinic cell proposed for the structure of kaolinite.[71]   More detailed measurements have since proved the structure of kaolinite to be based on a single-layer cell with triclinic symmetry.[72] The best solution of the structure of dickite is one based on a monoclinic cell with two kaolin layers,[73] and the rare nacrite is monoclinic with a six-layer cell.[74]

Since dehydrated halloysite has the composition of kaolinite and a basal spacing of about 7.2 A, it is presumably composed of kaolin layers.   The completely hydrated halloysite has the composition $Al_2(Si_2O_5)(OH)_4 \cdot 2H_2O$ and a basal spacing of about 10.1 A.   The spacing increase of 2.9 A in the hydrated mineral corresponds to the thickness of a single sheet of interlayer water molecules for which a definite arrangement has been proposed.[75]   The nature of these sheets of water molecules is very difficult to determine from X-ray data, and other structures have been proposed.[76] Metahalloysite (largely dehydrated halloysite), the dehydrated mineral, and hydrated halloysite give very similar diffraction patterns largely

[71] J. W. Gruner, *Z. Krist.* **83**, 75 (1932).

[72] G. W. Brindley and K. Robinson, *Mineralog. Mag.* **27**, 242 (1946).

[73] J. W. Gruner, *Z. Krist.* **83**, 394 (1932); S. B. Hendricks, *Am. Mineral.* **23**, 295 (1938).

[74] S. B. Hendricks, *Z. Krist.* **100**, 509 (1938).

[75] Hendricks, *loc. cit.* ref. 73; S. B. Hendricks and M. E. Jefferson, *Am. Mineral.* **23**, 863 (1938).

[76] M. Mehmel, *Z. Krist.* **90**, 35 (1935); C. H. Edelman and J. C. L. Favejee, *ibid.* **102**, 417 (1940); L. T. Alexander *et al.*, *Am. Mineral.* **28**, 1 (1943).

consisting of bands characteristic of randomly displaced layer lattices.[77] Many fire clays contain a mineral that is intermediate between kaolinite and metahalloysite, and possibly distinctive enough to be classed as another kaolin mineral.[78]

The changes taking place in kaolin minerals on heating are of considerable theoretical and practical interest. A differential thermal analysis applied to kaolinite shows a prominent endothermic change in the region of 550° to 700°C, during which dehydration occurs:[79]

$$Al_2(Si_2O_5)(OH)_4 \rightarrow Al_2O_3 \cdot 2SiO_2 + 2H_2O \quad (at~550°C)$$
$$\text{kaolinite} \qquad\qquad \text{metakaolin}$$

The water lost at this temperature was present originally as OH groups, and the dehydrated mineral is left in the form of an amorphous mixture of silica and alumina virtually on an atomic scale. Since the dehydrated mixture is decidedly not a normal mixture of the two components, the name "metakaolin" has been suggested for it. With further increase in temperature, two or more exothermic reactions take place with the formation of new minerals. Between 850° and 1050°C, amorphous $Al_2O_3$ crystallizes to $\gamma$-$Al_2O_3$:

$$Al_2O_3 \cdot 2SiO_2 \rightarrow \gamma\text{-}Al_2O_3 + 2SiO_2 \quad (850°-1050°C)$$
$$\text{metakaolin} \qquad\qquad \text{amorphous}$$

Above 950°C mullite begins to form from the $\gamma$-$Al_2O_3$ and $SiO_2$, and above 1100°C the excess $SiO_2$ is transformed into cristobalite:

$$3\gamma\text{-}Al_2O_3 + 6SiO_2 \rightarrow 3Al_2O_3 \cdot 2SiO_2 + 4SiO_2 \quad (950°C~and~upwards)$$
$$\text{mullite} \qquad\qquad \text{cristobalite}$$
$$\text{(above 1100°C)}$$

Mullite does not appear, however, from the heating of halloysite until 1100°C.[80]

The montmorillonite group, commonly referred to as the montmorillonoids, includes a number of minerals of similar structure based on modified pyrophyllite layers superimposed irregularly. The most fully studied of these is montmorillonite, which comprises a particular subgroup

[77] G. W. Brindley, K. Robinson, and D. M. C. MacEwan, *Nature* **157**, 225 (1946); G. W. Brindley and K. Robinson, *Mineralog. Mag.* **28**, 393 (1948).

[78] G. W. Brindley and K. Robinson, *Trans. Brit. Ceram. Soc.* **46**, 49 (1947).

[79] R. W. Grimshaw, E. Heaton, and A. L. Roberts, *Trans. Brit. Ceram. Soc.* **44**, 69 (1945); R. E. Grim and W. F. Bradley, *Am. Mineral.* **33**, 50 (1948); P. Murray and J. White, *Trans. Brit. Ceram. Soc.* **48**, 187 (1949).

[80] H. Insley and R. H. Ewell, *J. Res. Nat. Bur. Stand.* **14**, 615 (1935); A. H. Jay, *Trans. Brit. Ceram. Soc.* **38**, 455 (1939); J. F. Hyslop, *ibid.* **43**, 49 (1944); J. E. Comeforo, R. B. Fischer, and W. F. Bradley, *J. Am. Ceram. Soc.* **31**, 254 (1948); H. M. Richardson, pp. 81–85 of Brindley, *op. cit.* ref. 65.

containing mainly $SiO_2$ and $Al_2O_3$, with a little MgO, and some replacement of $Al_2O_3$ by $Fe_2O_3$. The complicated isomorphous replacement occurring in the montmorillonoids makes their composition and formulas diffcult to express clearly. Table 4.7 lists for comparison the formulas of

TABLE 4.7.   CHEMICAL CONSTITUTION OF PYROPHYLLITE AND OF
TYPICAL MONTMORILLONOIDS

|  | *Chemical Constitution* |
|---|---|
| Pyrophyllite | $(Si_8)^{T*}(Al_4)^{O*}O_{20}(OH)_4$ |
| Montmorillonite | $(Si_8)^T(Al_{3.33}Mg_{0.67})^O O_{20}(OH)_4$ $\downarrow$ $Na_{0.67}$ |
| Saponite | $(Si_{7.33}Al_{0.67})^T(Mg)_6^O O_{20}(OH)_4$ $\downarrow$ $Ca_{0.33}$ |
| Beidellite | $(Si_{7.33}Al_{0.67})^T(Al_4)^O O_{20}(OH)_4$ $\downarrow$ $M^+{}_{0.67}$ |
| Nontronite (ferruginous) | $(Si_{7.33}Al_{0.67})^T(Fe_4)^O O_{20}(OH)_4$ $\downarrow$ $M^+{}_{0.67}$ |
| Hectorite | $(Si_8)^T(Mg_{5.33}Li_{0.67})^O O_{20}(OH)_4$ $\downarrow$ $M^+{}_{0.67}$ |

* The superscripts T and O refer, respectively, to the *tetrahedral* and *octahedral* coordination of the ions.

pyrophyllite and typical montmorillonoid minerals. The exchangeable cation is shown below the arrow.[81]

The powder X-ray patterns of the montmorillonoids are made up of two distinct diffraction types, basal (00*l*) lines and general (*hk*) bands. The (*hk*) bands are characteristic of the nature of the layers, and to some extent may be used to distinguish between members of the montmorillonite series and those of the nontronite-beidellite series. These bands also suggest the irregular random stacking of the layers. On the other hand, the basal spacings are subject to great variation with the state of the sample. If the montmorillonoid is saturated with a given inorganic cation and then dried, the interlayer spacing varies with the size of the cation. Contact with water or organic liquids or vapors causes wide

[81] C. S. Ross and S. B. Hendricks, *U. S. Geol. Survey Prof. Paper*, No. 205-B, (1945); D. M. C. MacEwan, in Chap. IV of Brindley, *op. cit.* ref. 65.

variations in the basal spacing, and saturation with large organic cations (including proteins) produces large interlayer separations.[82]

The most generally accepted structure for these minerals has thus evolved from the work of many investigators.[83] Isomorphous replacement according to the formulas of Table 4.7 leads to negatively charged pyrophyllite-type layers. These layers are stacked irregularly, giving a turbostratic structure, and the base-exchange cations interspersed between the layers provide interlayer binding and electrical neutrality. Water in varying amounts penetrates between the layers increasing the basal spacing from the value 9.13 A in pyrophyllite to a value usually close to 14 A. Despite the extensive development of the structure just outlined, it is challenged by another[84] which postulates the presence of OH groups attached to the layers and extending into the interlayer space. These extended groups arise from inverting certain $SiO_4$ tetrahedra so that the apex points away from the layer instead of toward the interior. The apical O ion must then be replaced by OH, and another OH must be placed in the hole in the octahedral layer to balance the charges. The number of such inverted $SiO_4$ groups is assumed to be just sufficient to account for the base-exchange capacity. Experiments on the methylation of montmorillonite, using diazomethane, lend support to the presence of acidic OH groups. It is virtually impossible, however, to prove or disprove the theory by X-ray diffraction methods.

The mineral *bentonite*, which occurs in huge deposits in the United States, is principally montmorillonite. It finds technical applications in cosmetics, as a filler for soap, as a plasticizer, and especially as a stabilizer of suspensions. A major application therefore is in the preparation of thixotropic "drilling muds" used in drilling for petroleum. The main function of these muds is to transport to the surface the rock cuttings made by the bit. They must also cool and lubricate the bit, and exert sufficient hydrostatic pressure to keep oil, water, and gas from entering the hole. At the same time the muds must be fluid enough to be easily pumped. The thixotropic property is important to prevent the cuttings from settling in the bore hole whenever circulation has to be stopped. Sodium bentonite in a concentration not exceeding 2 to 3% confers the necessary thixotropy.

[82] For a good summary with references, see MacEwan, *op. cit.* ref. 81.

[83] Principally: U. Hofmann, K. Endell, and D. Wilm, *Z. Krist.* 86, 340 (1933); C. E. Marshall, *ibid.* 91, 433 (1935); E. Maegdefrau and U. Hofmann, *ibid.* 98, 299 (1937); S. B. Hendricks, *J. Geol.* 50, 276 (1942).

[84] C. H. Edelman and J. C. L. Favejee, *Z. Krist.* 102, 417 (1940); C. H. Edelman, *Verre et Silicates Industriels* 12, (suppl.) 3 (1947).

The detection, identification, and estimation of the various clay and mica minerals in samples of clays, shales, soils, etc., is a major analytical undertaking, and only the briefest outline can be given here.[85]    Powder X-ray diffraction techniques are standard for such identification problems.[86]    A routine procedure usually requires at least three steps:

(1)  A powder photograph of the original sample is first made.    Nonclay minerals can be identified on this pattern, and preliminary identification of the clay minerals started.    Likely basal spacings and the corresponding minerals are:  7.2 A, kaolinite; 10 A, micas; 14 A, chlorites, vermiculite, and possibly montmorillonite.    If much organic matter is present, it should first be removed by treatment with 9% $H_2O_2$.

(2)  Any sesquioxides are next dissolved out (with ammonium oxalate-oxalic acid solution of pH 3.3 to avoid attacking the chlorites).    The sample residue is then boiled gently with a solution of an $NH_4$ salt which displaces the 14-A vermiculite line to about 11 A.    Following this the washed and dried residue is treated with glycerol which increases the 14-A montmorillonite spacing to 17.7 A.    A second X-ray photograph is now prepared, and lines at 11 A, 14 A, and 17.7 A indicate vermiculite, chlorite, and montomorillonite, respectively.    A further check on the chlorite after heat treatment is advised.

(3)  An oriented aggregate is prepared and heated to 500°C for several hours.    This sample is immediately sealed off and a third X-ray photograph taken.    The 14-A chlorite line persists through this treatment, and the kaolinite pattern disappears.    The vermiculite and montmorillonite basal spacings, in turn, drop to about 10 A.

This program requires the preparation of three diffraction patterns, and it is seldom safe to reduce the number.

**The Feldspar Group.**    The feldspars, the most general of all rock constituents, comprise two groups of silicates closely related in form and physical properties.    One group (orthoclase, etc.) is monoclinic or nearly monoclinic in symmetry, and cleaves parallel to (001) with an inclination angle of 90° or nearly 90°.    The other group (plagioclase feldspars) is definitely triclinic, and cleaves parallel to (010) with an inclination angle of about 86°.    All have hardness values between 6 and 6.5.    Their colors are commonly white or pale shades of yellow, red, or green, occasionally

---

[85] Two excellent reviews of this subject are: D. M. C. MacEwan, *Research* **2**, 459 (1949); the monograph by Brindley, *op. cit.* ref. 65.

[86] H. P. Klug and L. E. Alexander, *X-Ray Diffraction Procedures for Polycrystalline and Amorphous Materials*, John Wiley and Sons, Inc., New York, 1954, Chap. 7.

TABLE 4.8. COMPOSITION OF THE FELDSPARS

| Name | Formula | Symmetry | Specific Gravity |
|---|---|---|---|
| *Orthoclase Group* | | | |
| Orthoclase | $KAlSi_3O_8$ | Monoclinic | 2.56–2.58 |
| Soda-orthoclase | $(K, Na)AlSi_3O_8$ | Monoclinic | ... |
| Hyalophane | $\begin{cases} KAlSi_3O_8 \\ BaAl_2Si_2O_8 \end{cases}$ | Monoclinic | 2.805 |
| Celsian | $BaAl_2Si_2O_8$ | Monoclinic | 3.37 |
| Microcline | $KAlSi_3O_8$ | Triclinic | 2.54–2.57 |
| Anorthoclase | $(Na, K)AlSi_3O_8$ | (pseudomonoclinic) | 2.57–2.60 |
| *Plagioclase Group* | | | |
| Albite (Ab) | $NaAlSi_3O_8$ | Triclinic | 2.60–2.62 |
| Oligoclase | $Ab_6An$ to $Ab_3An$ | Triclinic | ... |
| Andesine | $Ab_3An$ to $AbAn$ | Triclinic | ... |
| Labradorite | $AbAn$ to $AbAn_3$ | Triclinic | ... |
| Bytownite | $AbAn_3$ to $AbAn_6$ | Triclinic | ... |
| Anorthite (An) | $CaAl_2Si_2O_8$ | Triclinic | 2.74–2.76 |

dark. They are aluminosilicates of potassium, sodium, calcium, and rarely barium (Table 4.8). Magnesium and iron are always absent.

Orthoclase is probably the commonest mineral silicate. It and the variety *adularia* are the low temperature forms of orthoclase. Above 900°C the high temperature variety *sanidine* is formed which does not readily change to orthoclase on cooling. Most varieties of sanidine contain prominent amounts of sodium. Optical data distinguish these distinct varieties and other members of the orthoclase group, all of which have almost identical crystal structures. All feldspar structures are based on the same three-dimensional linked framework of $SiO_4$ and $AlO_4$ tetrahedra with the cations $K^+$, $Na^+$, $Ca^{++}$, or $Ba^{++}$ situated in the interstices of the negatively charged framework. The differences between the orthoclase and plagioclase groups appear to arise largely from the presence of the larger cations in the former and the smaller cations in the latter.

The first complete structure determination of a feldspar was made on sanidine.[87] Chains made up of links consisting of four tetrahedra can be traced through the structure parallel to the *a* axis (Fig. 4.18). These, however, are not separate chains as in the pyroxenes, but they are linked through oxygen atoms to other chains on all sides to give a three-dimensional network of linked tetrahedra. Three out of four of the tetrahedra

[87] W. H. Taylor, *Z. Krist.* 85, 425 (1933).

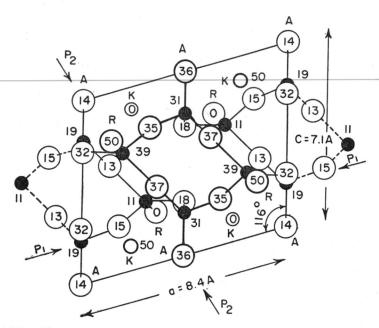

Fig. 4.18. The structure of orthoclase, showing the Si–O chain running parallel to *a*. Only atoms in the lower half of the unit cell are shown. (Bragg, *Atomic Structure of Minerals;* courtesy *Cornell University Press.*)

have silicon atoms at the center, and the remainder aluminum. Early diffraction data, unfortunately, could not distinguish between them. The potassium atoms are situated on the reflection planes in cavities providing six oxygen neighbors at 2.85 A and four at 3.1 A. More recently, highly accurate studies of orthoclase[88] and sanidinized orthoclase[89] have sought to explain the nature of the sanidine transformation as a disordering of the Al atoms relative to the Si atoms. The latter study established that the Al atoms in sanidine are completely disordered, but an ordered arrangement of the Al atoms in orthoclase was not conclusively demonstrated. The Al atoms in microcline, however, are partially ordered with respect to Si.[90] The unit cells of the other monoclinic feldspars are nearly identical in dimensions except that of celsian is slightly larger.[91] The replacement of $K^+$ by $Ba^{++}$ may reach 15% $Ba^{++}$ in hyalophane, the structure remaining essentially unaltered. But in the pure barium feld-

[88] S. H. Chao, A. Hargreaves, and W. H. Taylor, *Mineralog. Mag.* **25**, 498 (1940).
[89] W. F. Cole, H. Sörum, and O. Kennard, *Acta Cryst.* **2**, 280 (1949).
[90] S. W. Bailey and W. H. Taylor, *ibid.* **8**, 621 (1955).
[91] W. H. Taylor, J. A. Darbyshire, and H. Strunz, *Z. Krist.* **87**, 464 (1934).

spar, celsian, the unit cell is definitely larger, although the ionic sizes of $K^+$ and $Ba^{++}$ are nearly the same. Two other compounds have the composition $BaAl_2Si_2O_8$, paracelsian and hexagonal $BaAl_2Si_2O_8$. Paracelsian has a structure closely related to the feldspars, but its unit cell is strongly pseudo-orthorhombic.[92] Danburite is isostructural with it when the $BO_4$ groups of the former are considered to link the $Si_2O_7$ groups into a feldspar-type framework. Hexagonal $BaAl_2Si_2O_8$ contains hexagonal double sheets of composition $(Si, Al)O_2$ with $Ba^{++}$ ions between the sheets.[93]

Microcline, $KAlSi_3O_8$, and anorthoclase, $(Na, K)AlSi_3O_8$, are structurally very similar to orthoclase, but triclinic in symmetry. In both, however, the angles $\alpha$ and $\gamma$ differ from $90°$ by only a few minutes. The plagioclase feldspars, on the other hand, are grossly triclinic in symmetry, although built on a similar framework to the potash feldspars. Microcline and anorthoclase show almost universal twinning according to the albite and pericline laws, and both show laminar intergrowths with albite, $NaAlSi_3O_8$, in layers parallel to (100), forming *perthite*. Such intergrowths, even when on a submicroscopic scale, show a characteristic doubling of Laue spots, which vanishes on heating and reappears on cooling. This behavior is attributed to migration of the Na and K atoms. At high temperatures the Na and K atoms are evenly diffused throughout the framework of linked Si and Al tetrahedra producing a single crystal. At lower temperatures a segregation takes place through diffusion producing alternate potash-rich and soda-rich lamellae. Such interdiffusion of Na and K in the lattice at higher temperatures may be considered as similar to that occurring in the more open zeolite structures at room temperature.

Extensive studies of Korean and other feldspars verify the essential picture of these intergrowths. Microcline from Paotze contains 82% of K-rich triclinic feldspar and 18% of Na-rich triclinic feldspar; an anorthoclase from Chilposan contains 50% of a K-rich monoclinic phase and 21% and 29%, respectively, of two Na-rich triclinic phases; and a moonstone sample from Minchon is complicated by four different Na-rich phases (one monoclinic, three triclinic) comprising 58% of the material, the remainder being a K-rich monoclinic feldspar.[94] A specimen of an intermediate microcline, a microperthite from Kodarma, India, was used in the very refined study which demonstrated the partial ordering of Si and Al over the tetrahedral sites at room temperature.[90] This extremely

[92] J. V. Smith, *Acta Cryst.* **6**, 613 (1953).
[93] Ito designates this material as $\alpha$-celsian: *op. cit.* ref. 52, pp. 19–29.
[94] T. Ito and R. Sandanaga, *Acta Cryst.* **5**, 441 (1952).

careful study was possible because the weak extra X-ray reflections of the sodium feldspar component did not seriously overlap those of the K-rich phase.

The plagioclase feldspars have long been regarded as a perfect example of an unbroken series of solid solutions of the two end members albite, $NaAlSi_3O_8$, and anorthite, $CaAl_2Si_2O_8$. Minerals falling in certain composition ranges between the end members have well-known names (Table 4.8). X-ray, optical, and thermal studies have gradually revealed the extreme complexity of these feldspars. Early diffraction investigations[91,95] showed no fewer than three distinct structural types in the plagioclase series. The simplest is the triclinic cell of low-temperature albite, which is essentially similar to that of orthoclase. The corresponding anorthite cell is only a pseudo cell, the $c$ axis of the true cell being doubled. The intermediate plagioclase structures vary in an exceedingly complex manner from one to another, and are thought to be based on alternate slabs of albite-type and anorthite-type structures. Study of a large number of plagioclases of known composition, varying from nearly pure albite to nearly pure anorthite, suggests the following state of the system:[96,97]

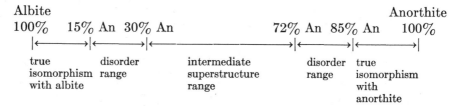

Body-centered anorthite (72% An) has had a complete structure analysis[94] which confirms the segregation of Al and Si atoms into definite positions in the crystal lattice. Further studies in the range of pure anorthite to $An_{70}Ab_{30}$ consider this whole range to be ordered as far as the Si–Al arrangement. The cell of pure low-temperature anorthite is primitive and completely ordered. Elevation of the temperature, however, or increase of the sodium content leaves the Si–Al arrangement undisturbed, but destroys the ordering of the $Ca^{++}$ (or $Na^+$) ions and promotes a change to a body-centered cell.[98]

[95] S. H. Chao and W. H. Taylor, *Proc. Roy. Soc.* (*London*) **176A**, 76 (1940).
[96] W. F. Cole, H. Sörum, and W. H. Taylor, *Acta Cryst.* **4**, 20 (1951).
[97] H. Sörum, *ibid.* **6**, 413 (1953).
[98] P. Gay, *Mineralog. Mag.* **30**, 169, 428 (1953–1954); P. Gay and W. H. Taylor, *Acta Cryst.* **6**, 647 (1953); F. Laves and J. R. Goldsmith, *ibid.* **7**, 465 (1954).

In addition to natural triclinic anorthite, synthetic $CaAl_2Si_2O_8$ has been observed in two additional polymorphic forms, orthorhombic and hexagonal.[99] Examination of the latter form proves it not to be isostructural with hexagonal $BaAl_2Si_2O_8$[93] even though they are dimensionally similar.[100]

The weathering of feldspar in nature to produce kaolinite was mentioned at the beginning of this chapter as one of the primary reactions in soil formation. In addition to the nature of the parent rock, climate, topography, vegetation, and time are also factors in the production of soil. Indeed, the same type of soil can develop after a suitably long period of time from rocks of widely different texture and composition.[101] Feldspars, particularly orthoclase, are important in ceramic technology. Hard porcelain may have up to 25% of feldspar in the clay mix from which it is fashioned, and the proportion in soft porcelain may be higher. The feldspar, during ignition, forms a glass phase especially important for the translucency of porcelain bodies. Anorthite is formed as a rough glaze-like layer over some ceramic bodies, and celsian is formed as a reaction product of optical glass melts with refractory fire-clay pots.

**The Zeolites.** The zeolites (Table 4.9) comprise a group of silicates whose structures are based on three-dimensional anion frameworks. From the chemist's point of view they are one of the most interesting groups of silicate minerals. A striking characteristic of the zeolites is their ability to reversibly take up and give up water. The loosely held water is continuously given up on heating and is regained on exposure to a moist atmosphere, without disruption of the crystal structure. Their physical properties, especially the optical properties, likewise vary continuously with the degree of hydration. The zeolites are not real hydrates, because they do not indicate real discontinuities in their water loss. For most zeolites this ideally reversible dehydration holds for a major part of the water present. Actually, the strength of the water binding differs with the zeolite, and even with the degree of hydration in some instances. For natrolite, from a state with fourteen molecules of water (per unit cell) down to complete dehydration, the heat of hydration is a constant 25 kcal/mole. For thomsonite, however, the heat effect is distinctly different for the states with twelve to eight and with eight to four molecules of water, and for the last four molecules the heat of hydra-

[99] J. R. Goldsmith and E. G. Ehlers, *J. Geol.* **60**, 386 (1952).

[100] G. Donnay, *Acta Cryst.* **5**, 153 (1952).

[101] R. E. Grim, *Clay Mineralogy*, McGraw-Hill Book Co., New York, 1953, pp. 330–345.

TABLE 4.9. CHIEF ZEOLITE MINERALS

| Name | Formula | Hardness | Specific Gravity | Structure References |
|---|---|---|---|---|
| Analcite | $NaAlSi_2O_6 \cdot H_2O$ | 5–5.5 | 2.22–2.29 | (1) |
| *Fibrous Zeolites* | | | | |
| Natrolite | $Na_2Al_2Si_3O_{10} \cdot 2H_2O$ | 5–5.5 | 2.20–2.25 | (2)(3) |
| Scolecite | $CaAl_2Si_3O_{10} \cdot 3H_2O$ | 5–5.5 | 2.16–2.4 | (3)(4) |
| Mesolite | $\begin{cases} Na_2Al_2Si_3O_{10} \cdot 2H_2O \\ 2CaAl_2Si_3O_{10} \cdot 3H_2O \end{cases}$ | 5 | 2.29 | (3)(5) |
| Thomsonite | $NaCa_2Al_5Si_5O_{20} \cdot 6H_2O$ | 5–5.5 | 2.3–2.4 | (3) |
| Edingtonite | $BaAl_2Si_3O_{10} \cdot 4H_2O$ | 4–4.5 | 2.694 | (3)(6) |
| *Chabazite Group* | | | | |
| Chabazite | $(Ca, Na_2)Al_2Si_4O_{12} \cdot 6H_2O$ | 4–5 | 2.08–2.16 | (7) |
| Gmelinite | $(Na_2, Ca)Al_2Si_4O_{12} \cdot 6H_2O$ | 4.5 | 2.04–2.17 | . . . |
| Levynite | $CaAl_2Si_3O_{10} \cdot 5H_2O$ | 4–4.5 | 2.09–2.16 | . . . |
| *Heulandite Group* | | | | |
| Mordenite | $(Ca, Na_2)Al_2Si_9O_{22} \cdot 6H_2O$ | 3–4 | 2.15 | (8) |
| Heulandite | $(Ca, Na_2)Al_2Si_6O_{16} \cdot 5H_2O$ | 3.5–4 | 2.18–2.22 | (7)(9) |
| Epistilbite | $(Ca, Na_2)Al_2Si_6O_{16} \cdot 5H_2O$ | 4 | 2.25 | . . . |
| Brewsterite | $(Sr, Ba, Ca)Al_2Si_6O_{16} \cdot 5H_2O$ | 5 | 2.45 | . . . |
| *Phillipsite Group* | | | | |
| Wellsite | $(Ba, Ca, K_2)Al_2Si_3O_{10} \cdot 3H_2O$ | 4–4.5 | 2.278–2.366 | . . . |
| Phillipsite | $(K_2, Ca)Al_2Si_4O_{12} \cdot 4\frac{1}{2}H_2O$ | 4–4.5 | 2.2 | . . . |
| Harmotome | $(K_2, Ba)Al_2Si_5O_{14} \cdot 5H_2O$ | 4.5 | 2.44 2.50 | (10) |
| Stilbite | $(Na_2Ca)Al_2Si_6O_{16} \cdot 6H_2O$ | 3.5–4 | 2.094–2.205 | (9) |
| Laumontite | $(Ca, Na_2)Al_2Si_4O_{12} \cdot 4H_2O$ | 3.5–4 | 2.25–2.36 | . . . |

(1) W. H. Taylor, *Z. Krist.* **74**, 1 (1930).
(2) L. Pauling, *Proc. Nat. Acad. Sci.* **16**, 453 (1930).
(3) W. H. Taylor, C. A. Meek, and W. W. Jackson, *Z. Krist.* **84**, 373 (1933).
(4) M. H. Hey and F. A. Bannister, *Mineralog. Mag.* **24**, 227 (1936).
(5) M. H. Hey and F. A. Bannister, *ibid.* **23**, 421 (1933).
(6) W. H. Taylor and R. Jackson, *Z. Krist.* **86**, 53 (1933); M. H. Hey and F. A. Bannister, *Mineralog. Mag.* **23**, 483 (1934); W. H. Taylor, *ibid.* **24**, 208 (1935).
(7) J. Wyart, *Bull. soc. franç. mineral.* **56**, 81 (1933).
(8) C. Waymouth, P. C. Thornley, and W. H. Taylor, *Mineralog. Mag.* **25**, 212 (1938).
(9) W. H. Taylor, *Proc. Roy. Soc. (London)* **145A**, 80 (1934).
(10) J. Sekanina and J. Wyart, *Bull. soc. franç. mineral.* **60**, 139 (1937).

tion is about 30 kcal/mole.[102] Usually, complete dehydration brings about intense changes, and is irreversible.

When dehydrated, other liquids, like alcohol, benzene, chloroform, carbon disulfide, and even mercury, can be adsorbed and desorbed in a

[102] M. H. Hey and F. A. Bannister, *Mineralog. Mag.* **23**, 51, 243 (1932); *Am. Mineral.* **16**, 408 (1931).

similar fashion.  Many gases may also be adsorbed to a great extent.
More than one material may be taken up by the same specimen.  A
dehydrated chabazite, for instance, took up 35% of mercury and then,
in addition, 25% of water.[103]  Equilibrium with gases may be established
in a matter of a few minutes, and the considerable evolution of heat which
accompanies their adsorption indicates a strong affinity between them and
the zeolites.  Only those molecules which do not exceed a certain diameter
can penetrate a given zeolite structure.  Thus, benzene and ether vapors,
and all gases with molecular weights above 50, are not resorbed by
chabazite,[104] and alcohols with a molecular length longer than about 6.6 A
cannot enter the framework of thomsonite.[105]  Because of their gas
adsorbing ability the zeolites show high catalytic activity in heterogeneous
gas reactions.

The water and gas molecules occupy cavities and channels present in
the zeolite framework.  In these openings are also found positive ions,
generally alkali-metal or calcium ions, which balance the negative charge
of the framework, whose composition in every case is $(Si, Al)O_2$.  A
three-dimensional network of $SiO_4$ tetrahedra as found in the various
varieties of silica is neutral.  If a portion of the $Si^{+4}$ ions of the tetrahedra
is replaced by $Al^{+3}$ ions, the network is left with a negative charge which
must be balanced by the insertion of positive ions.  These ions, as well
as the water, ammonia, carbon dioxide molecules, etc., are situated in
the afore-mentioned cavities and channels, which are large enough to
permit the free passage of the ions and gas molecules.  In the presence
of salt solutions these ions readily exchange, and the phenomenon of base
exchange is another characteristic of zeolites.  The sodium ions may be
replaced by silver or calcium, and vice versa.  The zeolite water softener
is based on this process.  The barium content of the natural mineral
edingtonite, $BaAl_2Si_3O_{10} \cdot 4H_2O$, can be replaced artificially by thallium,
potassium, silver, or sodium merely by placing the mineral in the corresponding salt solution.  In nature such reactions play an important role
in the secondary *metasomatic change* of magmatic rocks.

The first complete structure analysis of a zeolite was that of analcite,
$NaAlSi_2O_6 \cdot H_2O$.[106]  The structures of the fibrous zeolites, natrolite,
thomsonite, and edingtonite, however, are more readily pictured.[107,108]
The orthorhombic pseudotetragonal crystals of natrolite possess an eight-

[103] F. Grandjean, *Compt. rend.* 149, 866 (1909).
[104] O. Weigel and E. Steinhoff, *Z. Krist.* 61, 125 (1925).
[105] Hey and Bannister, *op. cit.*, ref. 144, p. 243; *Am. Mineral.* 17, 160 (1932).
[106] W. H. Taylor, *Z. Krist.* 74, 1 (1930).
[107] W. H. Taylor, C. A. Meek, and W. W. Jackson, *Z. Krist.* 84, 373 (1933).
[108] W. H. Taylor and R. Jackson, *ibid.* 86, 53 (1933); M. H. Hey and F. A. Bannister,
*Mineralog. Mag.* 23, 483 (1934); W. H. Taylor, *ibid.* 24, 208 (1935).

molecule cell with the dimensions:

$$a = 18.19 \text{ A}, \quad b = 18.62 \text{ A}, \quad c = 6.58 \text{ A}$$

On the basis of these dimensions, the composition, and the symmetry, Pauling[109] proposed the common structural feature of the fibrous zeolites, a chain of linked aluminum and silicon tetrahedra, Fig. 4.19. The chains are rigid and they exactly account for the dimensions along the $c$ direction to which they are parallel. These chains are linked to neighboring ones by sharing tetrahedron corners, thus building up a continuous framework of linked tetrahedra. In this process the chains are rotated about their axes until certain minimum interionic distances are attained. The ways in which these chains unite to form natrolite, edingtonite, $BaAl_2Si_3O_{10} \cdot 4H_2O$, and thomsonite, $NaCa_2Al_5Si_5O_{20} \cdot 6H_2O$, are diagrammatically shown in Fig. 4.20.

The very open framework structure of the zeolites explains their characteristic properties—namely, base exchange and the adsorption and loss of water and other gases. These channels, parallel to the $c$ axis in the fibrous zeolites, are evident as the diamond-shaped spaces between the squares in Fig. 4.20. The available spaces for cations are not nearly filled in most cases. The sodium ions, or other cations, take up positions in the channels between the strings such that they are surrounded by six to eight oxygens, part of which belong to the framework and part to water molecules present in the channel. The water molecules take up similar positions with two oxygen atoms of the framework on one side and one or two cations on the

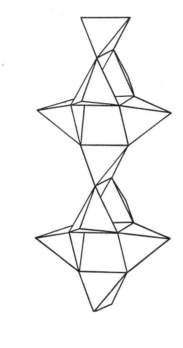

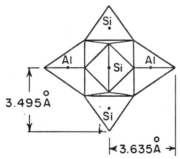

Fig. 4.19. The chain of linked aluminum and silicon tetrahedra found in the fibrous zeolites (elevation, above; projection along chain axis, below.) (Pauling, *Proc. Nat. Acad. Sci.* **16**, 453.)

[109] L. Pauling, *Proc. Nat. Acad. Sci.* **16**, 453 (1930).

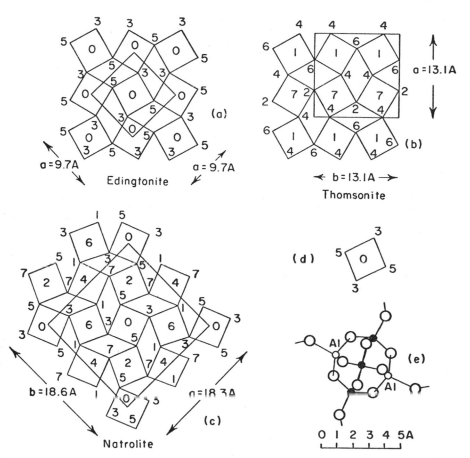

FIG. 4.20. The structural scheme in edingtonite, thomsonite, and natrolite. The squares represent the same projection of the strings as shown in Fig. 4.19. (Bragg, *Atomic Structure of Minerals*; courtesy *Cornell University Press*.)

opposite side. The configuration around the water molecules is thus triangular or tetrahedral.[110] The cation –O and $H_2O$–O distances usually are of the order of 2.5 to 3.0 A.

In feldspars every cavity is filled with a cation. In zeolites, with more spaces available for cations than are filled, two kinds of isomorphous replacement are possible, and both take place. The first type of replacement must be kept in mind in considering the composition of the framework, as it takes place during the original formation of the zeolite. This replacement is similar to that occurring in the feldspars and does not

[110] W. H. Taylor, *Proc. Roy. Soc. (London)* **145A**, 80 (1934).

change the number of cations:

$$KSi \rightleftharpoons BaAl$$
$$NaSi \rightleftharpoons CaAl$$

The second type of exchange may alter the number of cations and is responsible for base-exchange phenomena:

$$Ca \rightleftharpoons 2Na$$
$$Ba \rightleftharpoons 2K$$

In a zeolite like thomsonite, $NaCa_2Al_5Si_5O_{20} \cdot 6H_2O$, it is possible to replace half of the Ca by 2Na:

$$2Na^+ + NaCa_2 \rightleftharpoons Na_3Ca + Ca^{++}$$

The channels contain a sufficient number of suitable spaces to accommodate these extra ions.

The structures of the rest of the zeolites are less completely determined at this writing (1957). Chabazite is characterized by the extreme ease with which hydration, dehydration, and base exchange take place. Its rhombohedral cell, containing two molecules of the zeolite, is based on a framework of fourfold and sixfold rings of tetrahedra, but many structural details are uncertain.[111] Heulandite and stilbite may even be based on a sheet framework.[110] They are noted for their exceptional cleavage parallel to (010).

Very similar to the zeolites in their water resorbing and base-exchange properties are the permutites, synthetic silicate glasses prepared by fusing mixtures of quartz sand, feldspar, kaolin, and soda. These have an open framework structure of $SiO_4$ and $AlO_4$ tetrahedra of the glass type, and they differ from the natural zeolites only in the complete absence of crystalline symmetry and regularity. They find wide applications as "synthetic zeolites" for softening boiler feed water and water for laundering and dyeing.[112]

**The Ultramarines and Other Framework Silicates.** The ultramarines are a series of pigments based on a three-dimensional Si–Al–O framework. The natural mineral lazurite, with a composition approximating $Na_8Al_6Si_6O_{24} \cdot S_2$, gives the beautiful blue color to lapis lazuli, and various artificial ultramarines are known in a variety of colors. These are built on a cagelike network of squares and hexagons containing rather large

[111] J. Wyant, *Bull. soc. franç. mineral.* **56**, 81 (1933).
[112] For a detailed treatment of permutites, see W. Eitel, *The Physical Chemistry of the Silicates*, University of Chicago Press, Chicago, 1954, 1022–1040.

openings and cavities (Fig. 4.4).[113] The framework has the ideal composition $Al_6Si_6O_{24}^{-6}$, but the Si and Al are largely interchangeable. Incorporated in this network are cations equivalent to eight sodium ions, giving a positively charged structure of composition $Na_8Al_6Si_6O_{24}^{++}$. Various negative groups $NaSO_4^-$, $NaS_3^-$, $S_2^=$, etc., occupy the cavities and balance the positive charge.

The composition of the ultramarines may be varied widely. Increased sulfur content leads to deeper and more intense color. Higher silica content gives them a warmer glow. Boron may replace the silicon and aluminum, and selenium and tellurium may replace sulfur. A rather large number of elements may take the place of the sodium.[114] The colors produced by the various elements are listed in Table 4.10.

TABLE 4.10. COLORS PRODUCED BY VARIOUS ELEMENTS IN ULTRAMARINES

| Element | Color | Element | Color |
|---------|-------|---------|-------|
| Li | Blue or violet | Mn | Gray |
| Na | Blue, green, colorless | Ca | Colorless |
| K | Blue | Ba | Yellowish-brown |
| Tl$^I$ | Violet | Se | Blood red |
| Ag | Yellow or gray | Te | Yellow |
| Zn | Colorless to violet | | |

Ultramarine blue has the greatest commercial importance, being used as a pigment in oil paints and in inks for book and wallpaper printing. It also has the power to mask yellowish tints in materials like paper, sugar, and starch and is extensively used as a "blueing" agent in laundering. The blue pigment is prepared by fusing a mixture of clay, anhydrous sodium carbonate, and sulfur; or clay, sodium sulfate, and charcoal. Solvents have no effect on it, and it is stable toward dilute alkalies. It is easily attacked, however, by weak aqueous acids, liberating hydrogen sulfide and depositing silicic acid.

A number of other minerals have structures related to the ultramarine framework (Table 4.11). These are cubic in symmetry but appear not all to be based on the same space group. Sodalite is colorless, or occasionally blue; haüynite is blue; helvite is honey yellow; and noselite may

[113] F. M. Jaeger, H. G. K. Westenbrink, and F. A. van Melle, *Proc. Acad. Sci. Amsterdam* **30**, 249 (1927); E. Podschus, U. Hofmann, and K. Leschewski, *Z. anorg. allgem. Chem.* **228**, 305 (1936).

[114] F. M. Jaeger, *Proc. Acad. Sci. Amsterdam* **32**, 156 (1929); *Bull. soc. franç. mineral.* **53**, 183 (1930); *Baker Lectures, Vol. 7, Cornell University*, McGraw-Hill Book Co., New York, 1930. Part III; Podschus *et al.*, *loc. cit.*

TABLE 4.11. MINERALS RELATED TO ULTRAMARINE

| Name | Formula | Structure References |
|---|---|---|
| Ultramarine | $Na_8Al_6Si_6O_{24} \cdot S_2$ | (1) (2) |
| Sodalite | $Na_8Al_6Si_6O_{24} \cdot Cl_2$ | (3) (4) |
| Noselite | $Na_8Al_6Si_6O_{24} \cdot SO_4$ | (4) (5) |
| Haüynite | $Na_6Ca_2Al_6Si_6O_{24}(SO_4)_2$ | (4) (5) |
| Helvite | $(Mn, Fe)_8Be_6Si_6O_{24} \cdot S_2$ | (3) |
| Danalite | $(Mn, Fe, Zn)_8Be_6Si_6O_{24} \cdot S_2$ | (3) |

(1) F. M. Jaeger, H. G. K. Westenbrink, and F. A. van Melle, *Proc. Acad. Sci. Amsterdam* **30**, 249 (1927); E. Podschus, U. Hofmann, and K. Leschewski, *Z. anorg. allgem. Chem.* **228**, 305 (1936).

(2) F. M. Jaeger, *Proc. Acad. Sci. Amsterdam* **32**, 156 (1929); *Bull. soc. franç. mineral.* **53**, 183 (1930); *Baker Lectures, Vol. 7, Cornell University*, McGraw-Hill Book Co., New York, 1930. Part III; Podschus *et al.*, *loc. cit.*

(3) L. Pauling, *Z. Krist.* **74**, 213 (1930).

(4) T. F. W. Barth, *ibid.* **83**, 405 (1932).

(5) F. Machatschki, *Zentr. Mineral. Geol.* (A) No. 5, 136 (1934).

have a blue color imparted to it by heating in sulfur vapor. Sodalite is converted into noselite by heating in fused sodium sulfate, and, similarly, haüynite into sodalite by the action of fused sodium chloride.

The scapolites, a group of tetragonal minerals of variable composition, are based on a different framework. Typical members are marialite (Ma), $Na_4Al_3Si_9O_{24}Cl$, and meionite (Me), $Ca_4Al_6Si_6O_{24}(SO_4, CO_3)$, considered the end members of the series. Intermediate minerals are known as wernerite, $Ma_{60}Me_{40}$ to $Ma_{20}Me_{80}$, and mizzonite, $Ma_{80}Me_{20}$ to $Ma_{60}Me_{40}$. A structure has been proposed for these minerals based on columns of four-membered tetrahedral rings. The columns, in turn, are joined in such a way as to leave large collapsed octagonal cavities which contain the $SO_4$, $CO_3$, or Cl radicals.[109]

Several silicates are based on three-dimensional (Si, Al)$O_2$ frameworks related to one of the crystalline forms of silica (Table 4.12). Nephelite, for instance, is based upon the β-tridymite structure with NaAl substituted for part of the Si atoms. The K atoms occupy large holes and the Na atoms smaller holes in the framework.

The structures of pollucite, $CsAlSi_2O_6 \cdot nH_2O$,[115] and of leucite, $KAlSi_2O_6$,[116] are very similar to the structure of analcite, $NaAlSi_2O_6 \cdot H_2O$. Leucite and analcite can be converted into each other when heated with NaCl or KCl or the corresponding carbonates. Leucite is only pseudo-

[115] St. v. Náray-Szabó, *Z. Krist.* **99**, 277 (1938).
[116] St. v. Náray-Szabó, *ibid.* **104**, 39 (1942).

TABLE 4.12. SOME MINERALS BASED ON SILICA-TYPE FRAMEWORKS

| Name | Formula | Framework Type | Structure References |
|---|---|---|---|
| Nephelite | $(K, Na)AlSiO_4$ | $\beta$-tridymite | (1) |
| Eucryptite | $\beta$-LiAlSiO$_4$ | $\beta$-quartz | (2) |
| Kaliophilite | $KAlSiO_4$ | $\beta$-tridymite | (3) |
| Kalsilite | $KAlSiO_4$ | $\beta$-tridymite | (4) |
| $\alpha$-Carnegieite | $NaAlSiO_4$ | $\beta$-cristobalite | (5) |

(1) M. J. Buerger, G. E. Klein, and G. Hamburger, *Bull. Geol. Soc. Am.* **57**, 1182 (1946).
(2) H. G. Winkler, *Acta Cryst.* **1**, 27 (1948).
(3) B. Gossner and F. Mussgnug, *Z. Krist.* **73**, 187 (1930); F. A. Bannister and M. H. Hey, *Mineralog. Mag.* **22**, 569 (1931); J. S. Lukesh and M. J. Buerger, *Am. Mineral.* **27**, 226 (1942).
(4) G. F. Claringbull and F. A. Bannister, *Acta Cryst.* **1**, 42 (1948).
(5) T. F. W. Barth and E. Posnjak, *Z. Krist.* **81**, 135 (1932).

cubic (tetragonal) at room temperature, but becomes cubic when heated to about 600°C. The absence of water in leucite is unexplained. There is ample room for it, just as there is in pollucite. Pollucite, however, appears to lose its zeolitic capacity for water after it has been dehydrated.[117]

**Soluble Silicates.** Solutions of all alkali metal hydroxides dissolve silica at temperatures below 100°C forming solutions of the corresponding alkali metal silicates:[118]

$$SiO_2 + 2OH^- \rightarrow SiO_3^= + H_2O$$

This method has been used commercially to produce sodium silicates from opalite, a crude form of opal containing about 8% of water. Most American production of sodium silicate, however, is by fusion of mixtures of sand and sodium carbonate in open hearth type furnaces:

$$SiO_2 + Na_2CO_3 \rightarrow Na_2SiO_3 + CO_2$$

The reaction product, *waterglass* or *soluble glass*, is conventionally made in two $Na_2O:SiO_2$ ratios. The greatest tonnage is a pale bluish or greenish neutral glass of ratio 1:3.3, and the lesser production a yellowish alkaline glass of ratio 1:2.1. In Europe production is usually from $Na_2SO_4$ rather than $Na_2CO_3$ because of the more favorable price of $Na_2O$ as sulfate relative to carbonate prevailing there. A reducing agent, ordinarily some form of pure carbon, is required in production from sulfate.

[117] M. Fleischer and C. J. Kasanda, *Am. Mineral.* **25**, 666 (1940).
[118] Numerous general references on the chemistry and properties of the soluble silicates have appeared. One of the most complete is: J. G. Vail, *Soluble Silicates*, Reinhold Publishing Corp., New York, 1952, Vol. 1.

The dissolution of vitreous sodium silicates in water involves a series of engineering problems. In contrast to most salts, the dissolving process does not stop at any saturation point, but proceeds continuously until the entire mass sets up into a rigid and elastic body. For solution to proceed at a practical rate it is necessary to use (with a given amount of water) a much larger quantity of glass than is required even for the most concentrated solutions that can be handled. The solution must then be promptly removed or effectively diluted when the desired concentration is reached. Both continuous and batchwise processes have been devised for carrying on dissolution of these glasses. No less than twenty-nine liquid soluble silicate products are regularly manufactured. These solutions have an alkaline reaction as a result of hydrolysis, since silicic acid is extremely weak. They find many commercial uses, such as fireproofing and waterproofing of textiles and timbers, as a filler in cheap soaps, and as an adhesive in the manufacture of cardboard shipping cases. Table 4.13 presents estimates of the world production of soluble sodium silicate (in terms of short tons of anhydrous $Na_2O:3.3SiO_2$ glass) in 1949.

TABLE 4.13.   WORLD PRODUCTION OF SOLUBLE SODIUM SILICATE IN 1949*

| Country | Tons | Country | Tons |
|---|---|---|---|
| North America | 465,000 | Asia | 20,000 |
| Central Europe | 110,000 | Mediterranean area | 10,000 |
| United Kingdom | 60,000 | Central America | 10,000 |
| France | 40,000 | South America | 5,000 |
| Russia | Large | Scandinavia | 4,400 |
| Benelux area | 33,000 | Australia | 400 |

* J. G. Vail, *Soluble Silicates*, Reinhold Publishing Corp., New York, 1952, Vol. 1.

At least fourteen *solid* soluble silicates are regular items commercially. These range from completely vitreous to completely crystalline products. Both anhydrous and hydrated crystalline soluble silicates have been prepared (Table 4.14). One of the hydrates of sodium metasilicate, $Na_2SiO_3 \cdot 5H_2O$, a granular free-flowing powder readily soluble in water, is an important detergent and wetting agent.

The reactions of the salts of heavy metals with dilute solutions of alkaline silicates are not neatly stoichiometric. The precipitates formed depend on the alkalinity and the insolubility of the heavy metal silicates and are hydrous mixtures of varying composition and water content. Indeed, with their gelatinous properties they open up a whole field of colloid chemistry. A striking example of these reaction products is the "silicate garden." If crystals of heavy metal salt hydrates, such as

TABLE 4.14. SOME CRYSTALLINE SOLUBLE SILICATES*

| *Anhydrous* | | *Hydrated* | |
|---|---|---|---|
| $Li_4SiO_4$ | $Rb_2Si_2O_5$ | $Na_3HSiO_4 \cdot H_2O$ | $Na_6Si_{13}O_{29} \cdot 11H_2O$ |
| $Li_2SiO_3$ | $Rb_2Si_4O_9$ | $Na_3HSiO_4 \cdot 2H_2O$ | |
| $Li_2Si_2O_5$ | | $Na_3HSiO_4 \cdot 5H_2O$ | $K_2SiO_3 \cdot 0.5H_2O$ |
| | $NaLiSiO_3$ | | $K_2SiO_3 \cdot H_2O$ |
| $Na_4SiO_4$ | $KLiSi_2O_5$ | $Na_2SiO_3 \cdot H_2O$ | |
| $Na_6Si_2O_7$ | $K_4Li_2Si_6O_{15}$ | $Na_2SiO_3 \cdot 5H_2O$ | $K_2Si_2O_5 \cdot H_2O$ |
| $Na_2SiO_3$ | $K_{10}Li_4Si_7O_{21}$ | $Na_2SiO_3 \cdot 6H_2O$ | |
| $Na_2Si_2O_5$ | $K_{10}Li_2Si_7O_{20}$ | $Na_2SiO_3 \cdot 8H_2O$ | $K_2Si_4O_9 \cdot H_2O$ |
| | $K_5LiSi_2O_7$ | $Na_2SiO_3 \cdot 9H_2O$ | |
| $K_2SiO_3$ | | | |
| $K_2Si_2O_5$ | | | |
| $K_2Si_4O_9$ | | | |

* For physical properties and other data on these silicates, see Vail, *op. cit.*, pp. 111–150.

$Co(NO_3)_2 \cdot 6H_2O$ or $FeCl_3 \cdot 6H_2O$, are dropped into a 20% solution of sodium silicate, reactions immediately occur at the interface. A blue gelatinous membrane forms around the cobalt salt crystals, while the iron salt develops a similar brownish envelope. Osmosis through the membranes causes them to swell and burst, whereupon the escaping salt solution forms new membrane, and the process continues with the ultimate formation of attractive plantlike growths.

**Luminescent Silicates.** Substances are said to be luminescent if the absorption of radiant (or corpuscular) energy causes them to emit visible or near visible light of a longer wavelength. Such emission persisting only during excitation or for not longer than 10⁻⁹ sec after excitation is termed *fluorescence*, while that which persists for a longer time is known as *phosphorescence* or *afterglow*. Some varieties of natural willemite, $Zn_2SiO_4$, fluoresce strongly in ultraviolet light, in green, yellow, etc. Most interest centers, however, in the synthetic luminescent materials commonly termed *phosphors*. Among the prominent silicate phosphors are zinc silicate, zinc beryllium silicate, and cadmium silicate. Silicates of the alkaline earths and certain of the rare-earth metals are phosphors of lesser importance.

Preparation of phosphors is an exacting chemical operation. Since minute amounts of certain heavy metal ions may inhibit the luminescence, the materials used must be of such exceptional purity, 99.9999%, that they are designated luminescence pure (LP).[119] The highly pure silicates of accurate stoichiometric composition, however, may be only feebly luminescent if at all. They usually require the presence of a small

[119] H. W. Leverenz, *Luminescence of Solids*, John Wiley and Sons, Inc., New York, 1950, pp. 61–76.

amount of a suitable *activator* to produce a good phosphor.   Conventional $Zn_2SiO_4$ phosphors contain from 0.01 to 1% of manganese as an activator. Lead and europium may activate alkaline earth silicates.[120]

An important commercial use of phosphors is in the modern "fluorescent" lamp tubes.   These tubes contain mercury and argon or krypton at 3 to 18 mm pressure, and have a phosphor coating (about 1.7 mg of phosphor per cm²) on the inside wall.   White-emitting lamps may be coated with a mixture of pale-blue-emitting $Mg_2WO_5$:[W] and orange-yellow-emitting $(Zn:Be)_2SiO_4$:Mn phosphors.   During operation about 60% of the electrical energy input appears as the 2537-A mercury line which is the chief excitor of the phosphor coating.[121]   Other applications of phosphors are in television tubes, radar screens, luminescent inks, plastics, and tapes, and self-luminescent ("radium") dials.   The beryllium containing phosphors, like other beryllium compounds, are highly toxic.

**Glass.**   Glass[122] is as old as the earth, and its history has its beginning in the dim ages of antiquity.   Man during the Stone Age fashioned implements from obsidian, natural glass of volcanic origin.   For thousands of years, until about the time of the Bronze Age, obsidian was an article of commerce.   The first production of glass was probably accidental, and could have resulted from the fusion of sand and nitre in an open fire, as related by Pliny.   The oldest known piece of pure glass is an amulet molded of deep blue glass, of about 7000 B.C.   Thus glassmaking is an ancient art and was a highly developed industry of Syria before 1500 B.C. The Venetian glass workers made a very good product in the Middle Ages, and Venice was the center of glass manufacture for at least four centuries. The modern period in glass manufacture begins about 1600.   Flint glass was developed in 1675 and optical glass in 1790.   The art of cutting glass was perfected and a process for casting glass was invented in the seventeenth century.   As late as 1900 the manufacture of glass was still to be considered as a highly skilled art, and only very recently has actual scientific research been introduced into the industry with the achievement of remarkable advances.

Glass is one of industry's most important materials of construction.

[120] G. F. J. Garlick, *Luminescent Materials*, Clarendon Press, Oxford, 1949, pp. 84–87.

[121] Leverenz, *op. cit.*, pp. 415–421.

[122] General reference works on glass are numerous.   The following are suggested as an introduction: S. R. Scholes, *Modern Glass Practice*, Industrial Publications, Inc., Chicago, Revised Edition, 1952, 312 pp.; G. W. Morey, *The Properties of Glass*, Reinhold Publishing Corp., New York, 2nd Edition, 1954, 591 pp.; W. A. Weyl, *Colored Glasses*, Society of Glass Technology, Sheffield, 1951, 541 pp.; J. H. Dickson, *Glass*, Chemical Publishing Company, New York, 1951, 300 pp.; J. R. Vávra, *5000 Years of Glass-Making*, Artia, Prague, 1954, 192 pp., more than 200 full-page plates.

In a survey of 551 industrial plants it was shown that 42.2% use glass in their normal products.[123]  Its durability and thermal qualities are the properties most prized by the users, while its brittleness is considered its most unfavorable characteristic.  Glass ranked ninth in importance among twelve materials of construction.

1. *Properties of glass.*  All glasses have certain characteristic properties.  They are hard and elastic.  When struck a blow, they break in a curved fashion termed *conchoidal.*  They have no sharp melting point, but when heated soften by imperceptible degrees until they liquefy.  Glasses relatively rich in alkali metals show rather good conductivity of an electrolytic nature at higher temperatures but still well below the softening point.  The melt is characterized by high viscosity.  Optically, glasses are isotropic unless they are under stress.  They all show more or less tendency to devitrify.

TABLE 4.15. SOME DATA ON THE PHYSICAL PROPERTIES OF GLASSES

| Property | Borosilicate Chemical Resistant Glass | Window Glass | Possible Range of Values Obtainable in Glasses |
|---|---|---|---|
| Refractive index, $N_D$ | 1.474 | 1.51–1.53 | 1.467–2.179 |
| Density | 2.23 | 2.54 | 2.125–8.120 g/cc |
| Elasticity coefficient | 8,900,000 | 11,000,000 | 6,500,000–12,500,000 psi |
| Compressive strength | · · · | 130,000 | 90,000–180,000 psi |
| Tensile strength | · · · | 13,000 | 4,000–1,000,000 psi |
| Thermal conductivity | 0.0025 | 0.0022 | 0.0018–0.0028 cal/sec cm °C |
| Expansion coefficient | $33 \times 10^{-7}$ | $83 \times 10^{-7}$ | $8 \times 10^{-7}$–$140 \times 10^{-7}$ cm/cm °C |
| Softening point | 819°C | 670°–750°C | 500°–1510°C |
| Annealing point | 553°C | 500°–570°C | 350°–890°C |
| Volume resistivity | $10^{16}$ | $10^{12}$ | $10^8$–$10^{18}$ ohms/cc |
| Dielectric constant | 4.8–5.0 | 6.8–7.1 | 3.7–16.5 |
| Specific heat | 0.2 | 0.27 | 0.136–0.352 cal/g |

In Table 4.15 are listed data on certain physical properties of borosilicate and window glass, also the possible range in the values of these physical properties.  The data for window glass are typical.

2. *Composition of glass.*  Glass is usually composed of a mixture of various silicates, with some excess silicon dioxide.  The basic elements usually include an alkali metal and an alkaline earth metal; for example, common window glass is essentially a mixture of sodium and calcium silicates.  Potassium is substituted for the sodium to give a resistant

[123] *Materials Survey: Glass*, McGraw-Hill Book Co., New York, 1944.

*laboratory glass*, and lead is often used instead of calcium to give a *flint glass*. In some special glasses other acidic constituents than $SiO_2$ are used in whole or in part to give the desired properties. Table 4.16 shows the approximate percentage composition of certain types of glass.

TABLE 4.16.  APPROXIMATE PERCENTAGE COMPOSITION OF VARIOUS KINDS OF GLASS

| Glass | $SiO_2$ | $Na_2O$ | $K_2O$ | $CaO$ | $PbO$ | $Al_2O_3$ | $B_2O_3$ | $ZnO$ | $P_2O_5$ | $MgO$ | $BaO$ |
|---|---|---|---|---|---|---|---|---|---|---|---|
| Quartz......... | 100 | | | | | | | | | | |
| Soda lime...... | 76 | 13 | | 11 | | | | | | | |
| Potash......... | 71 | | 18 | 11 | | | | | | | |
| Flint.......... | 53 | | 14 | | 33 | | | | | | |
| Borosilicate..... | 81 | 5 | | | | 2 | 12 | | | | |
| Jena........... | 65 | 8.5 | | | | 4.5 | 11 | 11 | | | |
| Phosphate...... | | | 15 | | | 11 | 5 | | 57 | 12 | |
| Borate flint..... | | 4 | | | 7 | 11 | 66 | 12 | | | |
| Special......... | 68 | | | | | 3.5 | 13 | 3.5 | | | 12 |

Commercial glasses largely fall into three classes, based upon their chemical composition: *lime glasses, borosilicate glasses,* and *flint (lead) glasses.*

a. Lime glasses are made by heating a mixture of pure sand, sodium carbonate, and limestone. Sometimes sodium sulfate (salt-cake) or slaked lime is substituted. The properties of the resulting glass depend upon the proportions of the ingredients used. This soda-lime glass consists largely of sodium and calcium silicate and also is known as soft glass because it is readily softened by heat. A harder and more resistant glass results when potassium carbonate is used instead of sodium carbonate. The resulting potash glass is suitable for windows and bottles.

b. Borosilicate glasses have a part of the silica replaced by boric oxide. They have a low coefficient of expansion, high softening point, great resistance to chemical action, and considerable resistance toward shock. These properties make this kind of glass desirable for laboratory apparatus, kitchen ware, insulators, and thermometers. "Pyrex" and the various "Jena" glasses are of this type.

c. Flint or lead glasses are produced from sand, lead oxide, and potassium carbonate. They are heavy brilliant glasses of high refractive index. Cut-glass dishes and many optical instruments, such as lenses and prisms, are made from this type of glass. Glass containing barium is used in bifocal lenses.

3. *Structure of glass.* Early theories concerning the structure of glasses considered them to be "amorphous" or "supercooled liquids."

When the first X-ray diffraction patterns of glasses were observed, it appeared that they might be built up of exceedingly small crystals. The crystallite hypothesis, however, was soon shown to be out of harmony with the known physical properties of glass. It leads, for instance, to discrepancy between the observed and calculated density.

From consideration of substances that are obtainable in both the crystalline and vitreous states it has been concluded that the atoms in glasses are linked together by forces which are essentially the same as those in crystals. Modern theory[124] proposes that the atoms form extended three-dimensional networks in glasses just as in crystals, but lacking in a regular periodicity (Fig. 4.21). In such networks the "glass-

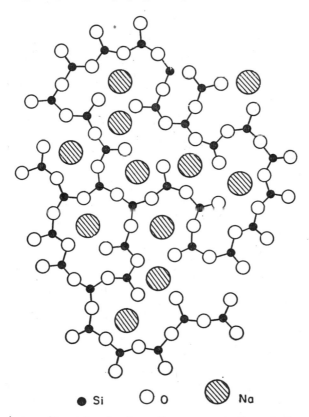

● Si    ○ O    ⦸ Na

FIG. 4.21. A two-dimensional schematic representation of the structure of soda-silica glass. (Warren and Briscoe, *J. Am. Ceram. Soc.* 21, 259.)

[124] W. H. Zachariasen, *J. Am. Chem. Soc.* 54, 3841 (1932); *J. Chem. Phys.* 3, 162 (1935).

forming" cations ($B^{+3}$, $Si^{+4}$, $P^{+3}$, $P^{+5}$, $As^{+3}$, $As^{+5}$, $Ge^{+4}$, and possibly $V^{+5}$, $Sb^{+5}$, $Cb^{+5}$, $Ta^{+5}$, and $Al^{+3}$) are surrounded by oxygen tetrahedra or by oxygen triangles which share only corners with each other.   The valences in such a network in general will not be balanced until typical large cations, such as $Na^+$, $K^+$, $Ca^{++}$, $Ba^{++}$ and $Pb^{++}$, are placed in the holes and interstices.   The holes in the nonperiodic framework will have a statistical distribution and, in the formation of an oxide-type glass, the holes are formed and filled at the same time the framework is being formed.   Such a picture is in harmony with the properties of glasses. A more general theory of vitreous structure based on the concept of glasses as supercooled liquids has also been presented.[125]   Several studies[126] of glasses have quantitatively treated the X-ray diffraction intensities, and apparently confirmed the Zachariasen picture.

4. *Coloring materials.*   Colorless, transparent glass can be made only when the purest raw materials are used.   A trace of iron gives a slightly green color to glass because of the presence of iron(II) silicate.   An addition of a small amount of manganese dioxide corrects this color by oxidizing the iron to the iron(III) condition; but an excess of the dioxide is avoided for it forms a purple color.   On the other hand, many substances are added to glass to form compounds which give it the desired color.   A few of these materials are listed in Table 4.17.

TABLE 4.17.   COLORING MATERIALS FOR GLASS

| Color | Material | Color | Material |
|---|---|---|---|
| Ruby | $Cu_2O$, Au, or Se | Blue | CoO |
| Green | $Cr_2O_3$, $Au_2O$, or FeO | Opaque | $SnO_2$ or $Ca_3(PO_4)_2$ |
| Yellow | $Sb_2S_3$, $AgBO_2$, $U_2O_3$, or Se | Fluorescent | $U_2O_3$ |
| Violet | $MnO_2$ | Milky | $SnO_2$ or $CaF_2$ |

5. *The making of glass.*   In the making of glass the mixture of materials is melted in pots or furnaces, and the molten mass is blown or formed into the desired shape.   Many articles, such as bottles, are blown with the aid of molds.   This molding process is usually carried out by very ingenious machines.   The glass is then carefully annealed in a kiln, where the temperature can be lowered gradually.   Plate glass is made by pouring molten glass upon a cast-iron table with a raised rim.   A hot iron

[125] Gunnar Hägg, *J. Chem. Phys.* **3**, 42 (1935).
[126] B. E. Warren, *Z. Krist.* **86**, 349 (1933); *J. Applied Phys.* **8**, 645 (1937); B. E. Warren and A. D. Loring, *J. Am. Ceram. Soc.* **18**, 269 (1935); B. E. Warren and J. Biscoe, *ibid.* **21**, 259 (1938).

roller is used to flatten the glass. The surface of the cooled glass is then ground and polished.

Formerly almost all glass-working and glass-forming operations were done manually. In making window glass a ball of molten glass on the end of an iron pipe was blown into a cylinder 6 ft long by a glass blower with powerful lungs. Then the cylinder was split lengthwise and flattened in an annealing oven. Bottles and glass vessels were blown into molds or shaped entirely by workmen. Now a modern machine can automatically produce 10,000 bottles per hour. This machine takes the required amount of molten glass from the furnace, places it in the mold, closes the mold, blows the bottle by compressed air, opens the mold, and starts the bottle through the annealing oven. Glass-blowing machines are preventing the death of many workers from tuberculosis, the dreaded disease of glass blowers.

At present large-quantity production of glass is carried out in a continuous type of furnace resembling a long tank. The furnace lining is of fire clay blocks or aluminum silicate (mullite). The raw materials, after careful and accurate mixing, are fed into one end of the furnace; at the other end molten glass is drawn off in a continuous stream or at intervals as desired. Flat window or plate glass comes from the furnace

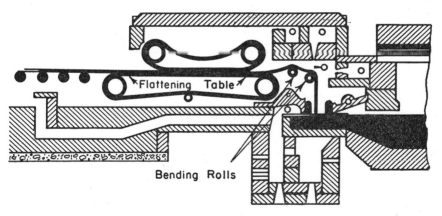

Fig. 4.22. Libbey-Owens-Colburn process of drawing window glass. (Scholes, *Modern Glass Practice;* courtesy *Industrial Publications, Inc.*)

in the form of a flat sheet (Fig. 4.22) or broad ribbon which is polished and annealed as it moves along on a carrier. A 100-ton glass-melting furnace at the Dearborn plant of the Ford Motor Company in 1939–40 poured a 51-in. wide sheet of glass without interruption for 600 days.

This production represents over 46,000 tons of glass, covering 42,100,000 sq ft.   Each day 3.25 miles of glass poured from the furnace.

All glass objects require careful annealing by slow cooling to prevent strains and breakage caused by the surface layer becoming so rigid as to keep the hotter interior from contracting to its normal volume at room temperature.   This process requires only a few hours with small glass objects, but a longer time as the pieces become larger.   The 20-ton glass mirror for the 200-in. telescope on Mt. Palomar in Southern California required a year to cool after casting.

6. *Safety glass.*   Safety glass, now standard equipment on all automobiles, has been constantly improved.   It consists of a flexible plastic sandwiched between two pieces of thin plate glass.   Adhesion of the glass to this flexible plastic prevents the glass from flying when broken. Originally the filler became discolored by sunlight, loosened by moisture, and brittle when cold, so that the glass lost its safety feature.   At present the plastic filler is usually a thin sheet of vinylite resin which is so elastic it acts like a sheet of transparent rubber.   It makes a permanent bond between the sheets of glass and possesses none of the faults of former fillers.

7. *Fibrous glass.*   Glass is being spun into very fine fibers, known as fibrous glass, and is of two types: one for thermal insulation, and the other for textile purposes.   A marble about 0.75 in. in diameter produces a thread which would extend from New York City to Omaha.   Fibrous glass is woven into cloth for fireproof curtains and the like, but problems of production involving the printing of glass fabrics have not yet been completely solved.   However, electrical tape, chemical filter cloth, and acid- and heat-resisting rope of fibrous glass are being made.   Fibrous glass is an excellent insulating material; and it is said to permit a substantial reduction in size and weight of motors and to permit them to operate at higher temperatures than those with other types of insulation. The lightest glass wool batting weighs only 0.5 lb/cu ft.   Substituted for old-fashioned insulation this product reduces the weight of a battleship by almost 500 tons.   The kapok-filled upholstery of airplanes may pick up 2 tones of moisture in a flight across the Pacific.   Fibrous glass does not adsorb moisture and may, therefore, be the solution to this problem.

8. *Foamglas.*   Cullet (waste and broken glass), after drying, grinding, and mixing with finely divided carbon, is heated to 1550°–1650°F. During the heating the oxides in the glass react with the carbon to form millions of tiny carbon monoxide- and carbon dioxide-filled cells in the glass.   The product is a froth or foam of glass with about the same weight as balsa wood or cork (one fifth that of ordinary glass).   It is extremely valuable for its buoyancy and insulating properties, since it is impervious

to water, is noncombustible, odorless, and unaffected by acid vapors and solutions.

9. *Structural glass.* Glass is becoming an important structural material in the building industry. Walls made of glass blocks admit light, insure privacy, and have high heat-insulating value. A special tempering process produces a glass four times as strong and flexible as normal for use in building partitions. The finished glass is heated to the softening point and suddenly chilled, thus leaving the outer surfaces under strong compressive stresses to which the glass owes its exceptional strength. Such glass, sold under such names as "Herculite" and Armourplate," withstands both thermal and mechanical shock incredibly well and is approved as a safety glass for automobile windshields in Great Britain. Other uses for it are as large plate glass doors without any frame, as showcases, portholes on ships, fire screens and oven doors, baseball backstops, etc. Items made of the glass cannot be cut, ground, or worked, since they fail and shatter when the outer envelope of compression is penetrated. Well-made tempered plate 0.25-in. thick will yield more than 40 fragments per sq in., and its safety properties, should it break, depend largely on this small fragment size. A special heat-absorbing glass, which transmits less than 43% of the total solar heat, is used in windows on south exposures and on trains crossing deserts. Colored glass is replacing tile for bathrooms and kitchen walls and is being used for shelves and table tops. Between 1920 and 1950 the amount of glass used in constructing the average American home increased from 9 to 18% of the total materials.

10. *Ultra-low-expansion glass.* Development of a glass with a very low coefficient of expansion is rapidly leading to mass production of glass cooking utensils. After forming a vessel of glass, the nonsiliceous components of it are leached out in an acid bath, leaving a network of nearly pure silica. Then the vessel is baked at a high temperature, whereupon it shrinks considerably and fuses into a completely transparent glass with properties resembling fused quartz. The resulting glass ("Vycor")[127] is resistant to breakage under severe temperature changes, as when plunged red hot into cold water.

11. *Polarizing glass.* Polarizing glass for the production of plane polarized light is another advance in glass technology. Polarization is accomplished by a thin film (0.001 in.) of cellulose ester in which oriented submicroscopic crystals of iodoquinine sulfate are suspended. This film is sandwiched between two pieces of glass as in safety glass. Polarizing

[127] H. P. Hood and M. E. Nordberg, **U.S. 2,221,709,** Nov. 12, 1940; **U. S. 2,286,275,** June 16, 1942.

glass has important applications in eliminating glare.  A streamliner on one of the railroads has windows of this glass to prevent glare from snow and desert sun.  Other possible applications are in the production of three-dimensional motion pictures, and for automobile windshields and headlight lenses.  Such lenses, however, reduce the output of light from headlights about 50%.  Polarizing glass is now used in daylight glasses to reduce glare.

12. *Some miscellaneous glasses and their uses.*  A clear, untreated glass reflects about 8 to 10% of incident light from its two surfaces.  An increase in the number of surfaces, as in a composite lens, may lead to light losses of 50% or more.  A process for preventing glare and reflection of light from glass involves the application of thin films of fluorides of metals to the surface of glass.  The thickness of the film (four millionths of an inch) is about a quarter of a wavelength of light.  Motion picture projectors with coated lenses are said to increase the screen illumination from 15 to 30%, by cutting down reflection and increasing transmission.

Special silica-free glasses, such as the Zn–Cd–Al phosphate glasses, are now being produced.  A glass whose major ingredient is $P_2O_5$ is not attacked by hydrofluoric acid.  Its working properties are about the same as those of ordinary glass.

"Scotchlite" is a reflective material consisting of many tiny glass spheres held to a backing by a special adhesive agent.  It has great reflecting quality when illuminated in the proper fashion.  Thus it is particularly adapted to use in advertising signs, warning signs, highway markers, and many other uses.

**Ceramic Products.**  Articles fabricated from natural clays or from artificial plastic mixtures of clay and other materials are known as *ceramic products*.[128]  The moist clay must possess sufficient viscosity that it can be molded under gentle pressure into the required shape and then retain that shape when the pressure is removed.  Another technique is frequently used in making the finer grades of ceramic wares.  A liquefied clay mix termed *slip* is poured into plaster molds in which the clay near the mold surface quickly solidifies, as a consequence of the rapid absorption of the water by the plaster.  The remaining liquid slip is then poured from the mold, leaving a hollow clay body of the desired

---

[128] Excellent general references on ceramics are numerous, such as: F. H. Norton, *Elements of Ceramics*, Addison-Wesley Press, Inc., Cambridge, 1952, 246 pp.; H. Salmang, *Die physikalischen und chemischen Grundlagen der Keramik*, Springer, Berlin, 3rd Edition, 1954, 335 pp.; A. T. Green and G. H. Stewart, Editors, *Ceramics: A Symposium*, British Ceramic Society, Stoke-on-Trent, 1953, 877 pp.; J. B. Kenney, *The Complete Book of Pottery Making*, Greenberg, New York, 1949, 242 pp.

form.   After drying, the clay object is strongly heated ("fired") in a kiln to produce a hard porous body called *biscuit*.   Transparent or colored fusible glasses (*glazes*) may be applied, with additional firings, to decorate the ware.   Table 4.18 summarizes the chief types of ceramic products.

TABLE 4.18.   THE CHIEF TYPES OF CERAMIC PRODUCTS

| | |
|---|---|
| Porcelain | Body dense, translucent, white |
| Stoneware | Body dense, opaque, white or colored (gray, yellow, brown) |
| Whiteware | Body porous, opaque, white or nearly white.   Not as strong as the foregoing. |
| Pottery | Body porous, opaque, colored |
| Bricks and Tiles | Porous, rather coarse grained, generally reddish in color |
| Refractories | Porous or dense, melting point above 1600°C |

Porcelain originated in China in early times, but was first manufactured in Europe at Meissen about 1710.   Modern hard porcelain is made from a clay mix of about 50% kaolin, 25% feldspar, and 25% quartz.   The fired porcelain consists of a vitreous matrix interspersed with needles of mullite, undissolved quartz grains, and minute air bubbles. For tableware a transparent glaze is applied by dipping the body into a suspension of kaolin, clay, feldspar, and marble in water, which, on heating, forms a high-melting glass.   Decoration of tableware and fancy porcelain with colored pigments may require a third firing.   Electrical, chemical, sanitary and other wares are produced in the United States, however, by a process that develops the body and glaze in a single firing.

Siliceous refractories[129] are vitally important to many industries. Fire clay, containing about 12 to 15% of $Al_2O_3$ and 50 to 54% $SiO_2$, is used especially for lining hearths, furnaces, and hot-blast heaters.   Firebricks are prepared from plastic fire clay and flint clay, and fired at 1250° to 1400°C to give a porosity of 15 to 20%.   A blast furnace and its stoves require nearly a million such bricks in its construction.   Open-hearth furnaces, Bessemer converters, and glass melting furnaces are lined with silica bricks.   Modern silica bricks are made from a quartzite sandstone (termed *ganister*) with 2% of lime as a bond.   The firing is prolonged at 1500° to 1550°C to convert as much of the quartz as possible to cristobalite and tridymite.   Silicon carbide is used in considerable quantities in kiln furniture and refractory brick.

**Portland Cement.**   The term *cement* usually applies to mortars called hydraulic cements, which have the property of hardening in water as well as in air.   Such cements have been known since early Greek and Roman times.   In 1824 a patent covering the making of a cement from

[129] A good general reference is: F. H. Norton, *Refractories*, McGraw-Hill Book Co., New York, 3rd Edition, 1949, 782 pp.

clay and slaked lime was taken out by Joseph Aspdin of Leeds, who named the product *Portland cement* because it resembled so closely the famous Portland (England) building stone. Although there are a number of different types of cements (Table 4.19), Portland cement is now by

TABLE 4.19. COMPOSITIONS OF TWO TYPES OF CEMENTS

| Compound | Portland Cement % | High Alumina Cement % |
|----------|-------------------|-----------------------|
| $SiO_2$ | 19–25 | 3–11 |
| $Al_2O_3$ | 5–9 | 38–48 |
| $Fe_3O_4$ | 2–4 | 2–15 |
| CaO | 60–64 | 35–42 |
| MgO | 1–4 | |
| $SO_3$ | 1–2 | |

far the most important. The American Society for Testing Materials defines Portland cement as "the product obtained by pulverizing clinker consisting essentially of hydraulic calcium silicates, to which no additions have been made subsequent to calcination other than water and/or untreated calcium sulfate, except that additions not to exceed 1.0% of other materials may be interground with the clinker at the option of the manufacturer, provided such materials in the amount indicated have been shown to be not harmful by tests carried out or reviewed by Committee C-1 on cement."[130]

Most cements[131] are mixtures of silicates (Table 4.19) which, when finely ground and mixed with water, undergo reactions resulting in the formation of hard, rocklike masses. Portland cement is made by calcining to incipient fusion in a rotary kiln the proper mixture of limestone or marl and clay or shale. Water and carbon dioxide are driven off, and the product fuses into clinkers. The latter are then air cooled, mixed with not more than 3% of gypsum (to control the rate of setting), and pulverized to the surface area specified for the particular type of cement (1600–1800 sq cm/g).

Only in recent years has satisfactory knowledge been obtained regarding the composition of cement and the reactions involved in the setting process. Much of this knowledge has been gained by the use of X-ray methods. The chief minerals in Portland cement clinker and their heats

[130] Am. Soc. Testing Materials, Specifications C-150-55.
[131] Useful general references are: R. H. Bogue, *The Chemistry of Portland Cement*, Reinhold Publishing Corp., New York, 2nd Edition, 1955, 793 pp.; *Proceedings of the Third International Symposium on the Chemistry of Cement*, Cement and Concrete Association, London, 1952, 870 pp.

of setting on hydration are:

|  | Cal/g |
|---|---|
| $3CaO \cdot Al_2O_3$ | 207 |
| $3CaO \cdot SiO_2$ | 120 |
| $4CaO \cdot Al_2O \cdot Fe_2O_3$ | 100 |
| $2CaO \cdot SiO_2$ | 62 |

The most important component of cement is the tricalcium silicate, $3CaO \cdot SiO_2$, whose structure[132] appears to be $Ca_3O(SiO_4)$. The reactions during the hydration and setting of cement are exceedingly complex and usually involve both hydrolysis and hydration of the components simultaneously. Moreover, variations in conditions can lead to different reaction products:[133]

$$Ca_3(SiO_3OH)_2 \cdot 2H_2O + 3Ca(OH)_2$$
afwillite
(hydration done in a ball mill)

$$2[3CaO \cdot SiO_2] + 6H_2O$$

$$Ca_3Si_2O_7 \cdot 3H_2O + 3Ca(OH)_2$$
a phase similar to the mineral tobermorite
(hydration done in paste form)

also

$$3CaO \cdot SiO_2 + 3H_2O \rightarrow 2CaO \cdot SiO_2 \cdot 2H_2O + Ca(OH)_2$$

Dicalcium silicate, $2CaO \cdot SiO_2$, apparently also can react in several ways to give hydrates and/or afwillite.[134] At room temperature only a tobermorite-type phase, $3CaO \cdot 2SiO_2 \cdot 3H_2O$, and a dicalcium silicate hydrate, $2CaO \cdot SiO_2 \cdot (2-4)H_2O$, seem likely in cement hydration.[135] There are perhaps seven or eight other calcium silicate hydrates formed in the temperature range 25° to 300°C,[135] and some of them doubtless have a part in the process of setting. Tricalcium aluminate, $3CaO \cdot Al_2O_3$, forms a hydrate, $3CaO \cdot Al_2O_3 \cdot 6H_2O$. The gypsum present retards the setting (which would otherwise be too rapid) by the formation of one or more sulfoaluminates, such as:

$$3CaO \cdot Al_2O_3 + CaSO_4 \cdot 2H_2O + 10H_2O \rightarrow 3CaO \cdot Al_2O_3 \cdot CaSO_4 \cdot 12H_2O$$

Years ago all Portland cement was of a fairly uniform composition and had a nearly constant set of properties. However, the demands of the construction industry during recent years have led to the development of a variety of cements to meet special needs. Some of these cements are discussed briefly.

[132] J. W. Jeffery, *Acta Cryst.* 5, 26 (1952).
[133] S. Brunauer, L. E. Copeland, and R. H. Bragg, *J. Phys. Chem.* 60, 112, 116 (1956).
[134] L. Heller, *Acta Cryst.* 5, 724 (1952).
[135] J. D. Bernal, paper [9] in: *Third International Symposium*, ref. 131, pp. 216–260.

*White Portland cement* is a standard cement made of very pure materials having a low iron content.

*High-early-strength cement* is used in construction work in which one step must follow another quickly, and in street work where adequate strength within 24 hours is demanded.

*Masonry cements* are plastic and of low shrinkage.

*Low-* and *moderate-heat-of-hardening Portland cements* have been developed for use in building the great dams constructed in recent years. Where such enormous masses of concrete are used it is highly desirable to have cements that develop little heat in the process of setting.

*Oil-well cements* have properties suiting them for use in the grouting of wells.

*Portland-pozzolana cements* resist chemical attack by agents such as the salts found in sea water. Pumicite, slag, and other materials that react with the calcium content of the cement are added to Portland cement to make it resistant.

**Slags.** In most ores the useful ore mineral, commonly an oxide, carbonate, or sulfide, is intimately associated with varying amounts of stony or earthy material termed *gangue.* During the smelting and refining processes, fluxes are added to react with the gangue and to separate it as a molten, fluid glass or *slag* which floats on the dense molten metal. Details differ with the ores and metals involved, and, likewise, the compositions of the resulting slags vary widely. Among the important sources of slags are: the iron blast furnace, the open-hearth steel furnace, the Bessemer converter, copper, lead, and precious-metal ore smelters, and electrochemical processes.

Blast-furnace slag[136] consists essentially of silicates and aluminosilicates of lime and other bases. When standard-grade hematite ore, $Fe_2O_3$, from the Lake Superior district is charged into the furnace, about 2 tons of ore, 1 ton of coke, 0.5 ton of fluxing stone (limestone, $CaCO_3$), and 4 tons of air are required to produce 1 ton of pig iron. At the same time about 0.5 ton of slag is produced. Molten slag, when rapidly chilled with water, solidifies substantially as a glass. When cooled more slowly it crystallizes into a relatively few mineral species. The most common mineral in blast-furnace slag is melilite, and member of the solid solution series extending from akermanite, $Ca_2MgSi_2O_7$, to gehlenite, $Ca_2Al(AlSiO_7)$. Slags low in lime and high in alumina may contain anorthite, and calcium metasilicate (pseudowollastonite), $CaSiO_3$,

[136] G. W. Josephson, F. Sillers, Jr., and D. G. Runner, *Iron Blast-Furnace Slag*, Bureau of Mines Bulletin 479, U. S. Government Printing Office, Washington 25, D. C., 1949, 304 pp.

also is found. With high lime content the orthosilicate, $Ca_2SiO_4$, may be present. Slags with much magnesia may contain monticellite and forsterite.

The tonnage of blast-furnace slag is enormous, and for many years it was strictly a nuisance of little economic value. Gradually this situation has changed, until in 1947 approximately 61% of the slag produced in the United States was commercialized in one form or another. It is produced chiefly as air-cooled slag. Granulated slag is produced by sudden chilling in water, and lightweight slag is the foamed product when molten slag is expanded in a limited quantity of water. Slag has numerous uses. It is an important aggregate for portland-cement concrete and for flexible-pavement bases and surfaces. It is used in cement and glass manufacture, for soil treatment, railroad ballast, sewage-filter media, roofing, and in the production of mineral wool.

*Mineral wool* or *rock wool* is a fibrous material of extensive use as an efficient insulator against heat and sound. It is made from molten rock or slag by directing a blast of stream against a thin stream of the melted material as it flows from a furnace. As the molten droplets are driven through the air, they form long thin threads, which solidify into fine fibers. This product is an especially satisfactory insulating material because it withstands fire, moisture, decay, and vermin.

In some processes the equilibrium of the slag with the underlying metal bath is of great importance. In the basic open-hearth furnace, for instance, FeO is soluble in both the metal and the slag in a fixed concentration ratio at a given temperature. The FeO in the metal oxidizes the metalloids (P, S, C), and the equilibrium ratio is maintained by diffusion of FeO from the slag to the metal. The concentration of FeO in the slag is maintained by the slag taking up oxygen from the furnace gases. In nickel-iron systems, additions of iron metal to a nickel melt under fused $NiSiO_3$ greatly decrease the NiO content of the slag, while the addition of nickel metal to an iron melt under an $FeSiO_3$ slag scarcely changes the FeO content in the metal.

Components of slags are frequently present as highly dispersed separate phases. Iron sulfide is often present in silicate slags as minute droplets of the sulfide, resulting in deep, black-colored, glassy slags resembling obsidian. The red color of copper refining slags is caused by finely dispersed $Cu_2O$.

# CHAPTER 5

## GERMANIUM AND ITS COMPOUNDS

**History.** By 1871 Mendeleev had developed his periodic arrangement of the elements to the stage where he could predict the existence of some of the then unknown elements and estimate many of their physical constants and chemical properties with remarkable accuracy. The classic example of this kind of prediction is found in the case of the element germanium. Mendeleev gave the name "ekasilicon" to this yet unknown element, since its position in the periodic table indicated that it would resemble silicon very closely in its chemical, physical, and metallurgical properties. When the element was isolated and identified in 1886 by Clemens Winkler,[1] its properties and physical constants were found to be very similar to those predicted by Mendeleev fifteen years earlier.

**General.** The association of germanium with silicon in the minds of chemists may have been unfortunate since it may have hampered the investigation and technological applications of germanium, factors also influenced by the supply and price differential of the two elements. There are, nevertheless, wide and important differences between the two elements, and these differences may be sufficiently important to establish germanium in its own place as a useful metal.[2] The oxide of germanium, for example, is the more easily reducible of the two, and free germanium is not as refractory as silicon.[3] As a result, germanium alloys itself more readily with other metals than does silicon. Germanium also differs from silicon in the degree to which it dissolves in other metals. The alloying behavior of germanium is between that of silicon and tin;[4] germanium stands between these two elements in their group in the periodic table.

NOTE. The authors are indebted to Dr. O. H. Johnson of the University of Minnesota for selected portions of this chapter.

[1] Clemens Winkler, *J. Prakt. Chem.* (2) **34**, 177 (1886).

[2] H. Nagafune, *Chemistry and Chem. Ind.* **6**, 165 (1953); C. A. Hampel, *Rare Metals Handbook*, Reinhold Publishing Corp., New York, 1954, pp. 161–172; D. C. Bradley and W. Wardlaw, *Science Progress* **42**, 1 (1954); J. L. P. Wyndham, *S. African Mining and Eng. J.* **154** I, 687 (1953); B. M. Kedrov, *Khim. Redkikh Elementov, Akad. Nauk S.S.S.R.* **1**, 7 (1954).

[3] R. I. Jaffee, E. W. McMullen, and B. W. Gonser, *The Electrochem. Soc. Preprint* 89–18 (1946).

[4] T. R. Briggs and W. S. Benedict, *J. Phys. Chem.* **34**, 173–177 (1930).

Thus it is found that silicon is immiscible with lead in both the liquid and the solid state, germanium is miscible with lead in the liquid state and immiscible in the solid state, whereas tin is not only miscible with lead in the liquid state but the two metals show appreciable mutual solubility in the solid state.

Germanium is in a position of great potential as well as actual utility.[5] It is produced in commercial quantities. Much of it is being used in experimental work, and real commercial usage depends upon the large-scale development of some of the applications (*vide infra*) in the electronics and electrochemical fields. A potential use for germanium compounds, such as $GeCl_2$, $GeCl_4$, $GeF_4$, $GeO$, and $GeOCl_2$, is in the lead-acid storage-battery industry. These compounds, when added to the electrolyte, appear to reduce the hygroscopicity of the plates and give improved overall performance.[6] Germanium compounds have long been used in the manufacture of glasses to give useful physical properties.

**Occurrence and Supply.** Winkler[7] discovered germanium and first isolated it while engaged in the analysis of the mineral argyrodite, $4AgS \cdot GeS_2$. The germanium content of this mineral is from 5 to 7%, but the mineral is comparatively rare and is not considered an important source. Another sulfide mineral, germanite, $7CuS \cdot FeS \cdot GeS_2$, found in Southwest Africa, contains 6% germanium. This mineral is a doubtful source of commercial quantities of germanium.[8]

The germanium supply on the market is produced from germanium-bearing by-products obtained in the smelting of zinc. Germanium has been extracted from a zinc oxide obtained from the zinc smelters of the New Jersey Zinc Company.[9] The Anaconda Copper Company[10] has also developed methods for the recovery of germanium from zinc-plant residues.

In 1947 the largest producer of germanium was the Eagle-Picher Company. In response to a demand for germanium crystals for use in radar applications, this firm developed procedures for recovering germanium from their cadmium-plant residues.

[5] R. I. Jaffee, E. W. McMullen, and B. W. Gonser, *The Electrochem. Soc. Preprint* 89–18 (1946).

[6] Carl Gutman *et al.*, U. S. 2,715,149, Aug. 9, 1955.

[7] Clemens Winkler, *J. Prakt. Chem.* (2) 34, 177 (1886).

[8] W. C. Johnson, L. C. Foster, and C. A. Kraus, *J. Am. Chem. Soc.* 57, 1828–1831 (1935); W. Keil, *Z. anorg. allgem. Chem.* 152, 101–104 (1926); W. Neubauer, *Berg- u. hüttermänn Monatsh. montan. Hochschule Loeben* 97, 113 (1952); *C.A.* 1548 (1953).

[9] L. M. Dennis and J. Papish, *J. Am. Chem. Soc.* 43, 2131–2143 (1921).

[10] F. L. Hess, *Mining and Met.* 19, 5–9 (1938).

There are numerous articles[11] dealing with the recovery of germanium dioxide from coal ashes and flue dusts in which it is found in amounts up to 1%. Since the production of germanium from cadmium-plant residues seems likely to be restricted to less than 2000 lb per year, it is possible that coal ashes and flue dusts may be a useful source of germanium should the demand increase appreciably beyond the present supply. Prices quoted in March, 1947, on 10-lb lots were $36.50 per lb for germanium tetrachloride, $60.00 per lb for germanium dioxide, and $140.00 per lb for germanium metal.

**Metallurgy.** This process is described in the following three sections.

1. *Extraction.* When a finely ground germanium-containing material is placed in concentrated hydrochloric acid and distilled, the germanium occurs in the distillate as volatile $GeCl_4$ along with the volatile chloride of arsenic. This procedure forms the basis for most of the methods devised for extracting germanium from its ores. The distillate is collected directly in water and is redistilled in a current of chlorine to oxidize the arsenic to the nonvolatile pentachloride. Relatively pure $GeCl_4$ is obtained as the distillate. The $GeCl_4$ is hydrolyzed to $GeO_2$ which is separated as a white filter cake and is ignited.

Other methods use extraction with 50% sodium hydroxide, followed by neutralization and acidification to precipitate arsenic[12] or a distillation of germanite ore in an atmosphere of nitrogen at 800°C to volatilize arsenic sulfide and sulfur. This process is followed by a reduction of the residue with ammonia at 825°C to change germanium(IV) sulfide to the volatile germanium(II) sulfide.[13]

2. *Reduction to metal.* Germanium(II) oxide sublimes at 710°C. The quantitative reduction of $GeO_2$ to metallic germanium is complicated by the formation of the volatile GeO as an intermediate product. To prevent excessive losses of the element, the reduction is accomplished under a layer of fused chlorides. Reduction of $GeO_2$ by hydrogen may be carried out at temperatures as low as 500°C. The hydrogen-reduced product is a dark-gray powder, lacking metallic luster.[14]

The most successful method for the production of metallic ger-

---

[11] F. H. Gibson and W. A. Selvig, *U. S. Bur. Mines Tech. Paper* **669**, 23 pp. (1944); V. M. Ratynski, *Compt. rend. acad. sci. U.S.S.R.* **40**, 198–200 (1943); G. Morgan and G. R. Davies, *Chemistry and Industry* **56**, 717–721 (1937); M. Inagaki, *J. Coal Research Inst.* **5**, 103, 326 (1954); W. Schreiter, *Metallurgie u. Giessereitech.* **4**, 417 (1954).

[12] F. Sebba and W. Pugh, *J. Chem. Soc.* **1937**, 1371–1373.

[13] W. C. Johnson, L. C. Foster, and C. A. Kraus, *J. Am. Chem. Soc.* **57**, 1828–1831 (1925).

[14] L. M. Dennis, K. M. Tressler, and F. E. Hance, *ibid.* **45**, 2033–2048 (1923).

manium[15] is the reduction of $GeO_2$ by carbon or by mixed potassium cyanide and carbon under a molten sodium-chloride flux.    Aluminum has been used to reduce $GeO_2$ to the metal but yields were low due to the formation of volatile GeO.    Germanium has been prepared by the electrolysis of $GeO_2$ in fused potassium fluogermanate or in molten cryolite.[16] Small pellets of the metal were obtained but the yields were low.

Germanium metal has for its principal impurities dissolved oxygen or oxides.    These impurities may be removed by repeated melting and solidifying the metal in an atmosphere of hydrogen or by prolonged vacuum treatment in the fused state.

3. *Germanium recovery at the Eagle-Picher Plant.*[17]    Most of the United States production of germanium is from the smelting of zinc ore derived from the Missouri–Arkansas–Oklahoma (Tristate ore) area.    British production, on the other hand, is substantially from coal processing.[18] Traces of germanium had been observed in zinc sulfide ores for many years, but they were disregarded until 1941 when the production of germanium became part of the war effort.    Spectroscopic analysis showed germanium to be concentrated in the cadmium fume from the sintering of zinc concentrates.    At the Henryetta, Oklahoma, Cadmium Recovery Plant, the cadmium fume is dissolved in sulfuric acid and the cadmium separated from other metals, such as zinc, lead, copper, iron, germanium, indium, and gallium.    By coordinating spectroscopic analyses with different possible treatments, it was possible to concentrate most of the germanium into residues that would make further treatment profitable.

Those residues sufficiently high in germanium are shipped to the Joplin Research Laboratory of the Eagle-Picher Company where they are distilled with excess concentrated hydrochloric acid containing at least 31% HCl.    The volatile $GeCl_4$, together with the volatile chlorides of other metals and some HCl, is caught in ice-cooled receivers.    The crude $GeCl_4$ is then purified, eventually resulting in a water-white $GeCl_4$ which is spectroscopically pure.

The pure $GeCl_4$ is hydrolyzed to germanium hydroxide.    One volume of $GeCl_4$ is diluted with five volumes of dilute ammonia.    The hydroxide is almost completely precipitated after 24 hours.    It is filtered, washed with a small amount of water, and dried at 150°C to form the dioxide.

[15] K. M. Tressler and L. M. Dennis, *J. Phys. Chem.* **31**, 1429–1432 (1927).

[16] R. I. Jaffee, E. W. McMullen, and B. W. Gonser, *The Electrochem. Soc. Preprint* 89–118 (1946).

[17] *Ibid.*

[18] A. P. Thompson and J. R. Musgrove, *J. Metals* **4**, 1132 (1952).

Germanium (IV) chloride may be distilled from germanite ore.[19]   The chloride is hydrolyzed directly to $GeO_2$, or, if needed, a further fractionation may be used followed by hydrolysis.   The chief impurity, $AsCl_3$, may be removed by treating the $AsCl_3$–$GeCl_4$ mixture with HCl saturated with chlorine.   The $AsCl_3$ is converted to $H_3AsO_4$.   Further traces of arsenic may be removed by multiple treatment with copper metal. Distillation of $GeCl_4$ in quartz has produced a product containing less than $6.30 \times 10^{-10}$ mole fraction of $AsCl_3$.[20]

Germanium metal is obtained from the dioxide by reduction with sodium cyanide, carbon, or hydrogen.   Metal of highest purity is at present most readily obtained by reduction with hydrogen at 900°C. Germanium produced by reduction with cyanide or carbon at 1200°C is somewhat less pure because of a slight reaction with the crucible but produces germanium of sufficient purity where slight contamination is not a factor.

Germanium of 98.7 to 99.7% purity has been produced by electroplating from a fused salt bath of $GeO_2 + Na_2B_4O_7$, $Li_2O$ or $SiO_2$, $Na_4P_2O_7$ and $Na_2O$, and NaF.   The process is carried out at the temperature near the melting point of germanium at an efficiency of 50 to 82%.[21]   Electroplating has also been accomplished from a 7% $GeCl_4$ solution in propylene glycol at 59°C at a current density of 0.4 amp/sq cm.   The plate is mirror bright and thicknesses up to 0.127 mm have been obtained.[22]

Germanium for asymmetrically conducting devices (rectifiers, transistors, etc.) has been purified by induction heating, *in vacuo*, at 1200° to 1500°C in a carbon vessel to remove arsenic, bismuth, and antimony by vaporization.   The germanium is then heated to 1000°C in an atmosphere of $90N_2:10H_2$ and granulated.[23]   The most successful method to date (1957) for obtaining highest purity germanium is by the zone melting process.   Preliminary purification may be achieved by the usual methods $(GeCl_4 \rightarrow GeO_2 \rightarrow Ge)$ followed by the passage of a bar of the metal through a heating coil or furnace.   The concept of increased solubility of impurities in the molten zone is utilized.[24]   Single crystals have been grown from the purified metal at a rapid rate by dipping a properly oriented seed crystal into a supercooled melt and withdrawing it at the

[19] O. Rosner, *Z. Erzbergbau u. Metallhattenw.* **8**, 1 (1955); *C.A.* **49**, 3757 (1955).

[20] M. Green and J. A. Kafalas, *J. Chem. Soc.* 1955, 1604.

[21] J. L. Andrieux and M. J. Barbier-Andrieux, *Compt. rend.* **240**, 2104 (1955).

[22] G. Szekely, *J. Electrochem. Soc.* **98**, 318 (1951); G. Szekely, **U. S. 2,690,422**, Sept. 28, 1954.

[23] **Brit. 703,606**, Feb. 3, 1954.

[24] E. E. Schumacher, *J. Metals* **5**, 1428 (1953); F. W. Dehmelt, *Chem.-Ing.-Tech.* **27**, 275 (1955); W. G. Pfann, *Chem. and Eng. News* **34**, 1440 (1956).

same rate that it grows.   Best results have been achieved by keeping the supercooled melt just above the freezing point.   Rates of 1 cm/min of growth are reported.[25]

**Physical Properties of Germanium.**   Germanium, like silicon, is a semiconductor.   The resistivity of the metal varies greatly with the impurities present, and this property has been made use of in developing a microwave rectifier, now in commercial production, in which the germanium is alloyed with a small amount of tin.   The tin partially dissolves in the crystals to form a lattice-imperfection semiconductor with very useful properties.

Rectifiers of this type are reported to handle higher inverse peak voltages than other similar types of rectifiers.   Currents handled by the germanium diode range from 30 to 70 milliamperes.   The low-resistance direction is from the tungsten-wire contact point to the germanium.

Germanium, when "doped" with minute traces of metals with fewer valence electrons (e.g., boron) or more valence electrons (e.g., antimony) than the parent metal, functions in a manner similar to silicon in the role of $p$- and $n$-semiconductors, respectively.[26]

Antimony doped single-crystal bars of $n$-type germanium heated at 800°C in a mixture of nitrogen and hydrogen remain as the $n$-type. When treated with HF and $H_2O_2$ or hot concentrated nitric acid, the $n$-type bars show conversion to $p$-type.   Copper electroplated on $n$-type germanium quickly converts to $p$-type on heat treatment.[27]   The phenomenon of $p$-$n$-type junction potentials has been utilized in studying the diffusion of impurities in germanium.   A comparison of this technique with radio-tracer technique gives good results.   The diffusion coefficients of In, Ga, Al, As, B, P, Sb, and Zn range at 900°C from $10^{-12}$ to $10^{-9}$ sq cm/sec.   The activation energy for bulk diffusion in germanium is about 2.5 ev or 57,000 cal/mole.

The dielectric constant of germanium is 15.8 ± 0.2 at 1 Mc/sec. There is a wide variation of dielectric constant with frequency for germanium in contrast to a small range for silicon (1%).   This variation is probably due to the lower resistivity of the germanium.[28]   The thermal

[25] E. Billig, *Proc. Roy. Soc.* (London) A229, 346 (1955); K. Lehovec *et al.*, *Rev. Sci. Inst.* 24, 652 (1955); H. E. Bridgers, *Chem. and Eng. News* 34, 220 (1956).

[26] W. C. Dunlop, Jr. *et al.*, *Phys. Rev.* 91, 206 (1953); E. M. Conwell, *ibid.*, 208; R. Bray and F. van der Maesen, *ibid.*, 231; A. V. Ioffe and A. F. Ioffe, *Zhur. Tekh. Fiz.* 24, 1910 (1954); E. H. Borneman *et al.*, *J. Appl. Phys.* 26, 1021 (1955); P. Aigrain *et al.*, *Semi-conducting Material* (*Proc. Conf. Univ. Reading*) 1951, 95–101; E. M. Conwell, *Proc. I.R.E.* 40, 1327 (1952).

[27] F. van der Maesen *et al.*, *Phillips Research Repts.* 8, 241 (1953).

[28] W. C. Dunlop, Jr., *Phys. Rev.* 94, 1531 (1954); *ibid.* 92, 1396 (1953).

conductivity of pure $n$-type germanium crystals along the 100 axis is 0.61 watt/(cm deg) at 5°C and 0.50 watt/(cm deg) at 95°C.[29]

Germanium has been compared with silicon and AlSb ($\Delta E$ values of 0.7 ev, 1.0 ev, and 1.6 ev, respectively) for use in the solar converter cell. The AlSb should be superior to either germanium or silicon for this purpose, and a maximum efficiency is estimated as 25%.[30]

Germanium resembles silicon in that it crystallizes in the diamond structure. An amorphous form is also known.[31] The surface tension of the liquid at the freezing point (under an atmosphere of argon) is 720 dynes/cm.[32] The value of $C_p - C_v$ for germanium may be calculated from the equation: $C_p - C_v = 9\alpha^2 VT/K_t$, where $\alpha$ is the coefficient of linear expansion, $K_t$ is the isothermal compressibility, and $V$ is the atomic volume.[33] The magnetic susceptibility has been determined and found to vary, depending upon the thermal history of the sample. A maximum is noted on the temperature susceptibility curve between 750° and 800°K.[34]

Germanium has been found to be pharmacologically inert and any significant toxicity of germanium compounds is due to other radicals in the molecules. The lethal dosage (L.D.$_{50}$) of $GeO_2$ injected intraperitoneally into rats is 750 mg/kg.[35]

Some special applications of germanium in the electrical area are described.

1. *Film resistors.* Germanium may be easily deposited as a film[36] by the decomposition of germane at above 370°C. Practical use is made of this property in the construction of film resistors. Magnesium germanide is formed by heating two parts of magnesium filings with three parts of germanium powder to red heat in an atmosphere of hydrogen. A 30 to 50% mixture of germane is obtained from the magnesium germanide by treatment with dilute hydrochloric acid. By decomposition of germane on a suitable surface of Pyrex glass, fused silica or dense ceramics, a film having high resistance characteristics is obtained.

Resistances measured over a 2.5-cm length of germanium film deposited inside 7-mm Pyrex tubing range from about 1000 ohms to several

[29] K. A. McCarthy and S. S. Ballard, *Phys. Rev.* 99, 1104 (1955).

[30] E. S. Rittner, *Phys. Rev.* 96, 1708 (1954); C. Kittel and A. H. Mitchell, *ibid.* 96, 1488 (1954).

[31] H. Krebs, *Angew. Chem.* 65, 293 (1953).

[32] P. H. Keck and W. Van Horn, *Phys. Rev.* 91, 512 (1953).

[33] M. E. Fine, *J. Chem. Phys.* 21, 1427 (1953); P. H. Keesom and N. Pearlman, *Phys. Rev.* 85, 730 (1952); Yü-Chan Hsieh, *ibid.*, 730; M. E. Fine, *J. Appl. Phys.* 24, 338 (1953).

[34] G. Busch and N. Helfer, *Helv. Phys. Acta* 27, 201 (1954).

[35] G. Rosenfeld and E. J. Wallace, *Arch. Ind. Hyg. Occupational Med.* 8, 466 (1953).

[36] T. R. Hogness and W. C. Johnson, *J. Am. Chem. Soc.* 54, 3583–3592 (1932).

megohms, depending upon the conditions of deposition. Such resistors have low-temperature coefficients, varying from 0.001 to 0.003 ohms/°C. Resistors with very low-temperature coefficients[37] can be made by depositing the germanium film over silver in a silvered Pyrex tube. Resistance values are lower, but temperature coefficients of less than 0.001 ohm/°C may be obtained in this way. This reduction of the temperature coefficient has been attributed to the formation of a eutectiferous alloy of silver and germanium with a temperature coefficient between that of the two metals.[38]

2. *Photoelectric effect.* Photosensitivity of germanium has been detected but the conditions and extent of this effect have not been definitely established.

3. *Microphone properties.* The resistance of a germanium powder compact will vary considerably with external pressure. Complete return to the original resistance after release of pressure does not result, however, and its possible application for microphone uses would seem to be limited by this factor.

**Alloys of Germanium.** Germanium forms a considerable number of alloys, among the most important of which are those with the coinage metals.

1. *Alloying.* Alloying of germanium may be carried out in air without too great a loss if chloride fluxes are used. Where control of composition is important, melting under hydrogen gives good results. Germanium does not form a carbide and may be melted in graphite crucibles with only minor contamination from the crucible.

2. *Gold alloys.* Germanium alloys with gold to form a gold-colored eutectic alloy having a minimum melting point at 356°C with a 12% germanium content. Alloying may be accomplished by bringing the two metals to the melting point of germanium, 960°C, in an atmosphere of hydrogen. Silicon forms a similar alloy with gold at 6% silicon, melting at 359°C, but it is more difficult to make since silicon does not dissolve readily in gold.

The Au–Ge alloy has good casting properties and good soldering characteristics for gold and copper alloys and for gold-plated articles. Because of its hardness it makes an excellent coating for gold or gold-plated articles and is easily applied by dipping the article in the molten Au–Ge eutectic alloy at 400° to 450°C. When used as a gold solder its

---

[37] R. I. Jaffee, E. W. McMullen, and B. W. Gonser, *The Electrochem. Soc. Preprint* 89–118 (1946).
[38] *Ibid.*

strength compensates for its lack of ductility, and joints soldered with this alloy deform in the metal without breaking the solder.

Germanium expands on solidification, and this valuable characteristic is evidenced in gold alloys with as little as 6% germanium. This expansion on solidification results in precision castings, and the alloy has been used for dental inlays with apparently good results.

3. *Silver alloys.* A eutectic alloy melting at 650°C is formed by silver and germanium with a germanium content of 18%. Alloys containing up to 6% tarnish more readily than pure silver.[39]

4. *Copper alloys.* Copper dissolves about 10% germanium. At higher germanium contents intermetallic compounds are formed. Germanium bronzes are not attacked by hydrochloric or sulfuric acids. If the germanium content is less than 25% the alloys are attacked by nitric acid. Alloys containing more than 25% germanium are dissolved only by aqua regia. The copper alloys are hard and become more brittle with increasing germanium content.

5. *Aluminum and magnesium alloys.* Germanium-aluminum alloys exhibit a eutectic point at 52% germanium; this eutectic melts at 423°C. It is claimed that the addition of germanium to aluminum increases the hardness to a greater degree than does the addition of silicon, and it is possible that germanium may at least partially replace silicon in alloys of the duralumin type.[40] The rolling properties of duralumin are said to be improved by the addition of small amounts of germanium. An alloy containing 74% Al, 21% Ge, 2% Fe, and 3% Si, capable of giving a strong secondary emission of electrons has been patented for use as a cathode material in electron tubes.[41]

The magnesium-germanium system yields two eutectic branches separated by the germanide, $Mg_2Ge$.

6. *Germanium-molybdenum system.* X-ray examination of the system Ge–Mo has identified the following phases: $Mo_3Ge_2$, $Mo_2Ge_3$, $\beta$-$MoGe_2$, and $\beta$-$MoGe_2$, as well as $Mo_3Ge$. There is no reaction of these phases with nonoxidizing acids or bases but they are readily attacked by $H_2O_2$ and $HNO_3$. They dissolve in fused pyrosulfates and react almost explosively with fused $NO_3^-$–$CO_3^=$ mixtures.[42]

7. *Germanium-manganese system.* Manganese forms a phase $Mn_5Ge_3$ with a B8 structure.[43]

[39] L. Jordan, L. H. Grenell, and H. K. Herschman, *Natl. Bur. Standards Technol. Paper 348* 21, 478–481 (1926–27).

[40] W. Kroll, *Metall. u. Erz.* 23, 682–685 (1926).

[41] *Soc. Fran. Radio-Electrique*, **Fr. Pat.** 845,087 (1939).

[42] A. W. Searcy and R. J. Peavler, *J. Am. Chem. Soc.* 75, 5659 (1953).

[43] L. Castelliz, *Monatsh.* 84, 765 (1953).

**Chemical Properties of Germanium.**    Germanium metal is not appreciably affected by water, 50% NaOH, concentrated HCl, 1:1 HCl or 1:1 $H_2SO_4$. The metal is tarnished by 10% NaOH and concentrated $HNO_3$. Dilute $HNO_3$ forms a coating of $GeO_2$ on the metal. Slight corrosion is observed with concentrated $H_2SO_4$ and with HF. The metal is dissolved by 3% hydrogen peroxide.

Hopkins[44] places germanium below hydrogen in the activity series since it will displace silver from its solutions but will not displace copper, mercury, tin, antimony, or bismuth. Einecke[45] places germanium between zinc and tin in the electromotive series. The activity of germanium is indicated by its rapid reaction with $NaNH_2$, liberating hydrogen.[46]

The electrochemical behavior of germanium is such that its presence causes considerable trouble in the electrolytic refining of zinc. It has been stated that a concentration of germanium as low as 1 mg/liter causes serious losses of efficiency in the zinc-refining process and that a concentration of 2 mg/liter interferes to the extent of preventing the deposition of zinc.[47] In the electrolytic zinc process the germanium is removed by adsorption on iron(III) hydroxide during leaching operation.

Germanium itself is only partially deposited by the electrolysis of acid solutions. It deposits electrolytically from alkaline solutions of the oxalate, tartrate, phosphate, carbonate, or hydroxide. The deposit is spongy in the presence of salts, but when it is plated from other solutions the deposit is bright and adheres well. It may be quantitatively deposited by careful control of conditions. A solution of $GeO_2$ in fused potassium or sodium carbonate also deposits germanium upon electrolysis.

**Chemical Compounds of Germanium.**    Germanium forms compounds in which the oxidation states are $+2$ and $+4$. Germanium(II) compounds are less common than those of germanium(IV). They are (with the exception of the sulfide) unstable and are easily oxidized or reduced.[48] Table 5.1 includes some of the thermodynamic properties of germanium compounds.

1. *Germanium monoxide, Germanium(II) oxide.*    Hydrous germanium monoxide may be prepared[49] by dissolving germanium dioxide in a slight

[44] B. S. Hopkins, *Chapters in the Chemistry of the Less Familiar Elements*, Vol. 1, Stipe Publishing Co. (1932).

[45] E. Einecke, *Chem. Ztg.* **61**, 989–991 (1937).

[46] R. Levine and W. C. Fernelius, *Chem. Revs.* **54**, 449 (1954).

[47] U. C. Tainton and E. T. Clayton, *Trans. Am. Electrochem. Soc.* **57**, 279 (1930).

[48] E. A. Boom, *Khim. Redkikh Elementov, Akad. Nauk S.S.S.R.* **1**, 121 (1954); O. H. Johnson, *Chem. Revs.* **51**, 431 (1952).

[49] L. M. Dennis and R. E. Hulse, *J. Am. Chem. Soc.* **52**, 3553–3556 (1930).

TABLE 5.1. SOME THERMODYNAMIC PROPERTIES OF GERMANIUM
AND ITS COMPOUNDS*

| | $\Delta H$, kcal/mole | $\Delta S$, cal/deg mole |
|---|---|---|
| Ge | | |
| Fusion, 1233°K.............................. | 8.3 | 6.7 |
| Sublimation†:    (Ge₁), 1150°K................ | 89 ± 2 | |
| Evaporation†:    (Ge₁), 1400°K................ | 79 ± 2 | |
| (Ge₂)........................ | 83 ± 3 | |
| (Ge₃)........................ | 81 | |
| (Ge₄)........................ | 70 | |
| Dissociation†:    (Ge₂)........................ | 75 | |
| GeH₄ | | |
| Transition:    C, III → C, II, 73.2°K........... | 0.050 | 0.68 |
| C, II → C, I, 76.5°K........... | 0.086 | 1.12 |
| Fusion:       C, I → deg., 107.26°K........... | 0.200 | 1.86 |
| Vaporization, 760 mm, 184.80°K............... | 3.361 | 18.19 |
| Ge₂H₆.......................................... | | |
| Vaporization, 760 mm, 304.0°K............... | 6.0 | 19.8 |
| Ge₃H₈.......................................... | | |
| Vaporization, 760 mm, 389.3°K............... | 7.7 | 20.0 |
| GeF₄ | | |
| Sublimation, 760 mm, 236.4°K................ | 7.8 | 33.0 |
| GeCl₄ | | |
| Vaporization, 760 mm, 356.3°K............... | 7.9 | 22.2 |
| GeHCl₃ | | |
| Vaporization, 760 mm, 348.5°K............... | 8.2 | 23.5 |
| GeF₂Cl₂ | | |
| Vaporization, 760 mm, 269°K................. | 5.9 | 21.9 |
| GeFCl₃ | | |
| Vaporization, 760 mm, 310.4°K............... | 6.6 | 21.3 |
| GeBr₄ | | |
| Vaporization, 760 mm, 187.1°K............... | 9.9 | 21.5 |

* *N.B.S. Circular 500.*
† R. E. Honig, *J. Chem. Phys.* **22**, 1610 (1954).

excess of 5 $N$ potassium hydroxide, adding sufficient hydrochloric acid
until the solution is about 5 $N$ with respect to HCl, then adding an excess
of 30% hypophosphorous acid and warming the mixture to 95°C for 2
hours.    Hydrous germanium monoxide is quickly oxidized by air, and
the filtering and washing procedures must be done in an inert atmosphere.
The hydrous germanium monoxide is completely dehydrated when it is
heated in nitrogen to 650°C.

Germanium monoxide is a jet-black crystalline substance which is inert
at room temperatures.    It is attacked only imperceptibly by hydrochloric
or sulfuric acids or by solutions of alkali hydroxides, but is slowly oxidized
by fuming nitric acid, potassium permanganate, or chlorine water.    It is

rather easily oxidized by an ammoniacal solution of hydrogen peroxide. Oxidation in dry air begins at 550°C.

When heated in an atmosphere of pure nitrogen, the monoxide sublimes at 710°C; when heated in nitrogen to a temperature above 500°C, germanium monoxide yields germanium dioxide and metallic germanium; when heated in boats of siliceous material, the monoxide reacts above 800°C to form yellow glazes.

It has been estimated that the $\Delta C_p{}^0$ value for GeO is $-3$ cal/deg mole and $\Delta S^0{}_{298}$ is 42 eu for the system: $1/2\text{Ge(s)} + 1/2\text{GeO}_2\text{(s)} \rightleftharpoons \text{GeO(s)}$. For the same reaction, except that gaseous GeO is formed, the average $\Delta H_o{}^0$ value is 54.1 kcal/mole and for the transition $\text{GeO(s)} \rightleftharpoons \text{GeO(g)}$, the calculated values of $\Delta H_o{}^0$ range from 46.8 to 49.0 kcal/mole.[50]

2. *Germanium dioxide.* Germanium dioxide is prepared by direct union of the elements, by igniting the sulfide, by oxidizing the sulfide with nitric or sulfuric acid, or by adding acids to dilute alkaline solutions of germanium salts. Germanium dioxide prepared from the sulfide has a solubility[51] of 0.447 g in 100 ml of water at 25°C. The aqueous solution of the oxide is acidic.

The properties of germanium dioxide vary greatly according to the method of preparation. The dioxide exists in two or possibly three forms.[52] When it is prepared by the hydrolysis of germanium tetrachloride or by the action of nitric acid on the sulfide, the germanium dioxide obtained dissolves with a hissing sound easily in HF, and it is appreciably soluble in water, aqueous ammonia, HCl, and NaOH. This modification exists as colorless polymorphic crystals which melt at 1116° ± 4°C and has a density of 3.61. When the dioxide is prepared by evaporating a water solution of germanic acid and heating the residue for some time at 380°C, an insoluble form is obtained. The transformation from the soluble form to the insoluble modification is slow, and only about 20% of the material is changed to this form at each heating. The unchanged soluble modification may be removed from the heated residue by extraction with boiling water. Almost all of the $GeO_2$ can be converted to the insoluble form by several repetitions of the original procedure.

The insoluble form is not only insoluble in water, but it is also unaffected by HF, HCl, NaOH or ammonia. It is obtained as a white powder or as tetragonal crystals which melt at 1086° ± 5°C and has a density of 6.00.

[50] W. L. Jolly and W. M. Latimer, *J. Am. Chem. Soc.* **74**, 5757 (1952).
[51] W. Pugh, *J. Chem. Soc.* **1929**, 1537.
[52] J. H. Müller and H. R. Blank, *J. Am. Chem. Soc.* **46**, 2358 (1924).

All forms of germanium dioxide fuse in the neighborhood of 1100°C to a viscous liquid which solidifies to a glass whose density is 3.30. This behavior is also characteristic of silicon dioxide.

Germanium dioxide readily forms colloidal systems. A germanium dioxide gel has been prepared by hydrolyzing germanium tetraethoxide, $Ge(OC_2H_5)_4$, with the calculated amount of water in alcoholic solution[53] according to a method developed for preparing silicon dioxide gels.[54] The germanium dioxide gel was found to have an adsorptive power for the vapors of benzene, ethyl ether, and carbon tetrachloride, comparable with that of silica gel.

Germanium(IV) oxide reacts with hypophosphoric acid in a medium of a hydrohalogen acid, such as HI, to form $3Ge(H_2PO_2)_2 \cdot GeI_2$, $GeHPO_3$, and $Ge_3(PO_4)_2 \cdot GeHPO_4$. A solution of $GeO_2$ in $H_3PO_4$ treated with $H_3PO_2$ gives $Ge(HPO_4)_2$. Prolonged heating of $GeI_2$ with 90% $H_3PO_2$ in contact with air gives a product that may be $Ge(H_2PO_2)_4$.[55] In none of the compounds formed in these reduction reactions is there evidence for $Ge^{II}$ in solution.

The reaction between $GeO_2$ and metallic germanium has been studied in terms of the equilibrium: $Ge(s) + GeO_2 \rightleftharpoons 2GeO(g)$ by vapor pressure technique (using a Knudsen effusion cell) at 758° to 859°K. Thermodynamic constants for the above equilibrium system (based on the formation of 1 mole of germanium) are reported as: $\Delta F^0 = 54,600 + 6.9T \log T - 62T$ cal/mole; $\Delta H^0 = 54,600 - 3T$ cal/mole; $\Delta S^0 = 59 - 6.91 \log T$ cal/deg mole. The heat of formation of $GeO_2$ (solid) is $-129 \pm 2.0$ kcal/mole.[56]

3. *Germanium(II) hydroxide.* Germanium(II) hydroxide, $Ge(OH)_2$, is precipitated when a solution of an alkali is added to a solution of germanium(II) chloride. It is soluble in an excess of the alkali. When first precipitated it is cream colored; it becomes red when it is heated. It has been suggested that a possible explanation for the color change is a tautomeric shift, in which the $Ge(OH)_2$ changes from a basic compound to an acidic compound:

$$Ge\genfrac{}{}{0pt}{}{\diagup OH}{\diagdown OH} \rightleftharpoons H{-}Ge\genfrac{}{}{0pt}{}{\diagup\!\!\diagup O}{\diagdown OH}$$

[53] A. W. Laubengayer and P. L. Brandt, *ibid.* **54**, 549 (1932).
[54] A. W. Dearing and E. E. Reid, *ibid.* **50**, 3058 (1928).
[55] D. A. Everest, *J. Chem. Soc.* **1953**, 4117.
[56] W. L. Jolly and W. M. Latimer, *J. Am. Chem. Soc.* **74**, 5757 (1952).

The acid form, when viewed in this manner, appears as an analogue of formic acid. It may be obtained by the hydrolysis of trichlorogermane,

$$HGeCl_3 + 2H_2O \rightarrow H-Ge \overset{O}{\underset{OH}{\big\backslash}} + 3HCl$$

This acid is sometimes called germanous acid and sometimes germano-formic acid. In the interests of consistency and simplicity it has been urged that germano-formic acid be called germanoic acid, conforming to the system of nomenclature used for carbon compounds in which formic acid is methanoic acid. Germanoic acid is slightly weaker as an acid than acetic acid.

4. *Germanium(II) sulfide.* Germanium(II) sulfide may be obtained from germanite as a lustrous-black, leafy sublimate.[57] It may also be prepared as a reddish-brown precipitate by the reduction of either germanium dioxide or germanium(IV) sulfide.[58] The GeS prepared by the latter method is a red amorphous powder which is readily soluble in HCl but only slightly attacked by $H_2SO_4$, $H_3PO_4$, or organic acids. It is oxidized by air above 350°C or by nitric acid, hydrogen peroxide, potassium permanganate, chlorine, or bromine. Germanium(II) sulfide is the most stable germanium(II) compound known and may be melted and vaporized without decomposition. It is slightly soluble in water and dissolves in alkalies and in yellow ammonium sulfide.

5. *Germanium(IV) sulfide.* Germanium(IV) sulfide, $GeS_2$, is a white powder obtained by bubbling $H_2S$ through a solution of a germanium(IV) salt or by adding an excess of strong mineral acid to a solution of GeS in ammonium sulfide. It dissolves slightly in water but hydrolyzes with the evolution of $H_2S$. Thermodynamic constants have been reported on the germanium sulfides (formed by direct combination) through a study of the dissociation pressures and hydrogen reduction of $GeS_2$ and GeS. For the system: $GeS_2 + H_2 \rightleftharpoons GeS + H_2S$, the value of $K_p = (H_2S)/H_2$, $\log K_p = - (4876/T) + 4.951$, $\Delta F^0 = 22,303 - 22.65T$. For the system $GeS + H_2 \rightleftharpoons Ge + H_2S$, $K_p' = (H_2S)/(H_2)$, $\log K_p' = - (2113/T) + 0.773$, $\Delta F^0 = 9665 - 3.536T$. These values, when combined with known values for $H_2S$, give the dissociation pressures, and the standard free-energy changes the dissociation of solid germanium

[57] W. C. Johnson, L. C. Foster, and C. A. Kraus, *ibid.* **57**, 1828–1831 (1935); E. Gastinger, *Z. Naturforsch.* **10b**, 115 (1955).
[58] *Inorganic Synthesis*, Vol. II, 104 (1946), McGraw-Hill Publishing Co., New York.

sulfides for the systems: $2GeS_2 \rightleftharpoons 2GeS + S_2$; $\log p_{S_2} = - (19.138/T)$ $+ 15.002$, $\Delta F^0 = 87,540 - 68.62T$ and $2GeS \rightleftharpoons 2Ge + S_2$; $\log p_{S_2}' = - (13,612/T) + 6.646$, $\Delta F^0 = 62,260 - 30.40T$.[59]

6. *Germanium(II) chloride.* Germanium(II) chloride, $GeCl_2$, is prepared[60] by passing $GeCl_4$ vapor over powdered metallic germanium at 430°C. In thin layers $GeCl_2$ appears as a white solid. The white color deepens through cream to light yellow as the layer becomes thicker. Decomposition begins at 75°C *in vacuo* and, as the temperature increases, the color changes through cream, lemon yellow, orange, reddish brown, dark brown, and finally, at 450°C, to black, at which point decomposition into $GeCl_4$ and metallic germanium is complete. Because of this ease of decomposition the compound cannot be sublimed. The ionic radius of $Ge^{++}$ is reported as 0.93 A.[61]

Germanium(II) chloride is insoluble in, or reacts with, many of the usual solvents. It is not affected by 95% ethanol or by chloroform. It is fairly soluble in $GeCl_4$. It hydrolyzes readily. Ammonia converts it into an orange-colored substance. Concentrated hydrochloric acid changes it to a white solid which soon dissolves in the acid with the probable formation of trichlorogermane.

Germanium(II) chloride is acted upon slowly by dry oxygen. After about 15 minutes of contact with the gas, the dichloride begins to turn white from the formation of germanium dioxide, and volatile $GeCl_4$ is given off. Chlorine rapidly converts $GeCl_2$ into $GeCl_4$, while bromine gives $GeCl_4$ and $GeBr_4$ without more than a trace of mixed halide being formed. Hydrogen sulfide reacts readily with the dichloride at room temperature to yield germanium(II) sulfide and HCl.

7. *Germanium(IV) chloride.* Germanium tetrachloride may be prepared by burning the metal in chlorine, by heating the metal or its disulfide with mercury(II) chloride, or by the reaction between germanium dioxide and hydrochloric acid. This latter method[62] is convenient since germanium dioxide is very easy to obtain and no special apparatus or technique is required.[63] Germanium tetrachloride is a colorless, mobile liquid with a density of 1.88. It boils at 83.1°C and freezes at −49.5°C. It fumes in air and is hydrolyzed with a crackling sound. It is stable but not very soluble in 6 $N$ hydrochloric acid. It dissolves in many organic solvents, such as ether and benzene, and readily enters into Grignard

[59] K. Ono and K. Sudo, *Bull. Research Inst. Mineral Dressing and Met., Tohoku Univ.* **10**, 181 (1954).
[60] L. M. Dennis and L. H. Hunter, *J. Am. Chem. Soc.* **51**, 1151 (1929).
[61] K. B. Yaksimirskii, *J. Gen. Chem. U.S.S.R.* **23**, 1851 (1953).
[62] Clemens Winkler, *J. Prakt. Chem.* **142**, 187 (1886).
[63] *Inorganic Synthesis*, Vol. II, 109 (1946), McGraw-Hill Publishing Co.

reactions. The tetrachloride serves as a starting material for the tetra-alkyl germanium compounds by its reaction with sodium in the presence of the appropriate alcohol.[64]

Hydrogen reduction of $GeCl_4$ in quartz at 900° to 1000°C results in the formation of a germanium(I) chloride. This compound forms on the cooler portions of the vessel as a light-yellow condensate and as a dark-brown material on hotter portions. Analysis gives $GeCl_{0.75-0.90}$ and the compound is probably $(GeCl)_x$. There are no X-ray lines corresponding to elemental germanium nor to $GeCl_2$. When heated for 90 hours at 210°C at low pressures, the monochloride is converted to $GeCl_4$ and some yellow $GeCl_2$. There is a slight decomposition on treatment with NaOH. It is decomposed by 6% $H_2O_2$, hydrolyzed by dilute acids, stable in cold concentrated $HNO_3$, forms a hydroxide with $NH_3$, is insoluble in organic solvents, explodes when flamed directly, but stable in vacuum to 370°C.[65]

8. *Germanium(IV) bromide.* Germanium tetrabromide, $GeBr_4$, has been prepared by treating heated metallic germanium with bromine vapor.[66] This method is laborious and an easier one involves the treatment of dioxide directly with hydrobromic acid; the yield is about 90%.[67] Germanium(IV) bromide is a colorless liquid which fumes on contact with air. It melts at 26.1°C and boils at 186°C. It shows the property of supercooling to a marked degree and may be chilled to as low a temperature as −18°C before it solidifies. It is soluble in absolute alcohol, carbon tetrachloride, benzene, and ether. It dissolves in acetone, but slow decomposition takes place with the evolution of bromine.

9. *Germanium(II) iodide.* Germanium(II) iodide, $GeI_2$, is prepared[68] by treating powdered germanium(II) sulfide with a large excess of hydriodic acid. It is golden brown to burnt orange in color and crystallizes in hexagonal plates. It is stable if kept dry but hydrolyzes slowly in the presence of moisture. The iodide is not oxidized by dry air. It disproportionates to Ge and $GeI_4$. It is only slightly soluble in benzene. The compound may also be prepared by reducing the tetrachloride with $H_3PO_2$ in an aqueous HI medium (*vide infra*). The iodide plates out as a yellow material which may be washed with hydrogen iodide solution and dried over $P_2O_5$.[69] On treatment with $CH_3I$ at 110°C, yellow $CH_3GeI_3$ is formed (mp 48°–50°C).

[64] O. H. Johnson and H. E. Fritz, *J. Am. Chem. Soc.* **75**, 718 (1953).
[65] R. Schwarz and E. Baronetzky, *Z. anorg. allgem. Chem.* **275**, 1 (1954).
[66] L. M. Dennis and F. E. Hance, *J. Am. Chem. Soc.* **44**, 299 (1922).
[67] A. W. Laubengayer and P. L. Brandt, *ibid.* **54**, 621 (1932).
[68] *Inorganic Syntheses*, Vol. II, 107 (1946), McGraw-Hill Publishing Co.
[69] L. S. Foster, *ibid.*, Vol. III (1950), p. 63.

The standard enthalpy change for the reaction:

$$GeI_2(solid) + I_3^- + 3H_2O \rightleftharpoons H_2GeO_3(aq) + 4H^+ + 5I^-$$

is $-26.0 \pm 1.0$ kcal/mole. From this value and solubility data on $GeO_2$, thermodynamic constants for the reaction

$$H_2O + GeO_2(ppt) \rightleftharpoons H_2GeO_3(aq)$$

have been reported as: $\Delta H^0 = +3.3 \pm 1.0$ kcal/mole; $\Delta F^0 = 1.86$ kcal/mole for the solution of $GeO_2$; and $\Delta S^0 = 4.7 \pm 3.4$ eu. For the reaction

$$2H_2O + GeI_2(solid) + I_3^- \rightleftharpoons GeO_2(solid) + 4H^+ + 5I^-$$

the value of $\Delta H^0$ is $-29.3 \pm 1.4$ kcal/mole.[70]

The force constant $k_e \times 10^{-5}$ dyne/cm for Ge-I has been established as 1.605. This value is higher than 1.464, predicted by a study of the ratio $k(AB)/k(AX)$ where A represents a Group IV element; B a Group VI element, and X a Group VII element from the same series as B.[71]

10. *Germanium(IV) iodide.* This compound is conveniently prepared[72] by the reaction of germanium dioxide with an excess of hydriodic acid. It is a reddish-orange solid which crystallizes in the cubic system. It decomposes above 440°C but readily sublimes in a vacuum at 100°C. It is soluble in carbon disulfide, benzene, methyl alcohol, chloroform, and many other organic solvents. It is ammonolyzed to germanium(IV) imide by liquid ammonia.

The heat and entropy of sublimation of $GeI_4$ can be represented by: $\Delta H^0 = 22{,}500 - 8T$ and $\Delta S^0 = 82.8 - 8 \ln T$. At 298°K, these functions have the values: $\Delta F^0 = 9.0$ kcal/mole, $\Delta H^0 = 20.1$ kcal/mole, and $\Delta S^0 = 37$ eu.[73]

11. *Germanium(IV) fluoride.* Germanium(IV) fluoride, $GeF_4$, is obtained as the trihydrate when a solution of $GeO_2$ in hydrofluoric acid is evaporated over sulfuric acid. $GeF_4 \cdot 3H_2O$ exists in the form of hygroscopic crystals which readily dissolve in water with slow hydrolysis. Mixed fluorides are obtained by the fluorination[74] of $GeCl_4$ with $SbF_3$ in the presence of $SbCl_3$. The compounds $GeFCl_3$, $GeF_2Cl_2$, $GeF_3Cl$, and $GeF_4$ have been obtained in this manner.

[70] W. L. Jolly and W. M. Latimer, *J. Am. Chem. Soc.* **74**, 5752 (1952).
[71] S. S. Metra, *J. Chem. Phys.* **22**, 2097 (1954); Y. P. Varshni, *Current Sci.* **22**, 199 (1953).
[72] *Inorganic Syntheses*, Vol. II, 112 (1946), McGraw-Hill Publishing Co.
[73] W. L. Jolly and W. M. Latimer, *J. Am. Chem. Soc.* **74**, 5754 (1952).
[74] H. S. Booth and W. C. Morris, *ibid.* **58**, 90 (1936).

Germanium reacts with $NO_2F_2$ (prepared from $NaNO_2$ and $F_2$) to give a white solid, $(NO_2)_2GeF_6$, at room temperature.[75] Force constants and the spectrum of germanium tetrafluoride have been reported.[76]

12. *Germanic acids and germanates.* Solutions of $GeO_2$ are slightly acidic. It has been proved that, at pH values in the range 8.4 to 8.8, the ion $Ge_5O_{11}^=$ exists in solution (rather than $GeO_3^=$) and the acid dissociation constant of $H_2Ge_5O_{11}$ is about $10^{-9}$. It has also been reported that $H_2Ge_5O_{11}$ exists only in the condensed state with $H_2GeO_3$ and that the dissociation constants for both acids are about equal.[77] An evaluation[78] of the true isohydric point vs the pseudoisohydric point seems to refute this claim with regard to condensation. Water-containing samples of $GeO_2$ do not contain a fixed amount of water as evidenced by heating for prolonged periods at 55°C. Apparently certain of the heat stable hydrates previously reported do not exist, at least as the molecule $H_2Ge_5O_{11}$. Water appears to be simply absorbed.[79] Melting point diagrams have indicated the existence of ortho-, meta-, di-, and tetra-germanates: $Li_4GeO_4$ (mp 1298°C), $Li_2GeO_3$ (mp 1239°C); $Na_2GeO_3$ (mp 1083°C); $Na_2Ge_2O_5$ (mp 799°C; and $Na_2Ge_4O_9$) (mp 1052°C).[80] The $Ge_5O_{11}^=$ ion is reported as being more stable than the $B_4O_7^=$, $As_3O_5^-$ and $As_2O_4^=$ ions from studies made on the effect of strong acids on the weak acids involving these ions.[81] Basic ion exchangers are reported to absorb the $Ge_5O_{11}^=$ ion in solutions of pH about 9. At pH values above and below 9, absorption diminishes, indicating lower stages of polymerization. It is assumed that above 9 the species $HGeO_3^-$ exists.[82]

A diphenolgermanic acid, $H_2Ge(C_6H_4O_2)_3$, is formed from diphenol and germanium dioxide.[83]

13. *Germanium-nitrogen compounds.* Germanium tetrachloride reacts with ammonia to form an imide, $Ge(NH)_2$. One heating to temperatures about 150°C, this compound is converted to $Ge_2N_3H$, and on further heating the nitride, $Ge_3N_4$, results. A nitride, $Li_5GeN_3$, is prepared by heating the individual binary nitrides to 850° to 1300°C. It is light in color, saltlike, and easily hydrolyzed. It crystallizes in the superstructure

[75] E. E. Aynsley *et al.*, *J. Chem. Soc.* 1954, 1119.
[76] L. K. Akers and E. A. Jones, *Phys. Rev.* 91, 236 (1953).
[77] G. Carpeni, *Bull. soc. chim. France* 1952, 1010.
[78] P. Souchay, *ibid.* 1953, 395.
[79] G. Brauer and H. Renner, *Z. anorg. allgem. Chem.* 278, 108 (1955).
[80] H. Remy, *Treatise on Inorganic Chemistry*, Vol. I, Elsevier Publishing Co., 1956, p. 521; H. Nowotny and A. Wittmann, *Monatsh.* 85, 558 (1954).
[81] P. Souchay and M. Teyssedre, *Compt. rend.* 236, 1965 (1953).
[82] E. A. Everest and J. E. Salmon, *J. Chem. Soc.* 1954, 2438.
[83] P. Bevillard, *Compt. rend.* 235, 880 (1952).

of the fluorspar lattice.   A mixed oxonitride, $Li_5GeN_3 + Li_2O$, results when germanium nitride is heated at 800° to 1100°C with $Li_2O$.[84]

14. *Magnesium germanide.*   Magnesium germanide, $Mg_2Ge$, may be prepared by heating germanium powder with fine magnesium turnings in an atmosphere of hydrogen.   The germanide is of interest principally for its value in the preparation of various hydrides of germanium.

15. *The germanes or germanium hydrides.*   In common with the other elements of Group IVA, germanium forms several known hydrides. These substances are known collectively as the germanes and individually as monogermane, or simply germane, digermane, trigermane, and so on; the prefix indicates the number of germanium atoms in the molecule. These germanes correspond to the alkanes of carbon chemistry and have the general formula $Ge_nH_{2n+2}$.

Monogermane is said to be obtained in yields of better than 70% by treating magnesium germanide with $NH_4Br$ in liquid ammonia.[85]   Purification is accomplished by bubbling the gases through a solution of sodium in liquid ammonia.   This treatment also reduces the higher germanes to the monogermane.   Germane of 99.7% purity is claimed by this method.

Digermane, $Ge_2H_6$, and trigermane, $Ge_3H_8$, have been isolated from the mixture of germanes obtained when magnesium germanide is treated with hydrochloric acid.[86]   The properties of the first three members of the series are given in Table 5.2.

TABLE 5.2.   THE PROPERTIES OF THE GERMANES

| Property | Germane | Digermane | Trigermane |
|---|---|---|---|
| Formula.................. | $GeH_4$ | $Ge_2H_6$ | $Ge_3H_8$ |
| Density, gas, g/liter......... | 3.42 | 6.75 | 10.08 |
| Density, liquid, g/cc........ | 1.523 at −142°C | 2.02 at −109°C | 2.20 at −105.6°C |
| Melting point, °C........... | −165 | −109 | −105.6 |
| Boiling point, °C........... | −90 | 29 | 110.5 |

16. *Germanium monohydride.*   Although no germanium compounds corresponding to the alkenes or alkynes of carbon are known, it is possible that the germanium monohydride, $(GeH)_x$, prepared by the reaction of sodium germanide with water, may belong to one of these groups.[87]   The

[84] R. Juza, *Z. anorg. allgem. Chem.* **273**, 48 (1953).
[85] C. A. Kraus and E. S. Carney, *J. Am. Chem. Soc.* **56**, 765 (1934); R. A. Ballinger and N. H. March, *Nature* **174**, 179 (1954).
[86] L. M. Dennis, A. B. Corey, and R. W. Moore, *J. Am. Chem. Soc.* **46**, 657 (1924).
[87] L. M. Dennis and N. A. Skow, *ibid.* **52**, 2369 (1930).

compound is a dark-brown solid which instantly dissociates with an explosive puff when the dry, or nearly dry, substance is brought into contact with air. In an inert gas or *in vacuo* the compound dissociates slowly. The monohydride is a strong reducing agent and unites with free halogens to form compounds of the type $GeX_4$.

**Organo Germanium Compounds.** The formation of organo-metallic compounds is an outstanding characteristic of the Group IV$A$ elements. The hydrogen atoms of the germanes may be replaced by various organic groups. Although the number of organo-germanium compounds isolated and investigated so far is less than 150, the number of such compounds is potentially large, and new compounds are being prepared and studied in increasing numbers.

Many of the tetraalkyl derivatives of germane have been prepared and there is reason to believe that any normal alkyl compound of this nature can be prepared. In the case of the isoalkyl radicals and the larger aryl groups, it has been found that steric effects are encountered with some of the larger groups.[88] Only a few of the alkyl and aryl derivatives of digermane and trigermane have been prepared.

Germanols (germanium alcohols) are unstable and only triphenyl germanol has been prepared. Germanoic acids tend to lose water readily and the anhydride appears to be the stable form. No germanium compounds analogous to the silicones have yet been prepared.

[88] O. H. Johnson and W. H. Nebergall, *ibid.* **71**, 4022 (1949).

# CHAPTER 6

## TIN

**History.** Tin has been known since ancient times. The metal itself was known and used, and bronze (an alloy of tin and copper) was in very common use. Objects made of tin have been found in early Egyptian tombs. Tin was brought to the Romans from the Cornish mines after Caesar's conquest of Britain.

Although tin was not used by the ancients to the same extent as lead, many of its properties were known. The influence of tin in alloying was so marked that it was sometimes called "diabolus metallorum," the devil of metals, because its presence made other metals hard and brittle.

**Occurrence.** The principal ore of tin is cassiterite, or tinstone, $SnO_2$. Its most important deposits occur in southwestern Asia. Table 6.1

TABLE 6.1. TIN CONTENT OF ORE FROM PRINCIPAL PRODUCERS (1939)

| Producer | Tin Content (long tons) |
|---|---|
| Malay States | 54,914 |
| Netherlands East Indies | 31,281 |
| Bolivia | 27,211 |
| Thailand (Siam) | 16,991 |
| Nigeria | 10,855 |

shows the tin content of the ore mined in the principal producing areas. The world production amounted to 181,000 long tons in 1939, the last year in which there was normal peacetime production preceding World War II.[1]

There is practically no production of tin in the United States because of lack of domestic deposits. Thus, this country is almost completely dependent on a relatively few overseas sources of tin. An important step toward lessening the dangers inherent in this dependence on distant sources of supply was taken in 1939 when Congress passed the Strategic Materials Act providing for the purchase of stock piles of this and other essential materials. In 1941 the United States government contracted with Bolivian interests for the annual purchase of tin ore concentrates equivalent to 18,000 short tons of refined metallic tin. This ore has been processed by the Tin Processing Corporation at a $3,500,000 smelter,

NOTE. The authors are indebted to Dr. O. H. Johnson for portions of this chapter.

[1] See *Chem. and Eng. News* **34**, 5666 (1956); *ibid.* **32**, 44 (1954).

known as the Longhorn Smelter, built for the purpose at Texas City, Texas. The Texas City (Longhorn) Tin Smelter[2] was invaluable during World War II and in the period from January 1, 1945, to November 30, 1945, produced 36,916 long tons of tin, principally from Bolivian ores with some Belgian Congo crude metal and ore concentrate. Consumption of tin in the United States[3] during the war years is given in Table 6.2.

TABLE 6.2. UNITED STATES CONSUMPTION OF TIN

| Year | Total Consumption (long tons) | Consumption of Primary Metal (long tons) |
|---|---|---|
| 1941.................... | 135,789 | 107,551 |
| 1942.................... | 86,096 | 56,862 |
| 1943.................... | 81,840 | 53,137 |
| 1944.................... | 90,352 | 61,926 |
| 1945 (est.).............. | 95,000 | 65,000 |

By primary metal is meant new tin recently smelted from ore. Total consumption includes tin recovered from scrap from various sources. Of the 143,548 long tons[4] produced in the United States during the three years, 1942–44, only 15 tons were from domestic ore. The United States normally consumes 40 to 50% of the world output. Because of the changes in the world economic conditions the United States consumption of new tin for the years following 1946 is expected to be over 100,000 tons of new tin, or 60 to 70% of the world production. The production in British Columbia in 1952 exceeded 1,000,000 lb.[5]

Prices for a fifty-year period varied from a low of 13.67 cents per lb in 1897 to a high of 88.75 cents per lb in 1918. During World War II the price was controlled and established at 52 cents per lb.

**Metallurgy.** Tin ores must generally be concentrated before reduction, inasmuch as their tin(IV) oxide content amounts to only about 1 to 5%. Lighter rock, such as silica, is washed away with water or by flotation in an oil froth. The next operation depends upon the source of the ore. Since $SnO_2$ is not magnetic, it may be freed from tungsten minerals and other magnetic impurities by means of magnetic separation. Other impurities may be removed by roasting, which volatilizes sulfur

[2] R. H. Ramsey, *Eng. Mining J.* **144**, No. 6, 56–61 (1943); F. S. Miller, *Symposium on Tin, ASTM Spec. Tech. Publ. No.* **141**, 3–20, 21–24 (1952); J. W. Cuthbertson, *Metallurgia* **48**, 277 (1953); *Tin News, The Malayan Tin Bureau*, Sept. 1954; *ibid.*, Oct. 1954.

[3] *Ibid.* **147**, 78–79 (1946).

[4] *Econ. Geol.* **41**, 308–327 (1946).

[5] *Chem. and Eng. News* **33**, 516 (1955).

and arsenic and converts metals, such as bismuth, zinc, iron, and copper, into their oxides. These oxides are subsequently removed by solution in sulfuric or hydrochloric acid. Tin(IV) oxide, $SnO_2$, is then reduced by carbon in a reverberatory furnace:

$$SnO_2 + 2C \rightarrow Sn + 2CO$$

The crude product is refined by liquation, a process which consists in cautiously heating the impure metal on a hearth until the readily fusible tin melts and flows away from the less easily fusible impurities.

Tin in a state of spectroscopic purity is prepared by converting the crude tin to the tetrachloride. The $SnCl_4$ is multiply distilled, mixed with sulfuric acid and separated, again distilled, converted to sodium stannate, and finally electrolyzed at 25 amp/sq dm. It is reported that tin of this purity is transformed to the α-modification at −30°C in 4 hours.[6] A high quality nonspongy form of tin has been plated from scrap in a system of a rotating bipolar drum electrode packed loosely with scrap, submerged in an alkaline aqueous solution (5% in NaOH) at 70° to 87°C for 1 to 5 hours at 2.7 to 3.9 v and 2.5 amp. The rotating drum is suspended between the anode and the cathode, above but not touching the anode. Anodic oxygen passing up through the scrap aids in the detinning operation.[7]

The Longhorn Smelter at Texas City[8] was located at that site for three primary reasons: (1) the availability of HCl as a waste product of nearby plants, (2) an adequate local supply of natural gas for heating the furnaces, and (3) the accessibility of the site by short and safe routes to Bolivian sources of tin ore.

The ore concentrates handled by this particular smelter are divided into three classes. Class A ore contains 50 to 60% tin with relatively small amounts of iron, antimony, and silica. Class B ore ranges from 40 to 50% tin with more impurities, and Class C ore has from 18 to 35% tin and contains considerable silica, iron as limonite, and other impurities.

**Properties.** Tin has three crystalline forms. The following diagram shows their relationship and transition temperatures:

$$\text{Cubic (gray or } \alpha) \xrightleftharpoons{18°} \text{tetragonal (white or } \beta) \xrightleftharpoons{161°} \text{rhombic } (\gamma) \xrightleftharpoons{231.9°} \text{liquid}$$

Density 5.75       Density 7.28       Density 6.56

The conversion of ordinary or tetragonal to cubic or gray tin does not

---

[6] K. Smirous, *Czechoslov. J. Phys.* **3**, 176 (1953).
[7] F. A. Lowenheim, **U. S. 2,665,473**, Oct. 13, 1953; see also section on *Tin(IV) Halides*.
[8] R. H. Ramsey, *Eng. Mining J.* **144**, No. 6, 56–61 (1943).

take place except at low temperatures or when gray tin is present. When once started, it proceeds rather rapidly. This conversion causes the tin to crumble to a powder, and, because of the consequent destruction of tin objects, the change is known as the *tin disease* or the *tin plague*. Although the change does not generally occur until the temperature falls rather far below the transition temperature, once it has begun it continues at any temperature below 18°C. Gray tin has a cubic lattice like that of the diamond.

Alpha-tin is an intrinsic semiconductor with an activation energy of 0.1 ev. The absolute value of the conductivity at 0°C is $5 \times 10^3$ ohm$^{-1}$ cm$^{-1}$.[9] The stability of gray tin is enhanced by the introduction of 0.75 weight per cent of germanium.[10]

The molecular weight of tin vapor in the temperature range 1600° to 1900°K is 91 ± 29 as determined by the Knudsen effusion method. The heat of sublimation of tin at 298°K is calculated to be 71.9 ± 2.0 kcal.[11] The specific heat of both tin and lead over a wide range in temperature from heating and cooling data has been reported. The data are found in Table 6.3.[12]

Certain of the properties of tin (and lead) have been studied at high pressures. The melting point of tin at 33,000 kg/sq cm is 315°C and that for lead is 527°C. In the pressure range of 8000 to 12,000 kg/sq cm, the average rise in melting temperature of tin is 2.9°C and that for lead is 6.8°C. In the range 20,000 to 30,000 kg/sq cm, the rise is 2.2°C for tin and 5.4°C for lead.[13]

As is true with most metals, the properties of tin vary depending upon the presence of small amounts of metal impurities.[14]

At ordinary temperatures tin is scarcely changed in air or in water; at higher temperatures a film of oxide forms over the surface. At white heat tin burns to the dioxide, which is yellow when hot and white when cold. The metal is acted on slowly by dilute acids, giving tin(II) salts

[9] G. Busch *et al.*, *Semi-conducting Materials* 1951, 188; G. Busch and E. Mooser, *Helv. Phys. Acta* 26, 611 (1953).

[10] A. W. Ewald, *J. Appl. Phys.* 25, 1436 (1954); U. Dehlinger and H. Schenk, *Z. Physik* 136, 344 (1953); E. R. Thews, *The Properties of Tin*, Greenford, Eng. Tin Research Inst., 1954, 55 pp.

[11] A. W. Searcy and R. D. Freeman, *J. Am. Chem. Soc.* 76, 5229 (1954); the value 70 ± 2 kcal/mole is also reported by L. Brewer and R. F. Porter, *J. Chem. Phys.* 21, 2012 (1953).

[12] G. M. Bartenev, *Uchenye Zapiski Moskov. Gosudarst, Univ. im. M. V. Lomonosova*, No. 134, Fiz. No. 5, 113, 126 (1949).

[13] V. P. Butozov and M. G. Gonikberg, *Doklady Akady. Nauk S.S.S.R.* 91, 1083 (1953).

[14] C. Mantell, *ASTM Spec. Tech. Pub. No. 141*, 57 (1953).

TABLE 6.3. THE SPECIFIC HEAT OF TIN AND LEAD

| Temperature, °C | Specific Heat, cal/g/deg | |
| --- | --- | --- |
| | Heating | Cooling |
| TIN | | |
| 50 | 0.0550 | 0.0552 |
| 100 | 0.0580 | 0.0580 |
| 150 | 0.0616 | 0.0620 |
| 166 | 0.0650 | 0.0650 |
| 185 | 0.0640 | 0.0642 |
| 200 | 0.0665 | 0.0672 |
| 250 | 0.0600 | 0.0600 |
| 300 | 0.0592 | . . . |
| 350 | 0.0584 | . . . |
| LEAD | | |
| 50 | 0.0312 | 0.0302 |
| 100 | 0.0331 | 0.0317 |
| 142 | 0.0380 | 0.0356 |
| 165 | 0.0340 | 0.0330 |
| 200 | 0.0347 | 0.0340 |
| 300 | 0.0365 | 0.0361 |
| 350 | 0.0408 | 0.0425 |
| 400 | 0.0394 | 0.0400 |

and hydrogen.   Concentrated nitric acid gives a hydrated tin(IV) oxide often called metastannic acid.   Tin dissolves in hot alkali hydroxides, forming stannates with the liberation of hydrogen.   Tin, as well as mixtures of tin, aluminum, and zinc, reduces $NaNO_3$ in the presence of $Ba(OH)_2$ at temperatures near the melting point of the base.   Ammonia is evolved.   With NaOH the reduction product is NO in the early stages with $NH_3$ finally being formed.   It is assumed that the reduction is due to [H] formed from the tin and the hydroxide ion.[15]

**Uses.**   Table 6.4 shows the uses of tin to be varied in character.   The principal use of tin is in the manufacture of tin plate.   In making this product, sheets of iron or steel, whose surface has been carefully cleaned by *pickling* in acid, are dipped into molten tin and then rolled to uniform thickness.   These tin-coated sheets (tin plate) find their greatest application in the making of the tin cans used for the storage and shipment of foods.   *Terneplate*, a heavier variety coated with a tin-lead alloy, is used

[15] J. Datta, *J. Indian Chem. Soc.* **29**, 465 (1952).

TABLE 6.4. Uses and Consumption (in Long Tons) of Tin

| Uses | Consumption | Uses | Consumption |
|---|---|---|---|
| Tin plate | 23,545 | Terneplate | 1,007 |
| Solder | 12,798 | Tin(IV) oxide (SnO₂) | 991 |
| Babbit metal | 4,157 | Pipes and tubing | 948 |
| Bronzes | 3,932 | Foil | 879 |
| Collapsible tubes | 3,427 | Galvanizing | 669 |
| Tinning | 1,773 | White metal | 434 |
| Type metal | 1,112 | Miscellaneous alloys | 257 |
| Chemicals | 1,076 | Miscellaneous | 478 |

as a roofing material. Solder, Babbitt metal, and other alloys (Table 6.5), foil, tubes, and chemicals use about half of the tin consumed. Block tin (pure tin) pipes are inert to the action of water. This property makes them suitable for use in soda fountains and in distilled water supply systems.

TABLE 6.5. Approximate Composition of Some Tin Alloys

| Alloy | Composition | | | | |
|---|---|---|---|---|---|
| | Sn | Cu | Pb | Sb | Bi |
| Pewter | 80 | | 20 | | |
| Gun metal (bronze) | 10 | 90 | | | |
| Type metal, standard | 26 | 1 | 58 | 15 | |
| Rose metal | 22.9 | | 27.1 | | 50 |
| Solder (soft) | 50 | | 50 | | |
| Antifriction | 75 | 12.5 | | 12.5 | |
| Babbitt metal | 89 | 3.7 | | 7.3 | |
| Bell metal | 22 | 78 | | | |
| Tinfoil | 88 | 4 | 8 | 0.5 | |
| White metal | 5 | 1 | 75 | 19 | |
| Bronze (speculum metal) | 33 | 67 | | | |
| Medal bronze | 1–8 | 92–7 | (0–2 Zn) | | |

The mechanism of corrosion within a sealed can is quite different from that of the process of corrosion of tin plate in the air.[16] Tin is considerably below iron in the electromotive series. When the tin-iron couple is exposed to a corrosive agent under normal conditions, the tin is unaffected while the iron is attacked. But, conditions are different inside a food can. In particular the supply of oxygen is limited and, after it has been absorbed in the first superficial attack on the tin plate, the conditions reverse in that the tin becomes anodic and thereafter acts as an

[16] J. Ireland, *Metallurgia* **31**, 75–79 (1944).

anticorrosion agent.[17]    It not only protects the steel by covering it but also exerts a potential which prevents direct attack on exposed steel.    This peculiar property of tin is an important factor in the success of tin plate in hermetic food containers and explains, in large part, the unsatisfactory performance of substitutes for this coating.

Necessary economies in the use of tin during World War II directed attention to the development of electrolytic tin plating.    By this process the amount of tin per unit of surface is reduced to about one half that required for hot dipped plate.[18]

The Tin Research Institute has developed a process for rustproofing tin cans by simply immersing them in a hot oxidizing solution.    This solution reacts superficially with the tin and with the iron at the exposed pores and forms an invisible oxide film which imparts greatly increased resistance to rusting.    The process shows great promise.

One of the metallurgical developments arising out of the shortage of tin has been the introduction of silver-lead and silver-lead-tin solders. At first much was expected from these so-called Argent solders since it was found that 1 to 2% of silver increased the fluidity of the molten solder so greatly that as much as 10% of tin could be omitted without loss of fluidity.    Continued use, however, showed that while silver contributed materially to an increase in fluidity, it also lessened the tendency of the solder to join two solid pieces of metal.    Tin appears to have a unique ability to wet the common engineering metals and to be the active and essential element in effecting a soft-soldered joint.

An important advance in the tinning of cast iron has resulted from wartime research.    It was formerly believed that hot-dipped tin coatings on cast iron were invariably inferior and that it was not practical to bond a white-metal bearing directly to cast iron.    It was the practice formerly, when a firm union between tin alloy and cast iron was required, to give the cast iron a preliminary coating of iron or copper.    Through the use of a low-temperature bath of fused salts, it is now possible to obtain a very satisfactory coating directly on cast iron.    Some success has been achieved in plating tin on aluminum using $SnCl_2$ as a cationic solution, or $K_2SnO_3$ or $Na_2SnO_3$ as an anionic solution.[19]

Speculum metals, or alloys of 40 to 45% Sn and the rest copper, are

[17] *Ibid.*

[18] R. M. Burns and W. W. Bradley, "Protective Coatings for Metals," 2nd Edition, *Am. Chem. Soc. Monograph No.* **129**. New York, Reinhold Publishing Corp., 1955; C. F. Powell *et al.*, *Vapor-Plating*, John Wiley and Sons, Inc., New York, 1955; A. Foschini, *Z. anal. Chem.* **139**, 408 (1953).

[19] J. M. Bryan, *Metal. Ind.* **83**, 461 (1953).

of renewed interest. Speculum is a difficult alloy to cast and fabricate. Application of electroplating techniques to speculum metal permits its use as a decorative finish on baser metals. The plate has a color and appearance closely resembling silver, has high reflecting qualities, and lacks the cold bluish tint associated with chromium plate. Speculum plate has considerable resistance to tarnish and will remain bright for a long period indoors. It is not recommended for outdoor use. It is electroplated by using separately controlled tin and copper anode circuits in a hot sodium stannate solution which also contains sodium cyano-cuprate(I) and an excess of NaOH and NaCN.

World War II research on substitutes for tin has only established the value of this metal more firmly and has brought on increased consumption through the development of new uses.

**General.** Tin forms two series of compounds: Tin(II) compounds, in which the valence of the element is +2, and tin(IV) compounds, in

TABLE 6.6. SOME THERMODYNAMIC PROPERTIES OF TIN AND ITS BINARY COMPOUNDS

| | | | $\Delta H$, kcal/mole | $\Delta S$, cal/deg mole |
|---|---|---|---|---|
| Sn | | | | |
| Transition: | (gray) → (white), 291°K | | 0.6 | 2.1 |
| | (white) → C, I, 476.0°K | | 0.002 | 0.004 |
| Fusion: | C, I → liq., 505.1°K | | 1.69 | 3.35 |
| SnO₂ | | | | |
| Transition: | C, II → C, I, 683°K | | 0.45 | 0.66 |
| SnH₄ | | | | |
| Vaporization: | 760 mm, 221.4°K | | 4.4 | 19.9 |
| SnCl₂ | | | | |
| Fusion: | 520°K | | 3.0 | 5.8 |
| Vaporization: | 760 mm, 896°K | | 21. | 23. |
| SnCl₄ | | | | |
| Fusion: | 239.9°K | | 2.19 | 9.13 |
| Vaporization: | 760 mm, 386°K | | 8.3 | 21.5 |
| SnBr₂ | | | | |
| Fusion: | 505°K | | 1.7 | 3.4 |
| Vaporization: | 760 mm, 911°K | | 22. | 24. |
| SnBr₄ | | | | |
| Fusion: | C, II → liq., 303°K | | 3.0 | 9.9 |
| Vaporization: | 760 mm, 478°K | | 10. | 21. |
| SnI₂ | | | | |
| Vaporization, 760 mm, 991°K | | | 24. | 24. |
| SnI₄ | | | | |
| Fusion: | 417.7°K | | 4.48 | 10.73 ($\Delta C_p = 5.7$) |
| Vaporization: | 760 mm, 617°K | | 13.6 | 22. |

which it has an oxidation state of +4. The lower oxide, SnO, is basic, giving tin(II) salts with acids, but it is also somewhat acidic and dissolves in alkalies to form stannites. Tin(IV), oxide, $SnO_2$, is also amphiprotic but is more acidic than basic. Tin(II) compounds readily pass by oxidation into tin(IV) compounds, and are consequently often used as reducing agents. Some thermodynamic properties of tin compounds are found in Table 6.6.

**1. Tin(II) Oxide, SnO.** Tin(II) oxide may be obtained as a gray powder by heating tin with a limited supply of air, and as a black powder by heating tin(II) oxalate, $SnC_2O_4$, out of contact with air:

$$SnC_2O_4 \rightarrow SnO + CO + CO_2$$

Tin(II) oxide changes to the dioxide when heated in air.

Tin(II) oxide has been identified in two allotropic modifications, blue-black $\alpha$-form and a high temperature $\beta$-modification, formed when the $\alpha$-SnO is heated in a vacuum to 550°C. When heated in air to 300°C there is oxidation to $SnO_2$. At 200°C SnO forms with fluorine two layers over the base material. The upper layer is $SnF_4$ and the lower is $SnO_2$. The nature of these layers has been identified by X-ray analysis. At 500°C the only product[20] is $SnF_4$. The monoxide is more volatile than either metallic tin or the dioxide.

The hydrated oxide, precipitated by the addition of an alkali metal hydroxide to a solution of tin(II) chloride, is readily soluble in an excess of the hydroxide to form a *stannite*. When sodium hydroxide is used, the crystals of sodium stannite obtained have the formula $Na[Sn(OH)_3]$. This substance is unstable at ordinary temperatures and decomposes to yield metallic tin as one of the products. The reaction for the formation of an alkali metal stannite probably takes place because of the following behavior of hydrated tin(II) oxide in the presence of the hydroxide ions:

$$[Sn(OH)_2(H_2O)] \rightleftharpoons H[Sn(OH)_3]$$

$$H[Sn(OH)_3] + H_2O \rightleftharpoons [Sn(OH)_3]^- + H_3O^+$$

The stannite ion is usually given the formula $HSnO_2^-$; this differs from the above complex by one molecule of water. The dissociation constant for

$$K = \frac{[Sn(OH)_3^-][H^+]}{[Sn(OH)_2]}$$

is $4 \times 10^{-10}$.

[20] H. M. Haendler et al., J. Am. Chem. Soc. **76**, 2179 (1954).

**2. Tin(II) Sulfide, SnS.** When tin and sulfur are heated together, a gray crystalline mass of tin(II) sulfide is formed:

$$Sn + S \rightarrow SnS$$

It is precipitated from a solution of a tin(II) salt by hydrogen sulfide as a dark-brown powder:

$$Sn^{++} + H_2S + 2H_2O \rightarrow SnS \downarrow + 2H_3O^+$$

The sulfide is insoluble in water and scarcely soluble in colorless ammonium sulfide. It dissolves in the polysulfides because of their oxidizing action, forming the thiostannates:

$$SnS + S_2^= \rightarrow SnS_3^=$$

Tin(II) sulfide, as well as tin(IV) sulfide, is rapidly fluorinated at temperatures as low as 25°C to give $SnF_4$.[21] When heated in hydrogen, SnS sublimes readily. The potential of metallic tin and SnS in saturated sodium chloride solution have been determined as $-0.466$ v and $-0.460$ v, respectively. There is no time dependence of the potential.[22]

**3. Tin(II) Halides.** Anhydrous tin(II) chloride is best formed by conducting hydrogen chloride over heated tin. From a solution in hydrochloric acid the dihydrate, $SnCl_2 \cdot 2H_2O$, crystallizes. This compound is known commercially as *tin salt*. It can be dehydrated by heating in a current of HCl gas. It is used in analytical work as a reducing agent. It converts mercury(II) chloride into mercury(I) chloride or free mercury. Tin(II) chloride reduces iron(III) salts to iron(II) salts:

$$Sn^{++} + 2Fe^{+3} + 6Cl^- \rightarrow [SnCl_6]^= + 2Fe^{++}$$

It reduces gold(III) chloride, $AuCl_3$, in dilute solution to *Purple of Cassius*, possibly colloidal gold. Tin(II) chloride hydrolyzes readily. Tin(II) chloride auto-oxidizes to the tetrachloride, the process possibly being catalyzed by chloride ion. It may also be that [Cl] is formed as an intermediate in the process.[23] Large quantities of $SnCl_2$ are used in the weighting of fabrics.

The other tin(II) halides are well known and characterized. Their behavior is similar to that of the chloride. Tin(II) bromide forms two hypophosphite derivatives: $3Sn(H_2PO_2)_2 \cdot SnBr_2$ (mp 150°C) and

[21] *Ibid.*
[22] N. S. Fortunatov and V. I. Mikhailovakaya, *Ukrain. Khim. Zhur.* **16**, 667 (1951).
[23] E. Abel, *Monatsh.* **85**, 949 (1954).

$Sn(H_2PO_2)_2 \cdot SnBr_2$ (mp 175°C). A corresponding iodide compound is known, $3Sn(H_2PO_2)_2 \cdot SnI_2$ (mp 135°C).[24]

Considerable interest has been evidenced in the use of tin(II) fluoride in dentifrices as an agent for decreasing the incidence of dental caries. A dentifrice analyzing 3.2 ppm Sn and 1.000 ppm fluoride has been proved effective for children in the age group of 6 to 15. It has also been reported that an unbuffered 2% solution of $SnF_2$ is significantly better than an unbuffered 2% NaF solution.[25] The $SnF_2$-treated enamel has a definite resistance to HCl solution action.[26]

**4. Tin(II) Sulfate, $SnSO_4$.** This compound crystallizes from a solution prepared by the action of tin on a mixture of concentrated sulfuric acid and nitric acid. The salt is water soluble. Up to approximately 0.2 $M$ $H_2SO_4$ there exist in solution $Sn^{++}$ ions and $SnSO_4$ according to a number of physicochemical measurements. At higher concentrations of sulfuric acid (0.3 to 0.6 $M$) there is some evidence for complexes,[27] as $[Sn(SO_4)_2]^=$ and $[Sn(SO_4)_3]^{-4}$.

**5. Tin(IV) Oxide, $SnO_2$.** In its oxidation state of $+4$, tin usually acts as an acid-forming element. As noted, the dioxide, $SnO_2$, is more acidic than basic in its chemical behavior. The dioxide occurs naturally as cassiterite. It is formed when the metal burns in air and when the hydroxide is ignited. If tin(IV) oxide is fused with alkalies, soluble stannates are formed:

$$2NaOH + SnO_2 \rightarrow Na_2SnO_3 + H_2O$$

Stannates are also formed by the addition of an excess of a solution of an alkali to a solution of tin(IV) chloride.

Tin(IV) oxide does not react with fluorine below 300°C to form the tetrafluoride; however, at 400°C the conversion is 80% complete.[28] With $N_2O_5$ the dioxide reacts to form $Sn(NO_3)_4$ and with $Cl_2O_6$ to form $SnCl_2(ClO_4)_2$ and $Sn(ClO_4)_4 \cdot 2Cl_2O_6$.[29]

**6. Tin(IV) Halides.** The chloride is prepared by the action of chlorine on metallic tin:

$$Sn + 2Cl_2 \rightarrow SnCl_4$$

[24] D. A. Everest, *J. Chem. Soc.* **1954**, 4698.

[25] J. C. Muhler *et al.*, *J. Dental Research* **33**, 606 (1954); C. L. Howell *et al.*, *J. Am. Dental Assoc.* **50**, 14 (1955).

[26] Y. Ericsson, *Acta Odontol. Scand.* **9**, 60 (1950).

[27] C. A. Discher, *J. Electrochem. Soc.* **100**, 480 (1953).

[28] H. M. Haendler *et al.*, *J. Am. Chem. Soc.* **76**, 2179 (1954).

[29] M. Schmeisser, *Angew. Chem.* **67**, 493 (1955).

It is a colorless liquid, boiling at 114.1°C. On cooling it forms a colorless solid which melts at −33°C. It fumes strongly in moist air. It dissolves in water with the evolution of a great deal of heat and undergoes hydrolysis. A number of solid hydrates, those with three, four, five, and eight molecules of water, have been identified. The pentahydrate is the most usual one.

Tin(IV) chloride is a compound of considerable importance in industry because its formation offers a means of reclaiming tin from scrap plate. Treatment of the latter with dry chlorine yields the relatively volatile tin(IV) chloride much more readily than it does iron(III) chloride. The separation of the two chlorides by fractional distillation is easy because their boiling points lie far apart.[30] Tin(IV) chloride boils at 114.1°C, whereas iron(III) chloride boils at 315°C.

The properties of the anhydrous chloride, such as its low melting point and inability to conduct the electric current, point to a nearly covalent molecule. Indeed, the existence of the ion, $Sn^{+4}$, in significant amounts *in solution* is questionable.

Sulfuryl chloride, $SO_2Cl_2$, serves as a good solvent for the covalent $SnCl_4$. The latter acts as a weak solvo–(chloride acceptor) acid, forming the ion $[SnCl_6]^=$. Conductometric titrations of $SnCl_4$ (an acid) by an alkyl ammonium chloride (solvo-base) result in the formation of such compounds as $(Me_4N)_4[SnCl_8]$, $(Me_4N)_3[SnCl_7]$, and $(Me_4N)_2[SnCl_6]$. Phosphorus(V) chloride (as a solvo-base) forms $(PCl_4)_4[SnCl_8]$ and $(PCl_4)_2[SnCl_6]$.[31]

The mechanism for the hydrolysis of a covalent halide such as $SnCl_4$ must be different from the hydrolysis of an ionic halide. The first step in the hydrolysis of tin(IV) chloride involves the coordinative addition of two molecules of water (see below). This reaction is logical because the $Sn^{IV}$ is coordinatively unsaturated, and by means of this addition of water the metal is enabled to attain its stable coordination maximum of six. It is of interest to note here the importance of the coordination of water as the initial step in hydrolysis. Thus, compounds such as carbon tetrachloride, $CCl_4$, sulfur hexafluoride, $SF_6$, and osmium octafluoride, $OsF_8$, are not hydrolyzed because the coordination maximum of the central element has been attained in each case, and therefore the initial additive step does not take place. On the other hand, tungsten hexachloride, $WCl_6$, is hydrolyzable inasmuch as the coordination maximum for tungsten is 8. A mechanism for the hydrolysis of tin(IV) chloride is

[30] B. Chatterjee, *Science and Culture (India)* **20**, 193 (1954).
[31] V. Gutmann, *Monatsh.* **85**, 393, 404 (1954).

the following:

$$SnCl_4 + 2 H_2O \longrightarrow [SnCl_4(H_2O)_2] \rightleftharpoons H_2[SnCl_4(OH)_2]$$
$$\quad -HCl$$

$$H[SnCl_3(OH)_2] \xrightarrow[\text{of } H_2O]{\text{addition}} [SnCl_3(OH)(H_2O)_2] \rightleftharpoons H_2[SnCl_3(OH)_3]$$
$$\quad -HCl$$

$$H[SnCl_2(OH)_3] \xrightarrow[\text{of } H_2O]{\text{addition}} [SnCl_2(OH)_2(H_2O)_2] \rightleftharpoons H_2[SnCl_2(OH)_4]$$
$$\quad -HCl$$

$$H[SnCl(OH)_4] \xrightarrow[\text{of } H_2O]{\text{addition}} [SnCl(OH)_3(H_2O)_2] \rightleftharpoons H_2[SnCl(OH)_5]$$
$$\quad -HCl$$

$$H[Sn(OH)_5] \xrightarrow[\text{of } H_2O]{\text{addition}} [Sn(OH)_4(H_2O)_2] \rightleftharpoons H_2[Sn(OH)_6]$$

The isolation of all of the intermediate products postulated in this hydrolysis appears, at the present time, to be impossible. However, the first addition product, $SnCl_4 \cdot 5H_2O$ or $[SnCl_4(H_2O)_2] \cdot 3H_2O$, and the product of the first step in the hydrolysis, $SnCl_3(OH) \cdot 3H_2O$ or $[SnCl_3(OH)(H_2O)_2] \cdot H_2O$, are both known.

Tin(IV) chloride reacts with fluosulfonic acid, $HSO_3F$, to give a 2:1 mixture of the compounds $SnCl_3(SO_3F)$ and $SnCl_2(SO_3F)_2$.[32] The tetrachloride forms 1:2 complexes with oxygen-containing molecules such as $H_2O$, EtOH, $Et_2O$, and $Me_2CO$ as well as 1:3 complexes with $H_2O$ and EtOH. The last mentioned type of complex (with $H_2O$ and EtOH) is ionic in nature while the first (1:2 ratio) is covalent as evidenced by low melting points and solubility in organic solvents. The 1:2 complexes are active as catalysts for styrene polymerization.[33]

The other tetrahalides are all known and characterized. They may be prepared by direct union of the elements. Thus, mossy tin and fluorine react to form $SnF_4$ above 190°C.[34] The addition of KI to $SnCl_4$ results in the precipitation of yellowish crystals of $SnI_4$. Complete exchange between iodine and $SnI_4$ (in $CCl_4$ medium) has been reported in less than 7 seconds.[35]

[32] F. Hayek et al., ibid. 85, 359 (1954).
[33] T. R. E. Devlin and D. C. Pepper, Cationic Polymerisation and Related Complexes 1952, 24–26, 26–27; Chem. and Eng. News 34, 5671 (1956).
[34] H. M. Haendler et al., J. Am. Chem. Soc. 76, 2179 (1954).
[35] M. Kahn and A. J. Freedman, ibid. 76, 929 (1954).

**7. Stannates and the Tin(IV) Acids.** The higher hydroxide of tin would be expected to have the formula $Sn(OH)_4$ and to be acidic in character, but neither the acid nor salts derived from it have been found. The *stannates* which do exist appear to be derived from the final product of the hydrolysis of tin(IV) chloride inasmuch as the solid salts, such as the alkali stannates, are of the composition indicated by the general formula, $M_2^{+1}O \cdot SnO_2 \cdot 3H_2O$. In the case of the sodium salt this may be written as $Na_2[Sn(OH)_6]$. In view of the formation of $Na_2SnO_3$, obtained by fusing tin(IV) oxide with sodium hydroxide, the formula for the stannate ion has generally been given as $SnO_3^{=}$. However, in the light of the composition of the solid stannates, and because of the known tendency of ions to become hydrated, it is preferable to consider the stannate ion in aqueous solution in the hydrated form as $[Sn(OH)_6]^{=}$. This is equivalent to $(SnO_3 \cdot 3H_2O)^{=}$.

As stated, there is no conclusive evidence for the existence of $Sn(OH)_4$, but there are two different forms of an acid whose simplest formula is $H_2SnO_3$. They are the *metastannic acids*. A substance of this composition could be derived from $Sn(OH)_4$ by the loss of a molecule of water:

$$Sn(OH)_4 - H_2O \rightarrow H_2SnO_3$$

The addition of a solution of ammonia to one of tin(IV) chloride produces a white, gelatinous precipitate of $\alpha$-stannic acid. It is readily soluble in acids, in alkalies, and in the alkali carbonates. $\beta$-stannic acid is obtained as a white powder by the action of concentrated nitric acid on tin. Unlike the $\alpha$-acid, it is insoluble in acids, and in concentrated alkali hydroxides and carbonates. The $\alpha$-form may be converted into the $\beta$-acid, but the reverse change has not been accomplished. X-ray examinations of the freshly prepared tin(IV) acids reveal an irregular arrangement of the molecules in each of the forms. The sodium and potassium stannates are used in electroplating. The latter gives a superior plate.

**8. Tin(IV) Sulfide, $SnS_2$.** If hydrogen sulfide is passed into a slightly acid solution of a tin(IV) salt, a bright-yellow precipitate of tin(IV) sulfide is obtained:

$$SnCl_4 + 2H_2S + 4H_2O \rightarrow SnS_2 \downarrow + 4H_3O^+ + 4Cl^-$$

This compound is insoluble in water and very dilute acids but dissolves readily in ammonium and sodium sulfides, forming thiostannates:

$$SnS_2 + S^= \rightarrow SnS_3^=$$

**9. Hexachlorostannic(IV) Acid, $H_2SnCl_6 \cdot 6H_2O$.** Colorless hygroscopic crystals (mp 19°C) of this substance may be obtained by the action of gaseous hydrogen chloride on a hydrate of tin(IV) chloride. The acid itself is of no practical importance, but ammonium hexachlorostannate(IV), $(NH_4)_2SnCl_6$, is well known as a mordant for silk. Although it is white in color it is known as *pink salt*.

**10. Other Tin(IV) Salts.** Tin(IV) sulfate, $Sn(SO_4)_2$, and tin(IV) nitrate, $Sn(NO_3)_4$, have been prepared. They hydrolyze rapidly in aqueous solution.

**11. The Stannanes or Tin Hydrides.** Only one tin hydride, $SnH_4$, is known. It is prepared by the hydrolysis of magnesium stannide:

$$Mg_2Sn + 4H_2O \rightarrow 2Mg(OH)_2 + SnH_4 \uparrow$$

Stannane is also prepared by treating $SnCl_2$ in HCl dropwise with 5% solution of $NaBH_4$. A gaseous mixture results. Water is first trapped at $-23°C$. A second cold-trapping at $-196°C$ is used, followed by distillation of the resulting liquid. The $SnH_4$ is removed at $-112°C$ at 84% purity.[36]

Stannane melts at $-150°C$ and boils at $-52°C$. It is relatively stable at ordinary temperatures when stored in clean vessels. Its decomposition is catalyzed by traces of metallic tin.

**Organo-Tin Compounds.** Its position in the periodic arrangement of the elements would indicate that tin could form a large number of organo-metallic derivatives. Thus numerous substituted stannanes, as $Sn(CH_3)_4$, are found. These compounds form mono-, di-, and trihalogen substitution products as well as the more familiar tetrahalogen compounds. Although polystannanes, hydrides containing more than one tin atom, have not been isolated, alkyl and aryl substitution compounds corresponding to these hydrides, such as hexaethyldistannane, $(C_2H_5)_6Sn_2$, have been prepared.

Stannoic acids, such as $CH_3SnOOH$, are known. Methylstannoic acid is prepared by the interaction of alcoholic methyl iodide with the potassium hydrogenstannite:

$$CH_3I + KHSnO_2 + KOH \rightarrow CH_3SnOOK + KI + H_2O$$

The free acid is obtained by passing carbon dioxide through its solution or by just neutralizing the alkaline solution with hydrochloric acid. The acid is a white infusible solid which decomposes on heating to give tin(II) and tin(IV) oxides, methane and methyl alcohol.

The stannoic acids are convenient starting materials for making the trihalogen compounds or stanniforms, by simply dissolving the weak

[36] G. W. Schaeffer and Sister M. Emilius, *J. Am. Chem. Soc.* **76**, 1203 (1954).

stannoic acids in stronger halogen acids:

$$RSnOOH + 3HX \rightarrow RSnX_3 + 2H_2O$$

Thus when methyl stannoic acid is dissolved in hydrochloric acid, methyl tin trichloride, $CH_3SnCl_3$, is obtained as colorless, deliquescent crystals, melting at 40°C. Methyl tin tribromide, melting at 52°C, and methyl tin triiodide, melting at 82°C, have been prepared in the same way.

Organo-tin oxides, or stannones, corresponding to ketones are known. $(CH_3)_2SnO$ is a typical example. Tin alcohols, or stannols, are also known and may be obtained from the stannoic acids by distilling the latter with caustic alkalies:

$$3CH_3SnOOH + 4KOH \rightarrow (CH_3)_3SnOH + 2K_2SnO_3 + 3H_2O$$

These compounds, which have strong and unpleasant odors, dissolve in the hydrohalogen acids to give monohalogen derivatives, such as $(CH_3)_3SnBr$.

# CHAPTER 7

## LEAD

**History and Occurrence.** Lead has been known since early historic times and is mentioned in the Bible in Job and in Numbers. Lead was used by the ancient Egyptians, and lead water pipes were commonly used by the Romans. Stained glass in the windows of the great cathedrals of the Middle Ages was set in lead. The metal was also widely employed as a roofing material.

*Galena*, PbS, is the most important mineral of lead. Less common minerals containing the element are *cerrusite*, $PbCO_3$, *anglesite*, $PbSO_4$, *pyromorphite* (green lead ore), $PbCl_2 \cdot 3Pb_3(PO_4)_2$, *mimetesite*, $PbCl_2 \cdot 3Pb_3(AsO_4)_2$, *stolzite*, $PbWO_4$, and *crocite*, $PbCrO_4$. Lead is sometimes found free in nature. Lead ores are widely distributed over the United States and in many other parts of the world. The 1946 mine production of lead in the United States is given in Table 7.1.

TABLE 7.1. MINE PRODUCTION OF LEAD IN THE UNITED STATES*

|  | Short Tons |
|---|---|
| Eastern States | 5,550 |
| Central States | 165,770 |
| Western States | 161,158 |
| Total U. S. production | 332,478 |

\* U. S. Bureau Mines, Mineral Market Report, MMS. No. 1491 (1947).

TABLE 7.2. REFINED LEAD PRODUCTION IN THE UNITED STATES*

|  | 1945 Short Tons | 1946 Short Tons |
|---|---|---|
| From domestic ores and base bullion | 356,535 | 293,309 |
| From foreign ores | 86,932 | 44,790 |
| From foreign base bullion | 118 | 98 |
| Total from primary sources | 443,585 | 338,197 |
| From scrap | 18,525 | 8,013 |
| Total refined lead | 462,110 | 346,210 |
| Average sales price per pound | $0.064 | $0.084 |
| Total calculated value of primary lead (exclusive of refined lead from scrap) | $56,778,880 | $56,817,096 |

\* U. S. Bur. Mines, Mineral Market Report, MMS. No. 1549 (1947).

NOTE. The authors are indebted to Dr. O. H. Johnson for selected portions of this chapter.

Table 7.2 gives the refined lead production in the United States for the years 1945 and 1946. Table 7.3 gives the world production for 1945 and 1946.[1]

TABLE 7.3. WORLD PRODUCTION OF LEAD*

| Area | Lead Content of Ore Produced at Mines<br>Long tons × 1000 | Smelter Production. Refined Lead Without Lead from Scrap<br>Long tons × 1000 |
|---|---|---|
| Europe | | |
| Belgium............... | . . . | 86.0 |
| France................ | 5.0 | 39.0 |
| Germany............... | 96.0 | 185.2 |
| Great Britain........... | 30.2 | 11.0 |
| Italy................. | 41.0 | 43.3 |
| Spain................ | 32.0 | 36.0 |
| U.S.S.R. in Europe....... | 19.0 | 19.0 |
| Others................ | 108.8 | 37.9 |
| Total in Europe......... | 332.0 | 457.4 |
| Asia | | |
| Burma................ | 89.9 | 81.4 |
| Japan................. | 12.0 | 12.0 |
| Korea................ | . . . | 10.0 |
| U.S.S.R. in Asia......... | 50.0 | 50.0 |
| Others................ | 16.9 | 2.4 |
| Total in Asia.......... | 171.8 | 155.8 |
| Africa (Total)............. | 63.9 | 27.3 |
| America | | |
| Mexico................ | 282.4 | 219.6 |
| Canada................ | 190.0 | 182.9 |
| United States........... | 331.4 | 336.0 |
| Others................ | 120.2 | 36.0 |
| Total in America....... | 924.0 | 774.5 |
| Australia (Total)........... | 278.8 | 227.3 |
| World Production.......... | 1770.5 | 1642.2 |

* W. Hofmann, *Blei und Bleilegierungen*, Edwards Bros., Ann Arbor, Mich. (1944).

**Metallurgy.** Lead ores are usually concentrated by a flotation method which also serves to separate zinc sulfide from galena. The

[1] See also *Chem. and Eng. News* **34**, 5666 (1956); *ibid.* **32**, 45 (1954).

flotation recipes are carefully formulated from mixtures of alcohols, thio-organic compounds, pine oil, and certain electrolytes to permit differential flotation of sulfides. The addition of KOH to an xanthate flotation mixture favors the combination of lead minerals (which would otherwise be inert) with the agent.[2] Aerofloat No. 25 added into the pulp mixture permits differential flotation of minerals in the order of galena, zinc blende, chalcopyrite, and finally pyrite.[3]

A part of the concentrate from flotation is roasted in air to convert the sulfide into the oxide and the sulfate:

$$2PbS + 3O_2 \rightarrow 2PbO + 2SO_2$$
$$PbS + 2O_2 \rightarrow PbSO_4$$

Much of the sulfur is eliminated as sulfur dioxide in this treatment. The roasted ore is then mixed with raw ore, limestone, coke, and sometimes a little iron ore, and smelted in a blast furnace. A number of reactions, some of them not definitely known, take place. Those leading directly to the formation of lead may be given as follows:

$$PbO + C \rightarrow Pb + CO$$

or

$$2PbO + C \rightarrow 2Pb + CO_2$$
$$PbO + CO \rightarrow Pb + CO_2$$

The galena in the raw ore acts as a reducing agent with lead oxide and lead sulfate:

$$PbS + 2PbO \rightarrow 3Pb + SO_2$$

and

$$PbS + PbSO_4 \rightarrow 2Pb + 2SO_2$$

Iron obtained as a result of the reduction of its ore also acts as a reducing agent:

$$PbS + Fe \rightarrow Pb + FeS$$

The limestone removes siliceous matter as a fusible slag of calcium silicate, while a molten *matte* containing the sulfides of iron and copper along with some lead is separated and subjected to further treatment for the removal of the lead. The molten lead tapped off from the furnace is subjected to a refining process. Copper, antimony, arsenic, bismuth, gold, and silver are often present in crude lead.

[2] S. V. Bessonov, *Izvest. Akad. Nauk S.S.S.R., Otdel. Tekh. Nauk* **1954**, No. 9, 108.
[3] M. Wada and K. Sawano, *Bull. Research Inst. Mineral Dressing Met. Tohoku Univ.* **8**, 15 (1952).

There has been much increased efficiency of lead smelting operations in recent years, but the improvements in smelting have been brought about by improvements in technique and changes in smelter design rather than by the introduction of any new metallurgical principles.[4] These improvements have resulted in reworking much of the discarded slag from earlier operations, in the saving of much additional metal for war requirements, and in the recovery of other valuable metals, particularly zinc.

**Refining of Lead.** Lead from the blast furnace is called *hard* lead because of the effect of the alloyed metals. This lead is melted and then stirred to promote the oxidation of antimony, arsenic, bismuth, and copper. These metals oxidize more readily than lead, and their oxides rise to the surface as dross. The softened lead, still containing bismuth, gold, and silver, is drained off for further treatment by one or the other of two methods.

1. *The Parkes process.* This process represents one of the many applications of the principle of partition to the solution of industrial problems.[5] It takes advantage of the fact that gold and silver are far more soluble in molten zinc than in lead. Zinc to the amount of 1 to 2% is stirred into molten crude lead. After a time the stirring is discontinued and the zinc is allowed to rise to the top of the molten mass to form a layer containing most of the gold and silver present in the crude lead. The zinc layer is then skimmed off and the operation is repeated a number of times. Gold and silver are separated from the zinc by distilling off the latter metal in retorts. The recovered zinc is then used to extract more gold and silver.

2. *The Betts process.* In this process the lead is refined by electrolysis. Thin sheets of pure lead are made the cathodes in a cell, heavy plates of crude lead the anodes, while the electrolyte is a solution of lead fluosilicate, $PbSiF_6$, containing 8 to 12% fluosilicic acid, $H_2SiF_6$, and a very small amount of gelatine. Addition of the latter causes a more coherent lead deposit. Silver and the other impurities adhere in part to the anode while the remainder collects as a slime (anode mud) at the bottom of the cell. The anode is scraped from time to time to remove the undissolved impurities. This deposit and the anode mud are worked to recover the metals they contain. The Betts process is well suited for the treatment

[4] V. Tafel, *Lehrbuch der Metalhüttenkunde, Bd. II*, 2nd Edition, 1953, 760 pp., Leipzig; H. Thompson, *Lead Handbook for the Chemical Process Industries*, Am. Smelting and Refining Co., New York, 1954, 44 p.; G. Heuser, *Metall.* 9, 675 (1955).

[5] T. D. de Souza Santos, *ABM (Bol. assoc. brasil. metais) (Sao Paulo)* 9, 219, 235 (1953); J. Feiser et al., *Z. Erzbergbau u. Metallhüttenw.* 7, 1 (1954); T. R. A. Davey, *J. Metals* 6, *AIME Trans.* 200, 838 (1954); L. Fagnani, *Metallurgia ital.* 46, 211 (1954).

of lead whose bismuth content exceeds about 2%. However, it is more expensive than the Parkes process and does not afford as complete recovery of the precious metals.

**Electrolytic refining.** Lead may be deposited in a satisfactory fashion from a number of electrolytes. Electrodepositions with high cathodic polarization at small current densities have been observed by adding tartaric acid and powdered Bakelite to sodium plumbate, $Na_2PbO_3$ solution.[6] Deposition from a sulfamic acid solution (as lead sulfamate) has proved successful with the best deposits formed when aniline, phenol, or resorcinol was added. A shift of the deposition potential in the negative direction with aniline as an additive indicates a strong absorption.[7]

Improvements in refining during the past few years have also taken the form of improved design and increased efficiency of old methods rather than any revolutionary change in principles.

**Properties.** Lead is a soft metal with a bluish-gray color when freshly cut. The bright luster soon disappears due to the formation of a film of oxide. Ordinary lead is a mixture composed principally of the isotopes 208 and 206. The 206 isotope results from the uranium series and the 208 is the end product of thorium disintegration. The uranium and lead concentrations in iron and stone meteorites are reported as: $1 \times 10^{-4}$ atom/$10^4$ atoms of silicon and $80 \times 10^{-4}$ atom/$10^4$ atom of silicon, respectively. Deep-seated basic rocks are less radiogenic and richer in $^{207}Pb$ than in granitic lead. The age of the earth from these considerations is estimated as $4.5 \times 10^9$ years.[8] Lead from uranium ores is composed largely of the lower isotope and has a density of 11.27 compared with 11.34 for ordinary lead. The density varies with the mechanical treatment of the lead. At its melting point of 327°C, the density is $10.65 \pm 0.01$ g/cc.[9] The thermal conductivity of lead at 18°C is 0.083 cal/sec/deg.[10] Some additional properties of lead not listed in the tables noted above are: $\Delta H$ (fusion) kcal/g atom = 1.18; $C_p$(liquid metal) between 150° and 550°C = 7.6; heat content, cal/g from 100° to 400°C = 16.2 for liquid metal.[11]

[6] N. N. Gratsianskii and P. F. Kalyuzhnaya, *Ukrain. Khim. Zhur.* **19**, 377 (1953).

[7] G. Z. Kir'hakov and I. A. Korchmarek, *Izvest. Akad. Nauk Kazakh. S.S.R.*, Ser. *Khim.* **1955**, No. 8, 54–58.

[8] C. Patterson, *Proc. Conf. Nuclear Processes in Geol. Setting, Univ. Chicago, Natl. Research Council, Natl. Sci. Foundation* **1953**, 36–40; H. Fr. Ehrenberg and G. Harlitz, *Z. Naturforsch.* **9a**, 951 (1954); *Chem. Eng. News* **31**, 4874 (1953).

[9] A. Schneider *et al.*, *Naturwiss.* **41**, 326 (1954).

[10] See also H. M. Rosenberg, *Phil. Roy. Soc. London* **A247**, 441 (1955).

[11] W. Oelsen, *Arch. Eisenküttenw.* **26**, 519 (1955); also reported for heat of fusion is the value $1.158 \pm 0.02$ kcal/g atom, W. Oelsen, *Z. Metallkunde* **46**, 555 (1955).

Lead lacks the necessary tensile strength for drawing into wire, but it may readily be cut and rolled. It is very plastic, especially when it is warmed to about 300°C, and may be "squirted" through dies to form wires or tubes and may be "wiped" on a joint of pipe.

It has been confirmed that lead does not dissolve hydrogen, nor does a 1% calcium alloy of lead. Lead-magnesium alloys (up to 17% Mg) dissolve increasing amounts of hydrogen with increasing amounts of magnesium due to the intermetallic $Mg_2Pb$ phase.[12] Lead, as well as certain of the other heavy metals, has been found to reduce sulfur dioxide directly to the dithionate. The reaction in aqueous solution is very slow due to the low solubility of the lead sulfite which is also formed.[13] Lead, as well as tin, reacts with soda amide, $NaNH_2$, at 350°C to give nitrogen and other products. This reaction is in contrast to that of germanium which reacts with the same reagent to give hydrogen.[14]

Lead oxidizes superficially in moist air, a protective film of oxycarbonate being formed. The metal burns to form lead monoxide, $PbO$. Lead combines directly with fluorine, chlorine, and sulfur. It is not attacked by pure water in the absence of air, but water containing air has a solvent action. This action is checked by the presence of a carbonate or a sulfate so that hard water may be carried in lead pipes without danger. Soft water, however, dissolves lead, and cases of lead poisoning have resulted from drinking soft water which has been carried in lead pipes. Lead is attacked by water containing air, nitrates, ammonium salts, carbon dioxide, and organic acids. Water led through lead pipes is therefore more injurious in the spring when the runoff water is rich in organic matter.

**Uses.** Table 7.4 includes the uses and the estimated amounts of lead consumed by various industries in the United States in 1945 and 1946.

**General.** Lead forms two definite series of compounds in which its oxidation states are +2 and +4, respectively.[15] Lead(II) hydroxide is amphiprotic. It is essentially basic, and so its acidic properties are weak. Plumbites, like the stannites, are formed by the action of an alkali on the hydroxide and the oxide. Crystalline sodium plumbite has been formed, but is so unstable as to prevent its isolation for analysis. However, there appears to be evidence for the existence in solution of hydrated ions, such as $[Pb(OH)_3]^-$ and $[Pb(OH)_4]^=$. The simple ion, $PbO_2^=$, is the one usually written in equations for reactions involving the plumbite ion.

[12] W. Mannchen and M. Baumann, *Metall.* 9, 686 (1955).
[13] L. Cambi *et al.*, *Rend. est. lombardo sci. Pt. I. Classe sci. mat. e nat.* 87, 251 (1954).
[14] L. Levine and W. C. Fernelius, *Chem. Revs.* 54, 449 (1954).
[15] J. Faucherre, *Bull. soc. chim. France* 1953, 1117.

TABLE 7.4. CONSUMPTION OF REFINED LEAD IN THE UNITED STATES*

| Use | 1945 Short Tons | 1946 Short Tons |
|---|---|---|
| Ammunition | 29,315 | 16,857 |
| Bearing metal | 14,104 | 11,012 |
| Cable covering | 86,158 | 69,004 |
| Caulking lead | 13,374 | 8,314 |
| Casting metals | 5,322 | 3,566 |
| Collapsible tubes | 7,428 | 7,189 |
| Foil | 2,185 | 2,143 |
| Pipes, traps, and bends | 24,061 | 27,372 |
| Sheet lead | 30,624 | 26,430 |
| Solder | 27,475 | 32,279 |
| Storage batteries | 60,179 | 53,413 |
| Terneplate | 2,178 | 4,839 |
| Type metals | 1,401 | 1,487 |
| White lead | 35,611 | 43,294 |
| Red lead and litharge | 157,171 | 128,513 |
| Tetraethyl lead | 75,890 | 37,902 |
| Chemicals and insecticides | 8,567 | 8,169 |
| Annealing | 5,525 | 5,514 |
| Galvanizing | 988 | 1,132 |
| Lead plating | 1,130 | 1,182 |
| Weights and ballast | 9,539 | 3,089 |
| Other | 32,205 | 22,497 |
| Total | 637,499 | 520,525 |

* U. S. Bur. Mines, Mineral Market Report, MMS. No. 1549 (1947).

A whole series of salts is derived from the hydroxide. They are somewhat hydrolyzed in solution, giving various insoluble hydroxy-salts with type formulas, such as $Pb(OH)X$ and $PbX_2 \cdot 2Pb(OH)_2$. The former have been shown to be dimeric and are formulated as coordination compounds,

$$\left[ Pb \left\langle \begin{matrix} HO \\ HO \end{matrix} \right\rangle Pb \right] X_2.$$

The second series is given the general formula

$$\left[ Pb \left\langle \begin{matrix} HO \\ HO \end{matrix} \right\rangle Pb \right)_2 \right] X_2.$$

Lead(IV) hydroxide is almost entirely acidic in nature, although it does yield a few well-defined compounds formed through its action as a base. Table 7.5 includes some thermodynamic properties of certain of the lead compounds.

All the soluble compounds of lead are poisonous. There is observed

TABLE 7.5. Some Thermodynamic Properties of Lead and Its Compounds*

| Lead and Its Compounds | | $\Delta H$, kcal/mole | $\Delta S$, cal/deg mole |
|---|---|---|---|
| Pb | | | |
| Fusion: | 600.6°K | 1.22 | 2.03 |
| Vaporization: | 760 mm, 2023°K | 43.0 | 21.3 |
| PbO | | | |
| Fusion: | C, I, yellow → liq., 1159°K | 2.8 | 2.4 |
| Vaporization: | 760 mm, 1745°K | 51. | 29. |
| PbF₂ | | | |
| Fusion: | C, I → liq., 1095°K | 1.8 | 1.6 |
| Vaporization: | 760 mm. 1563°K | 38.3 | 24.5 |
| PbCl₂ | | | |
| Fusion: | 771°K | 5.7 | 7.4 |
| Vaporization: | 760 mm, 1227°K | 29.6 | 24.1 |
| PbBr₂ | | | |
| Fusion: | 643.2°K | 5. | 7.8 |
| Vaporization: | 760 mm, 1187°K | 27.7 | 23.3 |
| PbI₂ | | | |
| Fusion: | 685°K | 5.2 | 7.6 |
| Vaporization: | 760 mm, 1145°K | 24.8 | 21.7 |
| PbS | | | |
| Sublimation: | 10 mm, 1238°K | 55. | 44. |
| Fusion: | 1387°K | 4.2 | 3.0 |
| PbSO₄ | | | |
| Transition: | C, II → C, I, 1139°K | 4.06 | 3.56 |
| Fusion: | C, I → liq., 1360°K | 9.6 | 7.1 |

\* *N.B.S. Circular 500.*

arterial hypotension and venous hypertension. There is usually a slowing of hippuric acid synthesis and an increase in bilirubin. Occasionally a positive test for urobilin is noted in the blood. Some success has been reported in treatment with folic acid and pentoxyl.[16] There is a high health hazard in any cold-working process of lead. Lead dust associated with coating operations is particularly dangerous. Symptoms associated with exposure in such working conditions are colic, anemia, and bilateral, median, and radial nerve paralysis.[17] Lead is a cumulative poison, and all workers with lead or its compounds must be protected from the inhalation of lead-containing dusts. Use of respirators and the observance of certain other precautions minimize the danger from this dreaded occupational disease.

[16] B. A. Atchabarov, *Vestnik Akad. Nauk Kazakh. S.S.R.* 11, No. 6, 89 (1955).

[17] L. Parmeggiani and N. Zurlo, *Med. lavoro* 46, 176 (1955); A. Copellini *et al.*, *ibid.* 46, 147 (1955); W. Reinl, *Z. Erzbergbau u. Metallküttenw.* 8, 325 (1955); J. W. Aldren Turner, *Lancet* 268, 661 (1955).

**Oxides of Lead.** Five oxides of lead have been claimed: $Pb_2O$, $PbO$, $Pb_2O_3$, $PbO_2$, and $Pb_3O_4$. Two of these are considered to be salts, while the existence of $Pb_2O$ is doubted.

1. *Lead suboxide, $Pb_2O$.* This oxide is said to be formed as a black powder when lead oxalate is decomposed below 300°C:

$$2PbC_2O_4 \rightarrow Pb_2O + 3CO_2 + CO$$

The existence of lead suboxide as a pure compound is extremely doubtful. Thermal decomposition data obtained on the vacuum heating of $PbC_2O_4$ proves that $Pb_2O$ does not exist. The actual decomposition may be represented by

$$2PbC_2O_4 \rightarrow (3 - x)CO_2 + (1 + x)CO + (1 - x)Pb + (1 + x)PbO$$

The value of $x$ varies linearly with temperature.[18] Similarly the thermal decomposition of barium oxalate yields $PbO$ at 370°C and no evidence for $Pb_2O$ is obtained.[19] The $Pb_2O$, then, is a mixture of lead and $PbO$ as proved by X-ray data.

2. *Lead(II) oxide, $PbO$.* The monoxide has long been known as *massicot* or as *litharge*. The former is the yellow powder obtained when lead is heated in air. Litharge is prepared as a buff-colored powder by fusing massicot and then pulverizing the product. The change in color is probably due to the presence of a little red lead.

Either red or yellow lead(II) oxide may be obtained by boiling $Pb(OH)_2$ with sodium carbonate. The former is the more stable form at ordinary temperatures, and solubility in water is in the order of a half a milligram in 100 g of water. The solubility of the yellow form is about twice this value. The red oxide is tetragonal, whereas the yellow is

rhombic, built of 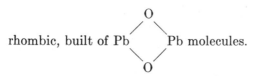 molecules.

Lead(II) oxide is only difficultly soluble in sodium hydroxide unless the latter reagent is very concentrated. Reducing agents, such as hydrogen, carbon, carbon monoxide, and alkali cyanides, convert $PbO$ to the metal at elevated temperatures.[20] The oxide reacts with gaseous hydrogen chloride at 195°C to give the anhydrous lead(II) chloride. It

[18] R. David, *Compt. rend.* **240**, 782 (1955).
[19] N. Unohara, *J. Chem. Soc. Japan.* **75**, 287 (1954).
[20] H. Remy, *Treatise on Inorganic Chemistry*, Vol. I, p. 545.

may be noted that at the same temperature CuO gives only a basic chloride.[21] A relatively stable hydroxyperchlorate complex of lead(II) is formed when PbO reacts with $Pb(ClO_4)_2$. The stability is attributed to the large ionic radius of the lead(II) ion.[22]

Lead(II) hydroxide, $Pb(OH)_2$, is formed by precipitation from lead(II) salts by dilute alkali. The compound is amphiprotic. The first dissociation constant for the equilibrium

$$Pb(OH)_2 \rightleftharpoons Pb(OH)^+ + OH^-$$

is $4 \times 10^{-5}$. The constant for the equilibrium

$$Pb(OH)_2 + H_2O \rightleftharpoons Pb(OH)_3^- + H^+$$

is approximately $10^{-12}$. Litharge is much used industrially, as noted in Table 7.6.

TABLE 7.6. DISTRIBUTION OF LITHARGE IN INDUSTRY

| Product | Consumption (Short Tons) |
|---|---|
| Storage batteries | 39,754 |
| Insecticides | 16,435 |
| Oil refining | 7,619 |
| Ceramics | 8,679 |
| Chrome pigments | 7,815 |
| Varnish | 2,428 |
| Rubber | 1,404 |
| Linoleum | 226 |
| Other uses | 5,158 |
| Total | 89,518 |

3. *Lead dioxide, lead(IV) oxide, $PbO_2$.* The dioxide is prepared by the action of chlorine or sodium hypochlorite on an alkaline solution of lead acetate or of lead monoxide. In each of these cases the reaction is between the plumbite ion and the hypochlorite ion:

$$PbO_2^= + ClO^- + H_2O \rightarrow PbO_2 \downarrow + Cl^- + 2OH^-$$

It is also formed by the action of nitric acid on red lead, $Pb_3O_4$:

$$Pb_3O_4 + 4H_3O^+ + 4NO_3^- \rightarrow PbO_2 + 2Pb^{++} + 4NO_3^- + 6H_2O$$

Lead dioxide is the chief constituent of the anode of the *charged* lead acid storage battery. It is deposited on the anode when solutions of lead salts are electrolyzed. It is a chocolate-brown powder, stable

---

[21] C. Chaleroux, *Compt. rend.* **239**, 1218 (1954).
[22] E. Hayek and E. Schnell, *Monatsh.* **85**, 472 (1954).

toward heat up to about 300°C; at higher temperatures it decomposes into litharge and oxygen.

Lead dioxide is formed first in the anodic electrolytic corrosion of lead. The $PbO_2$ is dissolved by salt formation and reduction followed by the passage of $Pb^{++}$ into solution. Alloying of lead with silver decreases the lead loss in this process by a factor of 10 and likewise decreases the amount of lead slime which falls from the anode.[23]

Lead(IV) oxide is sometimes labeled as a peroxide. No hydrogen peroxide is evolved on acidification and thus should not be so named. The structure is similar to that of $SnO_2$ and may be indicated as $O{=}Pb{=}O$. The lead atom is in the quadrivalent state.

Lead dioxide is an effective oxidizing agent, liberating chlorine from hydrochloric acid and, in the presence of acid, oxidizing manganese to a permanganate. Advantage is taken of the capacity of $PbO_2$ to oxidize HBr to $Br_2$ to maintain stored bromine. A small quantity of $PbO_2$ is added to the bromine container.[24] Freshly precipitated $PbO_2$ (hydrate) oxidizes $ClO_2$ rapidly to $HClO_4$. The $ClO_2$ is assumed to be the auto-decomposition product of $HClO_3$. A mixture of sulfuric acid and $PbO_2$ is treated slowly with $KClO_3$ and refluxed until no iodide test is obtained. On cooling, $KClO_4$ is formed in a theoretical yield.[25] Lead dioxide is amphoteric, giving unstable lead(IV) salts when acted on by acids, and plumbates when acted on by alkalies. These salts appear either as derivatives of orthoplumbic acid, $H_4PbO_4$, or of metaplumbic acid, $H_2PbO_3$. Thus, calcium orthoplumbate, $Ca_2PbO_4$, is obtained by heating together calcium oxide and lead dioxide, and potassium metaplumbate, $K_2PbO_3$, is formed when potassium hydroxide and lead dioxide are fused together. The hydroxoplumbates(IV) appear to be similar in structure to the hydroxoplatinates(IV) and hydroxostannates(IV). Heating does not lead simply to dehydration but to decomposition, forming oxygen, a base, and lead(II) oxide.

4. *Lead metaplumbate, lead(II,IV) oxide, or lead sesquioxide, $Pb_2O_3$.* This compound is prepared as an orange-yellow powder by treating a soluble lead(II) salt with a solution of a plumbate. Nitric acid dissolves half the lead, leaving the other half as lead dioxide. The compound is therefore best represented by the formula $PbPbO_3$.

5. *Lead orthoplumbate, lead(II,II,IV) oxide, or red lead, $Pb_3O_4$.* Red lead, or *minimum*, is formed when litharge is heated in the air to about

[23] G. Z. Kur'yakov and I. A. Korchmarek, *Zhur. Priklad. Khim.* **26**, 921 (1953); J. J. Lander, *J. Electrochem. Soc.* **99**, 467 (1954).

[24] R. Block *et al.*, U. S. **2,670,276**, Feb. 23, 1954.

[25] E. Ott, *Chem. Ber.* **86**, 1065 (1953).

450°C. If pure red lead is treated with nitric acid, two thirds of the lead dissolves and the other third remains as lead dioxide. For this reason the compound is given the formula $Pb_2PbO_4$. Commercial red lead always contains varying amounts of litharge. It is much used as a paint pigment. In a paint it seems to be very effective as a deterrent to the corrosion of iron and steel. It is assumed that red lead serves in corrosion prevention by the formation of cathodic protective layers containing $Pb(II)$. Such protection is in contrast to $PbCN_2$ which is active only because of basic properties of the decomposition products.[26]

A black modification of $Pb_3O_4$ (as well as the red) has been reported. Two methods are available for its preparation: the direct union of PbO with oxygen; and the degradation of $PbO_2$. Both processes must be carried out below 389°C, since above this temperature the black form changes to the red.[27] The chief use for red lead is in the manufacture of storage batteries, as indicated in Table 7.7. The ceramic industry uses

TABLE 7.7. INDUSTRIAL USES OF RED LEAD

| Industry | Consumption (Short Tons) |
|---|---|
| Storage batteries | 27,709 |
| Paints | 11,421 |
| Ceramics | 1,123 |
| Other uses | 2,723 |
| Total | 39,976 |

rod lead as an ingredient of certain glazes. Red lead also enters into the manufacture of a number of kinds of glass.

A process for making red lead from the element is described. Lead vapor, obtained by the vaporization of pure lead in an electric arc furnace, is passed into a chamber containing pure oxygen under carefully regulated conditions of temperature and pressure. The red lead produced by the reaction is claimed to possess higher corrosion-resisting properties and almost twice the covering power of standard red lead.

**Lead(II) Salts.** Lead(II) salts are more important and common than lead(IV) compounds (see Table 7.5).

1. *Lead(II) halides.* The *chloride* may be formed by the direct combination of lead and chlorine or by the action of hydrochloric acid on the oxide. It may also be precipitated from a solution of a lead salt by the addition of a soluble chloride. It may be distilled in an inert atmos-

[26] H. J. Schuster and J. d'Ans, *Naturwiss.* 41, 373 (1954).
[27] Remy, *op. cit.*

phere (as $CO_2$) without decomposition. It dissolves in hot water. Table 7.8 lists certain of the numerical and physical properties of $PbCl_2$. The theoretical expression representing the salt concentration for $PbCl_2$ (as well as $PbBr_2$) is

$$C = Ae^{-(\Delta E_s/2R)[(1/T)-(1/T_f)]}$$

where $C$ is the concentration in moles per liter, $T_f$ is the melting point of the salt, $A$ is 1.15 for $PbCl_2$ and 1.70 for $PbBr_2$. For $PbCl_2$, $T_f$ is 774°K and $\Delta E_s$ is 6.50. For $PbBr_2$, $T_f$ is 646°K and $\Delta E_s$ is 9.16. For $PbI_2$, the expression for $C$ is similar except that $A$ is 0.0158 and the exponential quantity contains $3R$ rather than $2R$. The values of $T_f$ and $\Delta E_s$ are 675°K and 14.13, respectively.[28] A mixed phosphate of $PbCl_2$ is prepared by suspending powdered natural calcium phosphate and $PbCl_2$ in water acidified with a small quantity of HCl. The resulting compound, $PbCl_2 \cdot 3Pb_3(PO_4)_2$, is readily susceptible to hydrogen reduction forming elemental phosphorus at the relatively low temperature of 600° to 800°C, suggesting a method of preparing this element.[29]

*Lead(II) bromide* is formed by precipitation methods similar to those of the chloride. The hydrate, $PbBr_2 \cdot 3H_2O$, is precipitated from solutions containing HBr. The properties of $PbBr_2$ are listed in Table 7.8. The bromide is formed in the combustion of lead tetraethyl fuels and poses a serious corrosion problem in internal combustion engines, due to the action of the hydrolysis products. Aluminum parts are particularly susceptible to this corrosive action. Epoxyresins have proved effective in the inhibition of this type of corrosion.[30] It has been reported[31] that $xPbO \cdot PbBr_2$ (where x may be 1, 2, 4, and 6) is first formed from the lead bromide. During flaming the oxybromide may be purged by the use of a detergent material, such as tricresylphosphate (TCP). Lead(II) bromide may be converted to a monobasic salt by titration with NaOH. If, on the other hand, the titration is carried out with such a base as diethylamine both mono- and tribasic salts are formed.[32]

*Lead(II) iodide* is formed by direct precipitation of iodide ion with any soluble lead(II) salt. The compound is intensely yellow in the solid state; however, the saturated solution is colorless indicating near com-

[28] T. G. Owe Berg, *Acta Chem. Scand.* **7**, 1313 (1953).

[29] J. C. Hutter, *Ann. chim.* (Paris) **8**, 450 (1953).

[30] S. K. Coburn, *Corrosion* **11**, 147t (1955); C. F. Schreiber, *ibid.* **11**, 119t (1955); A. Vaivads and L. Liepina, *Latvijas PSR Zinatnu Akad. Vesits* **1954**, 119; *C.A.* **49**, 5250 (1955).

[31] J. C. Street, *S.A.E.* **61**, 442 (1953); *ibid.*, 3–13.

[32] B. Charreton, *Compt. rend. 78ᵉ Congr. socs. savantes Paris et depts., Sect sci.* **1953**, 339; *C.A.* **49**, 8671 (1955); P. Deschamps, *Bull. soc. chim. France* **1954**, 454.

plete dissociation into Pb(II) and iodide ions (both of which are colorless). On heating, a color change from yellow to red to brown is noted. On cooling, the salt reverts to its original yellow color. Properties of $PbI_2$ are found in Table 7.8. The instability constant for the ion $PbI^+$ has been reported as $5.05 \times 10^{-3}$ as deduced from measurements on the solubility of $PbI_2$ in aqueous solutions of $Pb(NO_3)_2$. The $K$ solubility product[33] of $PbI_2$ is $1.05 \times 10^{-9}$. When $PbI_2$ is reacted with tetrasulfur tetranitride, $S_4N_4$, in nonaqueous solvents a red-brown thionitrosylate, $Pb(NS)_2$, is formed. This compound hydrolyzes to $SO_2$, $NH_4^+$, and Pb(II) ion in hot nitric acid. The bonding is reported as being from lead to nitrogen rather than lead to sulfur.[34]

*Lead(II) fluoride* is formed by precipitation through the action of HF on either lead hydroxide or the carbonate. It is the least soluble of the lead halides. As is noted in Table 7.8, the compound is dimorphous with

TABLE 7.8. SOME PROPERTIES OF THE LEAD(II) HALIDES

| Properties | $PbF_2$ | $PbCl_2$ | $PbBr_2$ | $PbI_2$ |
|---|---|---|---|---|
| Color | white (silky) | white (silky) | white | yellow |
| Solubility, g/100 g $H_2O$ | 0.064 (20°C) | 0.673 (0°C) | 0.4554 (0°C) | 0.044 (0°C) |
| | | 0.99 (20°C) | 0.8491 (20°C) | 0.063 (20°C) |
| | | 3.34 (100°C) | 4.71 (100°C) | 0.41 (100°C) |
| Density, g/cc | 8.24 | 5.9ᵃ | 6.66 | 6.16 |
| Melting point, °C | 855 (822. ± 2°)ᵇ | 498 | 373 | ~(402)ᶜ |
| Boiling point, °C | 1290 | 954 | 916 | ~(954)ᶜ |
| Crystal structure | α-Rhombic (stable RT) β-Cubic (>220°C) | Rhombic | Rhombic | Hexagonal (brucite) |
| Heat of formation,ᵈ $\Delta H_f$, kcal/mole | −158.5 | −85.85 | −66.21 | −41.85 |
| Free energy of formation,ᵈ $\Delta F_f$, kcal/mole | −148.1 | −75.04 | −62.24 | −41.53 |
| Entropy,ᵈ $S°$, cal/deg/mole | 29 | 32.6 | 38.6 | 42.3 |
| Equilibrium constant,ᵈ log $K_f$ (25°C) | 108.55 | 55.003 | 45.621 | 30.441 |
| Heat capacityᵈ | ... | 18.4 | 19.15 | ... |

ᵃ The value 5.90899 ± 0.00010 (4°C) is reported by J. I. Fernandez Alonso and L. Gasco, *Anales real soc. espan. fis. y quim.* **51B**, 5 (1955).

ᵇ D. A. Jones, *Proc. Phys. Soc.* **68B**, 165 (1955).

ᶜ Uncertain.

ᵈ *N.B.S. Circular 500.*

an α-form, stable near room temperatures, and β-form resulting when the α-form is heated above 220°C. The fluoride may be conveniently prepared by mixing equimolecular portions of $Na_2SiF_6$ and $PbSO_4$ at 500° to 700°C.[35] It is possible to grow crystals of the fluorite type from a $PbF_2$ melt in an oxygen-free atmosphere of nitrogen (2 to 10 mm pressure). The transparency of the crystals is high, and the cubic structure

[33] K. B. Yatsimirskii and A. A. Shutov, *Zhur. Fiz. Khim.* **27**, 782 (1953).

[34] M. Goehring *et al.*, *Z. anorg. allgem. Chem.* **278**, 1 (1955).

[35] U. S. 2,659,658, Nov. 17, 1953.

makes the crystals especially suitable for prism material in the 2800 A region. The crystal properties are also suitable for scintillation counters.[36]

2. *Lead(II) nitrate, $Pb(NO_3)_2$.* Lead nitrate is readily obtained by dissolving metallic lead or litharge in nitric acid. It is very soluble in water. The crystals are anhydrous and have the relatively high density of 4.53 at 20°C. At 4°C the density is 4.54808 ± 0.00021 g/cc.[37] Lead nitrate decomposes at about 470°C in the same manner as the nitrates of other heavy metals:

$$2Pb(NO_3)_2 \rightarrow 2PbO + 4NO_2 + O_2$$

Electrometric titrations of the system $Pb(NO_3)_2$ and NaOH indicate precipitates of the composition $Pb(NO_3)_2 \cdot Pb(OH)_2$ and $Pb(NO_3)_2 \cdot 5Pb(OH)_2$. The former exists over the pH range 5.0 to 7.0 and the latter 7.0 to >12. Up to a pH of 12, no appreciable amounts of $Pb(OH)_2$, PbO or the $PbO \cdot Pb(OH)_2$ complex are formed.[38]

The salt finds use as a mordant in the textile industry and as a source of other lead salts. It is also used in some explosive mixtures.

3. *Lead(II) acetate, $Pb(C_2H_3O_2)_2$.* The acetate is an important soluble salt of lead, formed by the action of acetic acid on litharge. It is known as *sugar of lead* because of its sweet taste. Its solution dissolves litharge, giving an oxyacetate. Lead acetate is used in the weighting of silk, in the preparation of other organic lead salts, and as a mordant. A solution of lead acetate reacts with hydrogen sulfide to yield the black insoluble sulfide, PbS. The appearance of this black substance on a piece of filter paper moistened with a solution of the acetate is used as a test for gaseous hydrogen sulfide.

4. *Lead(II) arsenate, $Pb_3(AsO_4)_2$.* This insoluble, white, crystalline salt is used as an agricultural insecticide.

5. *Lead(II) sulfide, PbS.* This compound occurs in nature as the important mineral galena. It is characterized by its high density and its cubic crystals. When prepared by precipitation it is a black solid, insoluble in water, dilute acids, or alkali sulfides. The solubility in water is about 0.8 mg/liter, a value higher than the normal calculation from the $K$ solubility product would indicate due to the hydrolysis of sulfide ion. Carbon monoxide has little effect in reducing the sulfide to lead, whereas hydrogen is an effective agent for this process. Molten PbS is soluble in all proportions in iron(II) sulfide and copper(I) sulfide. Acids with a complexing anion, as citric and even concentrated hydrochloric, dissolve

[36] D. A. Jones, *Proc. Phys. Soc.* **68B**, 165 (1955).
[37] J. I. Fernandez Alonso and L. Gasco, *loc. cit.*
[38] J. L. Pauley and M. J. Testerman, *J. Am. Chem. Soc.* **76**, 4220 (1954).

PbS liberating $H_2S$. Chlorine converts PbS to $PbCl_2$ and $SCl_2$. Air oxidation of PbS in a carbonate medium results first in the formation of the sulfate which reacts with sulfide eventually forming the free metal.[39] The crystal structure of PbS is similar to that of rock salt. The potential of artificially prepared pure PbS in saturated NaCl solution has been determined as $-0.510$ v. The potential of the metal in the same solution is $-0.606$ v. Elemental sulfur is produced during electrolysis.[40]

6. *Lead(II) sulfate, $PbSO_4$.* The sulfate of lead (lead vitriol) is a white crystalline solid, difficultly soluble in water and dilute acids.[41] Concentrated sulfuric acid dissolves $PbSO_4$ to a limited extent, due probably to the formation of the hydrogensulfate salt or to a sulfato complex. Acetate solutions dissolve $PbSO_4$, as does a tartrate solution, because of the formation of slightly ionized molecular species. Separations of $PbSO_4$ from other slightly soluble sulfates are possible using these reagents. It is formed by the addition of a soluble sulfate to a solution of a lead salt.

A so-called *basic lead sulfate* or *sublimed white lead* is prepared by roasting galena to a high temperature in a furnace to which a controlled amount of air is admitted. Analysis of the product shows 75% lead sulfate, 20% lead oxide, and 5% zinc oxide, the latter originating in the zinc ore (sphalerite, ZnS) which occurs in the galena used. The chief use of sublimed white lead is in the manufacture of paint. This pigment is nonpoisonous and is not darkened by hydrogen sulfide.

*Super-sublimed white lead* is an oxysulfate of the composition $PbO \cdot 2PbSO_4$ made by atomizing molten lead with air under 40 lb of pressure and natural gas under 15 lb of pressure into a furnace to which the proper amount of sulfur dioxide is admitted. The fine-grained powder is brighter than almost any other white pigment and is superior in whiteness to any other lead pigment.

7. *Lead(II) carbonate, $PbCO_3$.* The carbonate occurs in nature as *cerussite*. It is a white insoluble crystalline solid.

8. *Lead(II) hydroxycarbonate (white lead), $Pb(OH)_2 \cdot 2PbCO_3$.* Several hydroxycarbonates of lead are known. White lead, much used as a paint pigment, has a composition indicated by the formula $Pb(OH)_2 \cdot 2PbCO_3$. It has been prepared by a number of processes. Nearly all of them involve the intermediate formation of lead acetate and the conver-

[39] B. Reuter and R. Stein, *Physica* 20, 801 (1954).
[40] N. S. Fortunatov and V. I. Mikhailovskaya, *Ukrain. Khim. Zhur.* 16, 667 (1951); for other properties, see D. H. Parkinson and J. E. Quarrington, *Proc. Phys. Soc.* 67A, 569 (1954).
[41] Y. Sakamoto, *J. Sci. Hiroshima Univ. Ser. A,* 17, 407 (1954).

sion of this to the hydroxycarbonate by the action of carbon dioxide. The carbon dioxide may be produced by fermentation, as in the *old Dutch* process, or by the burning of coke, as in the Carter process.

In the Dutch process, lead cast into the form of grids called buckles (Fig. 7.1) is piled into an earthenware pot, the bottom of which contains

FIG. 7.1.   A lead buckle.

dilute acetic acid. A number of these pots, placed together as closely as possible on the floor of a chamber about 20 × 20 × 30 ft, are covered to a depth of 8 to 10 in. with spent tanbark obtained from tanneries. Boards placed loosely over the tanbark support another layer of pots and these in turn are covered with tanbark. The entire chamber is filled in this manner and is then sealed. Fermentation of the tanbark sets in and proceeds with the evolution of heat and carbon dioxide. Water and acetic acid volatilize and react with the lead to form a hydroxyacetate, which carbon dioxide then converts into the hydroxycarbonate.

After a period of from three to four months the reaction is sufficiently complete and the buckles are removed. They are ground under water to a fine powder. The heavier particles of hydroxycarbonate together with unchanged lead are allowed to settle out; the lighter particles remaining in suspension are then washed away. This suspension is thickened by settling to give what is known as "pulp lead"; it need not be dried if the pigment is to be made up into an oil paste for paints. In this event the wet pulp is mixed with raw linseed oil. Water is displaced and rises to the surface to form a layer which is run off. Ordinarily the oil paste is made up so as to contain 92% white lead and 8% linseed oil. Sometimes dry ground pigment is required. However, grinding is usually done wet because of the danger arising from the inhalation of the poisonous dust created during dry grinding.

In the *Carter* process the finely divided powder, made by atomizing molten lead in a stream of air or superheated steam, is allowed to react with acetic acid and carbon dioxide in sealed wooden cylinders. These are revolved slowly during the entire fifteen-day period of corrosion. Although the product is identical in composition with the white lead made by the Dutch process, there are differences in physical structure which cause painters to prefer one form or the other.

In the past the largest amount of lead for any single item, with the exception of storage batteries, has been used in making white lead. Out of a total of 98,429 short tons of white lead made in 1939, more than 90%

went into paint. None of the lead converted into white lead returns to the market as scrap. As shown in Table 7.4, conversion to white lead was the fifth most important use during World War II.

9. *Lead(II) chromate, PbCrO₄.* Lead chromate is formed as a bright-yellow precipitate when a solution of a lead salt is treated with a soluble chromate. It is largely used as a paint pigment and is known as chrome yellow. Ultraviolet light exposure results in [O] evolution followed by blackening. Additives such as the oxides of aluminum, tin, and titanium improve the light fastness.[42] Another pigment rather extensively produced and used is chrome red, obtained by boiling chrome yellow with a dilute alkali. It is an oxysalt having the formula $PbCrO_4 \cdot PbO$. Titrometric studies of $Pb(NO_3)_2$ and NaOH in the presence of $CrO_4^=$ show that a basic salt of the composition $Pb_2(OH)_2CrO_4$ is formed. The $K$ solubility product of this salt is represented[43] by: $[Pb^{++}]^2[OH^-]^2[CrO_4^=] = 2.1 \times 10^{-32}$.

10. *Lead(II) azide, Pb(N₃)₂.* Alkali metal azides precipitate slightly soluble colorless needles of lead azide from solutions of lead salts. The solubility at 18°C is 0.023 and at 70°C 0.09 g/100 ml of water. At 20°C the solubility is $8.5 \times 10^{-4}$ mole/liter. The concentration $K$ solubility product for $Pb(N_3)_2$ is $2.6 \times 10^{-9}$, and the thermodynamic solubility product is $1.8 \times 10^{-9}$. The $K$ solubility product of the basic salt $\beta$-$Pb(N_3)_2 \cdot PbO$ is $3 \times 10^{-15}$ at 20°C.[44] At 350°C the azide explodes. In the presence of NaOH the azide hydrolyzes to basic salts. The basic salts are formed directly by precipitating lead azide from a mixture of lead nitrate and $NaN_3$ in NaOH solution. Three forms of $Pb(N_3)_2 \cdot PbO$ have been characterized by X-ray examination. Likewise three forms of the compound $3Pb(N_3)_2 \cdot 5PbO$ are known, formed with varying equivalents of NaOH. Still other forms are $Pb(N_3)_2 \cdot 2PbO$, $Pb(N_3)_2 \cdot 3PbO$, $2Pb(N_3)_2 \cdot 7Pb(OH)_2$, and $Pb(N_3)_2 \cdot 4PbO$.

11. *Lead(II) cyanamide, PbCN₂.* This salt is prepared by the interaction of lead(II) acetate and an ammoniacal cyanamide solution. Lemon-colored crystals are formed. Above room temperature there is a tendency toward polymerization. At about 250°C, $PbCN_2$ begins to decompose in air. The main gaseous decomposition products are nitrogen and variable amounts of cyanogen and carbon dioxide. The lead is converted in air at 350°C to PbO and above 500°C to $Pb_3O_4$. In the absence of air the decomposition products are cyanogen, nitrogen, and metallic lead. The compound is used in antirust paints. The corrosion

[42] V. Watson and H. F. Clay, *J. Oil and Colour Chemists Assoc.* **38**, 167 (1955).
[43] B. Charreton, *Compt. rend.* **234**, 1623 (1952).
[44] W. Feitknecht and M. Sahli, *Helv. Chim. Acta* **37**, 1423 (1954).

inhibiting properties arise from the slow hydrolysis to $Pb(OH)_2$, urea, and $(NH_4)_2CO_3$. There is, therefore, a buffering action preventing low pH solutions from contacting the base metal.[45]

**Lead(IV) Compounds.** These compounds are relatively few in number. Of the tetrahalides of lead, only the chloride and fluoride are known with certainty.

1. *Lead tetrahalides.* *Lead tetrachloride, $PbCl_4$,* can be prepared in solution by passing chlorine into a suspension of lead chloride, $PbCl_2$, in concentrated hydrochloric acid at a temperature of 10° to 15 °C. Addition of solid ammonium chloride to the solution precipitates the yellow crystalline ammonium hexachloroplumbate, $(NH_4)_2PbCl_6$. This salt reacts with concentrated sulfuric acid to give lead tetrachloride as a heavy, yellow, fuming liquid (density = 3.18 at 0 °C). It decomposes at room temperature to lose half its chlorine. Water decomposes it with the formation of lead dioxide and hydrochloric acid. Several reactions involving $PbCl_4$ have been studied and the thermodynamic values reported.[46]

$$PbCl_4 + I_2 \rightarrow PbCl_2 + 2ICl - 19{,}793 \pm 64 \text{ cal}$$

$$PbCl_2 + Cl_2 \rightarrow PbCl_4 + 7{,}003 \pm 76 \text{ cal}$$

$$Pb + 2Cl_2 \rightarrow PbCl_4 - 78.85 \text{ kcal/mole}$$

The heat of solution of $PbCl_4$ in $CCl_4$ is endothermic, $+706.7 \pm 8.1$ cal.

2. *Lead(IV) fluoride, $PbF_4$,* has been prepared by the direct fluorination of $PbF_2$. The compound forms as colorless tetragonal needles with a density of 6.7 and with a heat of formation of 222 kcal/mole.[47] The pseudohalide, *lead(IV) azide, $Pb(N_3)_4$* is known. When $Pb_3O_4$ is treated with hydroazoic acid, $HN_3$, a red solution of the tetrazide is formed. Rapid decomposition follows with the formation of the more stable lead(II) azide. No tetrazide forms when $HN_3$ is acted on $PbO_2$.

3. *Lead(IV) tetraacetate, $Pb(C_2H_3O_2)_4$,* is a colorless, crystalline solid obtained by dissolving powdered red lead in a warm (50° to 80 °C) mixture of glacial acetic acid and acetic anhydride. It melts at 175 °C. This substance is a very powerful oxidizing agent, and it has properties which make it particularly useful for bringing about certain specific reactions in organic chemistry. It is readily hydrolyzed to yield lead dioxide. Glacial acetic acid, in which the tetraacetate is freely soluble, is the solvent usually employed.

[45] D. Costa and C. Bolis-Connella, *Ann. chim.* **43**, 769 (1953).
[46] F. Ya. Kul'ba, *Zhur. Obshchei Khim.* **24**, 1700 (1954); *C.A.* **49**, 6714 (1955).
[47] Remy, *op. cit.*, p. 556.

**Organic Compounds of Lead.**   Lead hydride, PbH$_4$, is unstable and has not been prepared in pure form.   It is said to have a boiling point of approximately $-13\,°\text{C}$.[48]

Many derivatives of this lead hydride are known in which the hydrogen atoms are replaced by organic radicals, but the only one of industrial importance is the tetraethyl derivative.   Lead tetraethyl, Pb(C$_2$H$_5$)$_4$, is produced to the extent of about $2.25 \times 10^6$ lb per day[49] for use by the petroleum industry in the production of antiknock gasoline.   About 88% of all American gasolines contain lead tetraethyl.   Gasolines leaded to an octane rating of 80 or higher are known as Ethyl or premium gasolines. The ethyl fluid used contains not only lead tetraethyl (approx. 63%) but also ethylene dibromide (approx. 26%), ethylene dichloride (approx. 9%), and a dye (approx. 2%).   The amount of lead tetraethyl in automobile gasoline ranges from 0.75 ml to the legal maximum of 3 ml per gallon of gasoline.   Because of its highly toxic nature, lead tetraethyl cannot be sold as such to the individual user but is mixed with the gasoline at the refinery.

Lead tetraethyl is a covalent compound, liquid at ordinary temperatures and boiling at $202\,°\text{C}$.[50]   The commercial process for its manufacture consists in the interaction of a sodium-lead alloy with ethyl chloride at moderate temperature and pressure:

$$4\text{PbNa} + 4\text{C}_2\text{H}_5\text{Cl} \rightarrow \text{Pb}(\text{C}_2\text{H}_5)_4 + 4\text{NaCl} + 3\text{Pb}$$

The lead derivative is separated by steam distillation, and the lead sludge is smelted into pig lead.   A lead-sodium alloy of 20 to 22 weight per cent sodium is capable of effecting alkylation with an alkyl sulfate or phosphate at 110° to 150°C, which process eliminates the use of the usual alkyl halides in the preparation of lead tetraethyl.[51]   An alloy has been prepared for this use by plating sodium in the molten condition on a copper or copper alloy surface.   In this condition the sodium is highly sensitive for the preparation of Pb(Et)$_4$.[52]

[48] F. Paneth and E. Rabinowitsch, *Ber.* **58**, 1138 (1925).

[49] D. P. Thornton, Jr., *Petroleum Processing* **7**, 846 (1952).

[50] J. P. Nicherson, *J. Chem. Educ.* **31**, 560 (1954).

[51] H. Shapiro and I. T. Krohn, U. S. **2,688,628**, Sept. 7, 1954.

[52] Brit. **707,074**; **707,075**, Apr. 14, 1954; see also Brit. **718,619**, Nov. 17, 1954; U. S. **2,635,105**; Brit. **712,644**, July 28, 1954; U. S. **2,644,827**; N. Whitman, U. S. **2,657,225**, Oct. 27, 1953.

PART II

# THE METALLIC BORIDES, CARBIDES, SILICIDES, AND RELATED COMPOUNDS

# CHAPTER 8

## THE METALLIC BORIDES, CARBIDES, SILICIDES, AND RELATED COMPOUNDS

**Introduction.** Most compounds involve chemical combination through electron transfer (electrovalence) or electron sharing (covalence). The bonds, however, are seldom purely ionic or purely covalent but possess some mixed character. For instance, the bond in sodium chloride, NaCl, is probably not entirely ionic in character but possesses about 5% covalent character; the bond in the hydrogen molecule, $H_2$, usually regarded as a purely covalent bond, possesses about 5% of ionic character; while such compounds as zinc sulfide, ZnS, and silver iodide, AgI, possess bonds of very definite intermediate character. Compounds formed in the above manner possess certain characteristics. They show constant composition and obey the elementary rules of valence. As solids, their physical properties are much more closely related to the nonmetals than to the metals, for they are brittle, nonconducting, without metallic luster, and are transparent or translucent in thin sections.

Many of the metals combine with hydrogen or with less electronegative nonmetals, such as carbon, silicon, boron, and nitrogen, to form substances which frequently are more or less metallic in nature. All such substances (or compounds) that exhibit a metallic luster possess bonds which are partially metallic in character and show many properties which are in contrast to those of ionic and covalent compounds. In addition to their metallic luster they commonly show ability to conduct a current, variation from the simple valence rules, and deviation from the laws of constant composition.

Not all carbides, nitrides, borides, silicides, and hydrides are metallic in nature. Some of them are definitely of the ionic and covalent types. Thus calcium carbide, $CaC_2$, and calcium hydride, $CaH_2$, are ionic, saltlike compounds, while neodymium carbide, $NdC_2$, and titanium hydride, TiH, are metallic in appearance, contrary to the rules of valence, and are capable of dissolving an excess of either component. The greater the degree of metallic bonding the more metallic will these compounds be and the greater they will deviate in their properties from the ionic-covalent types. It is thus particularly desirable to consider here all carbides, nitrides, hydrides, and related compounds of metallic character, so that the two extreme types, the saltlike and the metallic, may be contrasted.

251

**The Metallic Bond.** The characteristic properties of metals make it very evident that their interatomic bonding forces are not the usual ionic or covalent types. The nature of the metallic binding forces, however, has become established. Considerable evidence supports the view that the metallic binding is a multiplicity of resonating covalent bonds.[1] An atom in a metal crystal at one instant shares its bonding or valence electron with one of the neighboring atoms, and at a later "instant" shares it with another neighboring atom. In this fashion the valence bond formed resonates among the various nearest neighbors of each atom, and includes not only the states expected from synchronized resonance but also those involving conversion of atoms into ions. To have such free resonance among the atoms, it is necessary for each atom receiving a bond to have an unoccupied orbital (designated the *metallic* orbital) for the electron that jumps to it. Actually, a metallic orbital on only about 75% of the atoms is all that is required; the remaining atoms may use all of their orbitals for bond formation or for occupancy by unshared pairs of electrons. It is merely necessary for these latter atoms to be surrounded by atoms having metallic orbitals. The valence bonds of the central atom can then resonate among the surrounding neighbors by pivoting about the central atom.

This concept of the metallic bond as an uninhibited resonance of covalent-type bonds is consistent with the strength, malleability, and ductility of metals. The energy of the resonating bond in a metal crystal is about twice that of a nonresonating bond. The high mobility of the bonding electrons explains the metallic luster and the high electrical and thermal conductivity of metals. Indeed, this theory is not greatly contradictory to the older electron-gas theory[2] which explained many of the physical properties of metals but was less satisfactory for interpreting the chemical nature of the metallic bond. For instance, the nonintegral metallic valencies shown by the transition elements are interpreted by the new theory as averages resulting from resonance of each atom among two or more electronic structures with integral valencies. The valency 2.44 assigned to white tin corresponds to the presence in white tin of about 75% bivalent Sn and 25% tetravalent tin. Effective metallic valencies of 3.5 for Ga, 4.5 for Zn, and 5.5 for Cu are explained in a similar fashion.

The purest examples of resonating metallic bonds are in the metals

[1] L. Pauling, *Proc. Roy. Soc. (London)* **196A**, 343 (1948).

[2] For details of this theory, see N. F. Mott and H. Jones, *The Theory of the Properties of Metals and Alloys*, Oxford Clarendon Press, London, 1936; F. Seitz, *The Modern Theory of Solids*, McGraw-Hill Book Co., New York, 1940.

and in the solid solutions and intermetallic phases of alloys, where the theory is providing useful systematization. Binding of this type also characterizes many carbides, silicides, and borides.[1] Intermediate or mixed bond types, such as ionic-metallic and covalent-metallic, may also be expected.

**Berthollide Compounds.** The simple laws of valence and constant composition really define a certain restricted type of compound, since both laws were formulated in a day when the known chemical compounds were very simple ones. Indeed, at that time, Berthollet warned that the law of constant composition should not be applied to all chemical compounds, but his suggestion was not taken seriously. Now numerous compounds with variable composition are known, and his viewpoint has been completely substantiated. Crystal analysis has contributed greatly to the knowledge of these substances; sometimes referred to as *berthollides*. Many compounds with metallic character have variable composition, and some of the very well-known compounds are also of this type.

Variability of composition may arise through several structural phenomena, and three groups of such compounds have been designated: substitution, addition, and subtraction compounds. Substitution compounds have lattices with all equivalent positions filled, but one kind of atom or ion may be more or less continuously replaced by another species. This phenomenon is common among the silicates and is referred to as isomorphous replacement. For instance, olivine is ideally $Mg_2SiO_4$, but usually varying amounts of the $Mg^{++}$ have been replaced by $Fe^{++}$ so that the composition approximates the formula, $6Mg_2SiO_4 \cdot Fe_2SiO_4$. When boron, carbon, nitrogen, and hydrogen react with metals, particularly the transition metals, the metalloid atoms take positions in the interstices of the metal lattice. Such interstitial structures are addition compounds. Variation in the number of interstices filled may lead to homogeneous phases over a considerable range of composition. The intermediate alloy phases, such as the $\beta$, $\gamma$, and $\epsilon$ phases, may dissolve an excess of either component and thus become examples of addition compounds. The subtraction compounds vary slightly from simple stoichiometric proportions as a result of vacant lattice points in their structures. The familiar compounds FeO and FeS have long been known to show variations in composition corresponding apparently to solution of excess oxygen and sulfur respectively. X-ray diffraction studies have shown that the true state of affairs is a deficiency of iron atoms. FeO is based on an ideal FeO structure with some of the iron atoms missing, the true formula corresponding to $Fe_{0.95}O$ to $Fe_{0.91}O$. For each iron atom ($Fe^{++}$) missing, two $Fe^{++}$ in the structure have their charges raised to $Fe^{+3}$. In this way electrostatic valence requirements are preserved in the structure on the macroscopic scale. The tungsten bronzes, $NiO$, $Cu_2O$, $FeSe$, and other compounds are similar examples.

**Interstitial Compounds.** Because of their small atomic size, the elements hydrogen, boron, carbon, nitrogen, and (occasionally) oxygen combine with metals, particularly the transition metals, by entering the interstices of the metal lattice. Solid solutions of these elements in metals are formed in this way, and phases with distinctive structures or compositions are also formed. Compounds of the metals with these elements have metallic character only when the metal is a transition metal. Thus the hydrides and carbides of the alkali metals are ionic and saltlike; the familiar $CaC_2$ shows no metallic properties.

The work of Hägg[3] is primarily responsible for the present picture of the fundamental structure of these compounds. When the interstices in the metal lattice are large enough to accommodate readily the metalloid atoms with little or no distortion, phases or compounds with simple structures and simple stoichiometry will be formed. This situation will prevail when the metalloid atom is small compared with the metal atom. The geometrical requirements for this condition are met when the ratio of the radius of the metalloid atom, $R_X$, to the radius of the metal atom, $R_M$, is less than 0.59. When the ratio $R_X : R_M$ exceeds 0.59, the interstices are too small for the metalloid atoms, distortion of the metal lattice results, and much more complicated structures are formed. The compounds tend toward the simple compositions $M_4X$, $M_2X$, $MX$, and $MX_2$

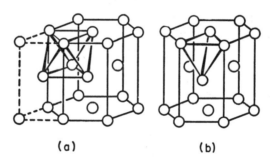

**(a)**    **(b)**

FIG. 8.1. Outline of possible positions for interstitial atoms in a hexagonal close-packed metal. (a) The octahedral holes, (b) the tetragonal and triogonal interstices. (Hume-Rothery and Raynor, *The Structure of Metals and Alloys;* courtesy *Institute of Metals.*)

[3] G. Hägg, *Z. physik. Chem.* **B12**, 33 (1931).

when the radius ratio is favorable, i.e., below 0.59. The $M_2X$ phases usually have the metal atoms in a hexagonal close-packed lattice, Fig. 8.1a. The $MX$ compounds, however, are generally based on cubic close-packing with the metalloid atoms usually going into the largest interstices, those at the centers of the cube edges, to form the sodium chloride structure, Fig. 8.2a. A few interstitial phases are based on body-centered

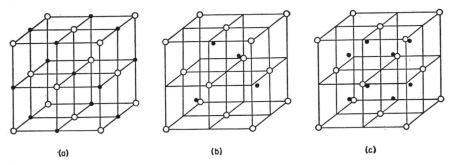

(a)          (b)          (c)

Fɪɢ. 8.2.   Possible positions for interstitial atoms in a cubic close-packed metal.   (a) All the largest (octahedral) interstices filled, leading to a NaCl-type structure.   (b) Half the smaller (tetrahedral) interstices filled producing the ZnS-type structure.   (c) All the smaller interstices filled, resulting in a CaF$_2$-type structure.

cubic or simple hexagonal metal lattices. Expansion usually occurs as the metalloid atoms enter the interstices of the metal lattice, and distortion from cubic to tetragonal or lower symmetry may occur. Indeed, the type of metal packing may change during the formation of such compounds. For instance, pure titanium is hexagonal close-packed at room temperature and body-centered cubic above 882°C; yet the metal atoms in TiC are in face-centered cubic packing. Tantalum metal, likewise, is body-centered cubic, but TaC has the NaCl structure.

There will be instability if the metalloid atom is too small for the interstice. Hydrogen atoms are so small ($R_H$ = about 0.4 A in interstitial phases and compounds) that some interesting geometrical relations develop. In the series Ti–H, Zr–H, and Ta–H,[4] the phases TiH, ZrH, and TaH might be expected to have NaCl structures, Fig. 8.2a, as observed for TiC and TaC. This mode of behavior, however, would demand a hydrogen radius of 0.6 to 0.7 A in TiH and ZrH for contact between the hydrogen and the metal, a distance too large for hydrogen. It is concluded, therefore, that the hydrogen goes into the smaller tetra-

[4] G. Hägg, *Z. physik. Chem.* **B11**, 433 (1931).

hedral interstices of the face-centered cubic titanium lattice.   There are eight such spaces, at the centers of the eight identical cubelets into which the face-centered unit cell can be divided.   When four of these spaces are filled, as in Fig. 8.2b, a zinc blende structure results, which is probably the structure of TiH and ZrH.   It should readily be possible to fill the four remaining spaces with hydrogen to give a structure like that of $CaF_2$, Fig. 8.2c.   Actually the system Ti–H shows a completely homogeneous range from 50 atomic per cent hydrogen to 67 atomic per cent hydrogen, and $TiH_2$ is believed to have a $CaF_2$ structure.[5]   However, $ZrH_2$ is distorted to face-centered tetragonal, more simply described by an equivalent body-centered tetragonal cell,[6] and $TaH_2$ is not known.   Similarly, $Ti_2H$ and $Zr_2H$ are hexagonal phases and are believed to have an incomplete wurtzite structure, Fig. 8.1a.   $Ta_2H$, however, seems to be based on the original body-centered cubic packing found in tantalum metal,[7] and the maximum absorption of hydrogen corresponds to a formula of about $TaH_{0.8}$,[8] and has a face-centered rhombic structure.

The frequent occurrence of the NaCl structure among the interstitial monocarbides and mononitrides, irrespective of metal structure and metal radius, has been considered by Rundle.[9]   In such electron-deficient structures it is suggested that two hybrid *sp*-orbitals combined with two *p*-orbitals are used in the nonmetal-to-metal bonds.   Two of the bonds will thus be ordinary electron-pair bonds, and four of them will be half-bonds, although resonance would make them all equivalent with a strength of two thirds.   The octahedral arrangement of these strong bonds can explain the structure, hardness, brittleness, conductivity, and high melting point of this type of interstitial compound.

**Carbides.**   Carbides may frequently be prepared by heating the appropriate metal with carbon.   In many cases this reaction takes place far below the fusion point of the two components.   Sometimes the oxide of the metal, when heated with excess carbon, yields the carbide, reduction first taking place followed by combination of the metal and carbon.   The use of the electric furnace to furnish the necessary heat is desirable in many of these reactions.   In some cases the carbides can be prepared by

[5] T. R. P. Gibb, Jr., and H. W. Kruschwitz, Jr., *J. Am. Chem. Soc.* **72**, 5365 (1950).
[6] R. E. Rundle, C. G. Shull, and E. O. Wollan, *Acta Cryst.* **5**, 22 (1952).   Another study, D. A. Vaughn and J. R. Bridge, *J. Metals (Trans.)* **8**, 528 (1956), interprets the phases of the Zr–H system as a single phase in which changes in composition shift the axial ratio of the tetragonal structure through unity so that, at various temperatures, two tetragonal and one cubic hydride appear to exist as different phases.
[7] F. H. Horn and W. T. Ziegler, *J. Am. Chem. Soc.* **69**, 2762 (1947).
[8] G. Brauer and R. Hermann, *Z. anorg. allgem. Chem.* **274**, 11 (1953).
[9] R. E. Rundle, *Acta Cryst.* **1**, 180 (1948).

passing hydrocarbon vapors (naphthalene vapor) over the heated metal (incandescent filament or strip of metal). A few of them, $Cu_2C_2$, $Ag_2C_2$, $HgC_2$, $Au_2C_2$, can be prepared by passing acetylene into metallic salt solutions. These, being derivatives of acetylene, are often called *acetylides*. The formation of $Cu_2C_2$ is quantitative and can be used for the determination of copper.[10] The compounds $NaHC_2$ and $KHC_2$ are formed by passing $C_2H_2$ into solutions of the alkali metals in liquid ammonia. On heating them above 200°C, they decompose to acetylene and the normal carbide:

$$2NaHC_2 \rightarrow Na_2C_2 + C_2H_2$$

Most of the carbides are extremely stable toward heat and oxygen. The alkali and alkaline-earth carbides, however, are relatively easily attacked and are very strong reducing agents when heated. Many of the carbides are very resistant to the action of acids, but alkalies attack most of them. Several of the heavy metal acetylides, $Ag_2C_2$, $Cu_2C_2$, $HgC_2$, etc., when dry explode easily on rubbing. $Hg_2C_2 \cdot H_2O$, however, is reported as not explosive but decomposing at 100°C.

Data on some of the known carbides are summarized in Table 8.1.

TABLE 8.1. FORMULAS AND PROPERTIES OF SOME BINARY CARBIDES

| Follow Simple Valence Rules | | | | | Contrary to Simple Valence Rules | |
|---|---|---|---|---|---|---|
| Daltlike (Chiefly) | | | | | Metallic (Chiefly) | |
| Not Hydrolyzed | Hydrolyze Yielding | | | | Not Hydrolyzed | |
| | $C_2H_2$ | | $CH_4$ | Mixture of Hydrocarbons | | |
| SiC | $Li_2C_2$ | $MgC_2$ | $Be_2C$ | $CeC_2$   $MnC_2$ | $Mo_2C*$ | $NbC*$ |
| TiC | $Na_2C_2$ | $CaC_2$ | $Al_4C_3$ | $LaC_2$   $UC_2$ | $B_4C$ | $TaC$ |
| ZrC | $K_2C_2$ | $SrC_2$ | | $NdC_2$   $Mg_2C_3$ | $U_2C_3$ | $MoC*$ |
| HfC† | $Rb_2C_2$ | $BaC_2$ | | $PrC_2$   $Mn_3C$ | $VC$ | $WC$ |
| | $Cs_2C_2$ | $ZnC_2$ | | $SmC_2$   $Ni_3C$ | | $W_2C*$ |
| | $Cu_2C_2$ | $CdC_2$ | | $YC_2$   $Co_3C$ | | $Nb_2C*$ |
| | $Ag_2C_2$ | $BeC_2$ | | $ZrC_2$   $Cr_3C_2$ | | $Ta_2C*$ |
| | $HgC_2$ | $Al_2(C_2)_3$ | | $ThC_2$   $Cr_5C_2$ | | |
| | $Au_2C_2$ | $Ce_2(C_2)_3$ | | $Fe_3C$ | | |

* These carbides become superconducting at some temperature above 1.20°K.
† *Chem. and Eng. News* **32**, 1128 (1954).

[10] J. Scheiber, *Z. anal. Chem.* **48**, 529 (1909).

A large group of the carbides possess two atoms of carbon per molecule which crystal structure studies have revealed are present as a $C_2^{-2}$ group in the crystal. Many of these must be regarded as salts of acetylene acting as a diprotic acid. Actually, their ionic conductivity and saltlike character have been demonstrated by the electrolysis of solid $Na_2C_2$.[11] The alkaline-earth and alkali-metal carbides yield acetylene on hydrolysis. Both $Be_2C$ and $Al_4C_3$, yielding $CH_4$ on hydrolysis, are to be regarded as salts of methane acting as an acid:

$$CaC_2 + 2H_2O \rightarrow Ca(OH)_2 + C_2H_2$$
$$Al_4C_3 + 12H_2O \rightarrow 4Al(OH)_3 + 3CH_4$$

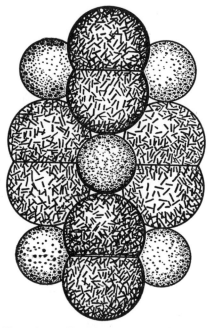

FIG. 8.3. Packing of the $Ca^{+2}$ ions (small spheres) and $C_2^{-2}$ groups in the crystal of $CaC_2$. (Wyckoff, *Crystal Structures*, Vol. I; courtesy *Interscience Publishers, Inc.*)

The rare-earth carbides and certain of the transition-metal carbides are hydrolyzed yielding a mixture of hydrocarbons.

Stackelberg[12] has attempted to show the relation between the crystal structures of the carbides and their hydrolysis products. The univalent metal carbides are largely prepared from acetylene and would be expected to yield acetylene on hydrolysis. Carbides of the general formula $MC_2$ commonly crystallize with the $CaC_2$ structure[13] and possess discrete $C_2^{-2}$ groups (Fig. 8.3). This fact satisfactorily accounts for the hydrolysis to acetylene in the case of the alkaline-earth carbides, but the formation of a mixture of hydrocarbons on the hydrolysis of the rare-earth carbides is less readily explained.

The approximate composition of the hydrolysis products of some of the carbides is given in Table 8.2.

The hydrolysis of the rare-earth metal, thorium, and uranium carbides to give mixtures of hydrocarbons rather than acetylene alone may be re-

[11] A. v. Antropoff and J. Fr. Müller, *Z. anorg. allgem. Chem.* **204**, 305 (1932).
[12] M. von Stackelberg, *Z. physik. Chem.* **B27**, 53 (1934).
[13] M. von Stackelberg, *ibid.* **B9**, 437 (1930).

TABLE 8.2. COMPOSITION OF HYDROLYSIS PRODUCTS OF CERTAIN CARBIDES

| Product | LaC$_2$, CeC$_2$, PrC$_2$, NdC$_2$ % | ThC$_2$ % | Mg$_2$C$_3$ | Mn$_3$C | Fe$_3$C | UC$_2$ % |
|---|---|---|---|---|---|---|
| C$_2$H$_2$ | 70–80 | 50 | | | | Trace |
| C$_2$H$_4$ | Few | few | | | $x$ | Few |
| CH$_4$ | 20–30 | 30 | | $x$ | $x$ | ca. 25 |
| CH$_3$C≡CH | | | Chiefly | | | |
| Solid and liquid hydrocarbons | | | | | $x$ | ca. 66 |
| Free carbon | | | | | $x$ | |
| H$_2$ | None | 20 | | $x$ | $x$ | ca. 5 |

lated to the fact that these elements rarely are divalent. It has been suggested that they are acting with a lower valence in their dicarbides and that in hydrolysis they go to a normal higher valence state, La(OH)$_3$, Th(OH)$_4$, etc., along with the formation of hydrogen and acetylene:

$$2LaC_2 + 6H_2O \rightarrow 2La(OH)_3 + 2C_2H_2 + H_2$$

Other hydrocarbons then arise from secondary reactions between the hydrogen and acetylene. Mn$_3$C, however, yields white manganese(II) hydroxide on hydrolysis. The reported hydrolysis of Mg$_2$C$_3$ to yield chiefly allylene suggests the presence of C$_3^{-4}$ groups in the crystal.[14] An unusual reaction is that of Al$_4$C$_3$ with HgCl$_2$ in the presence of water and hydrochloric acid:[15]

$$2Al_4C_3 + 3HgCl_2 + 18HCl \rightarrow 3Hg(CH_3)_2 + 8AlCl_3$$

It takes place in the cold, with separation of drops of mercury dimethyl.

Silicon carbide has a structure in which each kind of atom is tetrahedrally surrounded by four of the other kind. One of its most remarkable properties is its polymorphism, there being 15 to 17 known crystalline modifications of the compound. These different forms arise from different orientations of these tetrahedra with respect to one another in the lattices. The carbides[16] TaC, TiC, ZrC, NbC, HfC, ThC, UC, VC, and PuC have the same crystal structure as sodium chloride, Fig. 8.2a,

[14] N. V. Sidgwick, *The Chemical Elements and Their Compounds*, Oxford Clarendon Press, London, 1950, pp. 223–224.

[15] S. Hilpert and M. Ditmar, *Ber.* 46, 3738 (1913).

[16] For a detailed discussion of the hard refractory carbides see: P. Schwarzkopf and R. Kieffer, *Refractory Hard Metals*, The Macmillan Company, New York, 1953, pp. 47–220.

while the remaining carbides are more complicated in structure. The structure of $Cr_3C_2$ is of special interest. It appears to have infinite carbon-carbon chains, similar to those of the long-chain hydrocarbons, extending through the crystal. The chains are zigzag and have a C–C distance only slightly larger, 1.665 A, than in the normal paraffin hydrocarbons. The chromium atoms are inserted between the chains in such a way that each carbon atom is surrounded by six chromium atoms at the corners of an approximately regular trigonal prism (C–Cr = 2.02–2.07 A).[17] The more complex $Cr_{23}C_6$—formerly considered to be $Cr_4C$—has a unit cube containing ninety-two chromium and twenty-four carbon atoms.[18] In its lattice the Cr atoms form alternate cubo-octahedra and cubes with Cr atoms at their centers. The carbon atoms then occupy positions in which they octahedrally surround the chromium cubooctahedra. Crystallizing with the same lattice are the compounds $Mn_{23}C_6$, $Fe_{21}W_2C_6$, $Fe_{21}Mo_2C_6$, $Cr_{21}W_2C_6$, $(Fe, Mo)_{23}C_6$, and other variable phases with the same total number of metal atoms. Another simpler stoichiometric carbide ratio is the cubic lattice of $Fe_3W_3C$.[19] Other phases with this structure are $Fe_3Mo_3C$, and many variable phases of composition $M_6C$. The $M_{23}C_6$ and $M_6C$ phases are important in the alloy steels.[20]

Several other carbides have unusual compositions and/or structures. The well-known cementite, $Fe_3C$, has an orthorhombic cell containing four molecules. Each carbon atom is placed at the center of a nearly regular trigonal prism of iron atoms in which Fe–Fe varies from 2.49 A to 2.68 A and Fe–C lies between 1.85 A and 2.15 A.[21] Two phases of composition $Fe_2C$, one with an hexagonal cell, have been described.[22] The corresponding cobalt carbide, $Co_2C$, has been prepared.[23] $UC_2$ has the $CaC_2$ structure,[24] but $ThC_2$ has a monoclinic cell in which the carbon atoms are still in $C_2$ groups.[25] Their C–C distance (1.5 A), however, is considerably longer than the acetylenic carbon-carbon distance. The diamond-hard boron carbide, $B_4C$, contains linear $C_3$ chains.[26]

[17] K. Hellström and A. F. Westgren, *Svensk Kem. Tidskr.* **45**, 141 (1933).
[18] A. F. Westgren, *Jernkontorets Ann.* **117**, 501 (1933).
[19] A. F. Westgren, *ibid.* **117**, 1 (1933).
[20] H. Krainer, *Arch. Eisenhüttenw.* **21**, 33, 39 (1950); D. J. Blickwede, M. Cohen, and G. A. Roberts, *Trans. Am. Soc. Metals* **42**, 1161 (1950).
[21] H. Lipson and N. J. Petch, *J. Iron and Steel Inst.* **142**, 95 (1940); N. J. Petch, *ibid.* **149**, 143 (1944); W. Hume-Rothery *et al.*, *ibid.* **145**, 143 (1942).
[22] L. J. E. Hofer, E. M. Cohn, and W. C. Peebles, *J. Am. Chem. Soc.* **71**, 189 (1949).
[23] L. J. E. Hofer and W. C. Peebles, *ibid.* **69**, 893 (1947).
[24] R. E. Rundle *et al.*, *ibid.* **70**, 99 (1948); L. Litz *et al.*, *ibid.* **70**, 1718 (1948); U. Esch and A. Schneider, *Z. anorg. Chem.* **257**, 254 (1948).
[25] E. B. Hunt and R. E. Rundle, *J. Am. Chem. Soc.* **73**, 4777 (1951).
[26] H. K. Clark and J. L. Hoard, *ibid.* **65**, 2115 (1943); **67**, 2279 (1945).

A remarkable property of the metallic carbides is their ability to dissolve excess of either of the pure components. Indeed, almost any composition from the pure metal to the stoichiometric compound is possible in some instances. Only the carbides of the transition elements are metallic in nature, and these are true interstitial compounds and phases, the metalloid atoms, C, occupying the interstices between the atoms of the metal lattice. Interstitial solid solutions of carbon in iron are the basis of steel. As might be anticipated, several pairs of the cubic isomorphous carbides show a continuous series of solid solutions: TiC–VC, TiC–NbC, ZrC–NbC, NbC–TaC, (Ta, Nb)C–VC, VC–TaC, TiC–TaC, TaC–ZrC, TiC–ZrC.[27,28] The pair VC–ZrC is reported to show no solubility, and the pairs ZrC–WC, NbC–WC, VC–WC, TaC–WC, VC–Mo$_2$C, ZrC–Mo$_2$C, NbC–Mo$_2$C, and TaC–Mo$_2$C show limited solubility, the cubic carbide in each case being the solvent.[27]

Carbides of the alkali and alkaline-earth metals are colorless and transparent when pure. Commercial CaC$_2$, however, is a gray, opaque, brittle solid owing to the presence of impurities. Aluminum carbide, Al$_4$C$_3$, is bright yellow as are also most of the rare-earth dicarbides and Be$_2$C. Copper acetylide, Cu$_2$C$_2$, and cerium carbide, CeC$_2$, are red, but most of the remaining carbides are metallic in appearance. The latter have a high electrical conductivity, with a negative temperature coefficient, showing it to be true metallic conduction. More remarkable is the fact that several of the carbides show the phenomenon of superconductivity (see Table 8.1). Thus Nb$_2$C becomes superconducting at 9.18°K, a temperature higher than for any other carbide.

In keeping with their chemical stability, most carbides are very hard, brittle compounds of high melting point. In fact NbC, TaC, and HfC have melting points in the vicinity of 4000° to 4200°C, the highest of any compounds measured. Their hardness makes them very valuable as abrasives and cutting tools. *Carborundum*, SiC, is one of the commonest and best abrasives, being only a little less hard than the diamond. Its use in making grinding wheels, whetstones, etc., has already been mentioned. Also WC, and more recently TaC, have found great use in the making of high-speed cutting tools. The pure carbides are too hard and brittle to be used directly as tools. They are crushed to a fine powder and mixed with a suitable binder, as powdered iron, manganese, or cobalt. This powdered mixture, when pressed into the desired shape and then sintered, forms the material for the tool. The nature and amount of

[27] H. Nowotny and R. Kieffer, *Metallforschung* **2**, 257 (1947).
[28] J. T. Norton and A. L. Mowry, *Trans. A.I.M.E.* **185**, 133 (1949).

the binder have considerable effect upon the hardness and strength of the final product.    Tantalum carbide tools are much more resistant than even the tungsten carbide tools and show no wear after a period of use several times the lifetime of the latter.    An important new laboratory tool is the boron carbide mortar and pestle.    Boron carbide, $B_4C$, has a hardness of 9.5 on the Mohs scale and is exceeded in hardness by few substances. These mortars are much harder than porcelain or agate (hardness 7). Ores, rocks, glass, and even silicon carbide and emery may be powdered in these boron carbide mortars.

**Graphitic Compounds.**    The graphitic compounds[29] are interstitial compounds closely allied to the carbides in certain respects and are logically introduced at this point.    Graphite itself, one of the crystalline allotropic modifications of carbon, is a nearly perfect example of the layer-lattice type of structure, and many of its unusual properties arise from this feature.    The pure material consists of plane sheets of carbon atoms arranged in a regular hexagonal array such that each atom is linked to three equidistant neighbors (Fig. 8.4).    The carbon to carbon distance in these sheets is 1.42 A, and the bond is essentially covalent with single-bond-double-bond resonance.    Pauling and Brockway[30] have as-

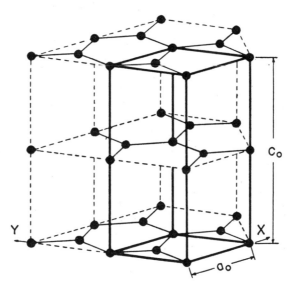

Fig. 8.4.    The structure and unit cell of graphite.    (Wyckoff, *Crystal Structures*, Vol. I; courtesy *Interscience Publishers, Inc.*)

[29] For a good review of earlier work, see H. L. Riley, *Fuel* **24**, 8, 43 (1945).
[30] L. Pauling and L. O. Brockway, *J. Am. Chem. Soc.* **59**, 1223 (1937).

sumed these bonds to have one third double-bond character. These carbon sheets are stacked on one another with an interplanar spacing of about 3.4 A. This rather wide spacing is accompanied by relatively feeble bonding between the layers. The actual bonding forces are chiefly of a residual or van der Waals type, but there is also appreciable metallic character in the linkage. This feature gives rise to the metallic luster of graphite and its good electrical conductivity. The ease with which the feebly bonded layers can slide over one another leads to the important lubricating properties observed for graphite. These peculiar structural characteristics of graphite also result in rather interesting compound formation with certain reagents, through the insertion of atoms, ions, or molecules between the layers.

1. *Graphitic oxide.* When graphite is treated with strong oxidizing agents, such as a mixture of nitric acid and potassium chlorate, it swells in one direction and forms a material varying in color from green to brown to sulfur yellow.[29] Chemical analysis of the product leads to formulas such as $C_{11}H_4O_{5-6}$, and it was formerly assumed that a series of these substances, called graphitic acids, existed. The work of Hofmann and his colleagues[31] has largely served to clear up the true nature of these materials. The hydrogen has been shown to be present as water molecules and not as hydroxide groups, and even very carefully dried samples contain molecular water. The material is actually a graphitic *oxide* with an atomic ratio of carbon to oxygen varying from 6:1 to 6:2.5.[32]

The oxygen atoms appear to be attached to both sides of the sheets at about 1.4 A above or below the sheets. Each oxygen is apparently held by covalent bonds, furnished by the fourth valency, to a pair of adjacent carbon atoms of the sheet, in the epoxy manner similar to that in ethylene oxide. The utilization of these electrons in bonding the oxygens partially reduces the $\pi$-bond character of the layers and results in the loss of the metallic luster and electrical conductivity of the graphite. Another consequence of this oxidation is an expected increase in flexibility of the layers in graphitic oxide as compared to graphite which electron micrographic observations appear to verify.[33] Water, varying in amount up to 95%, is adsorbed on the graphitic oxide sheets. The interplanar spacing is no longer the 3.4 A of graphite but increases to values between 6.4 and 11.3 A, depending upon the oxygen and water content. The limit of the swelling process is apparently reached when each sheet attains

[31] U. Hofmann *et al.*, *Ber.* **61**, 435 (1928); **63**, 1248 (1930); *Z. Elektrochem.* **37**, 613 (1931); *Kolloid-Z.* **58**, 8 (1932); **61**, 297 (1932); *Ann.* **510**, 1 (1934).
[32] G. L. Ruess, *Kolloid-Z.* **110**, 17 (1945); *Monatsh.* **76**, 381 (1947).
[33] R. J. Beckett and R. C. Croft, *J. Phys. Chem.* **56**, 929 (1952).

a unimolecular layer of water molecules on both surfaces.   The substance is homogeneous in spite of its variable composition, and it has been shown that the symmetry of each sheet is maintained by a statistical distribution of the oxygen atoms.   Graphitic oxide is thus an outstanding example of the Berthollide type of compound.

2. *Graphitic salts.*   When graphite is treated with concentrated sulfuric acid containing a small amount of such oxidizing agents as $HNO_3$, $HClO_4$, $CrO_3$, etc., it swells and produces a material with a steel-blue luster known as *blue graphite*.[29]   Addition of even slight amounts of water to the material decomposes it with the regeneration of the graphite.   The last traces of the sulfuric acid are difficult to remove, however, and strongly held oxygen to the extent of 1 to 2% is invariably present.   The regenerated graphite is thus more hydrophilic than the original graphite, and this type of treatment has found some application in the technical purification of graphite.   Blue graphite is essentially graphite hydrogensulfate and corresponds closely to the formula $C_{24}^+HSO_4^- \cdot 2H_2SO_4$ when of maximum sulfate content.   The material appears to be essentially saltlike in character, but it is not known exactly how the negative charges of the sulfate layers are balanced by the graphite layers.   Possibly $H^+$ ions are adsorbed between the graphite layers, thereby providing the necessary positive charges for electrical neutrality.   Sulfuric acid is just one of many compounds (Table 8.3[34]) that are occluded or "intercalated"

TABLE 8.3.   SOME COMPOUNDS THAT INTERCALATE GRAPHITE*

| | | | | |
|---|---|---|---|---|
| $H_2SO_4$ | $CrO_2Cl_2$ | $SbCl_5$ | $RuCl_3$ | $CuS$ |
| $HNO_3$ | $CrO_2F_2$ | $BiCl_5$ | $RhCl_3$ | $FeS_2$ |
| $HClO_4$ | $CuCl_2$ | $TaCl_5$ | $PdCl_4$† | $V_2S_5$ |
| $H_2SeO_4$ | $CuBr_2$ | $FeCl_3$ | $PtCl_4$ | $Sb_2S_5$ |
| $H_3PO_4$ | $AuCl_3$ | $CrCl_3$ | $ICl$ | $Sb_2O_5$ |
| $H_4P_2O_7$ | $AlCl_3$ | $MoCl_5$ | $ICl_3$ | $MoO_3$ |
| $H_3AsO_4$ | $AlBr_3$ | $WCl_6$ | $YCl_3$ | |
| $HF$ | $GaCl_3$ | $UCl_4$ | $SmCl_3$ | |
| | $InCl_3$ | $UO_2Cl_2$ | $GdCl_3$ · | |
| | $TlCl_3$ | $ReCl_4$ | $YbCl_3$ | |
| | $ZrCl_4$ | $CoCl_3$† | $DyCl_3$ | |
| | $HfCl_4$ | | $EuCl_3$ | |

* Chiefly from R. C. Croft, *Nature* **177**, 725 (1953).
† Normally unstable, but stable when intercalated in graphite.

by graphite to produce lamellar compounds.   The graphite hydrogensulfate richest in sulfuric acid corresponds to the insertion of a layer of $HSO_4^-$ groups between every pair of graphite sheets (Fig. 8.5).   Spacings perpendicular to the sheets are thereby expanded to 7.98 A.   In the case

[34] W. Rüdorff, *Z. physik. Chem.* **45**, 42, 174 (1939).

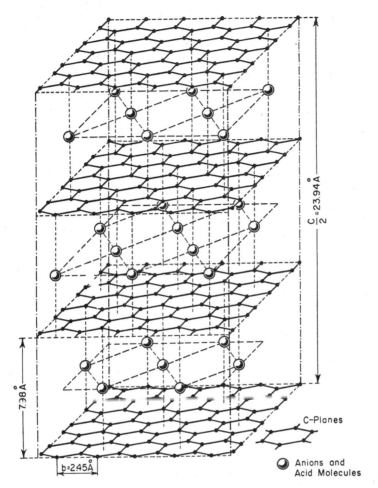

FIG. 8.5.   The structure of graphite hydrogensulfate.   (Rüdorff, *Z. physik.*
*Chem.* **45**, 42.)

of the nitric acid and perchloric acid compounds, this distance is 7.84
and 7.94 A, respectively.[34]   Removal of sulfuric acid from the hydrogensulfate apparently takes place in discrete stages.   One stage results in a
layer of sulfate groups between alternate pairs of graphite layers, while
other stages have only every third, fourth, etc., interlayer spacing expanded to about 8 A by the inserted acid layers.   The electrical resistance, its temperature coefficient, the Hall coefficient, and other properties of graphite hydrogensulfate and its residue compounds have been

studied.[35]   The hydrogenfluoride, whose formula is $C_{24}^+HF_2^-\cdot4HF$, shows very similar X-ray diffraction patterns to the hydrogensulfate.[36]

Lamellar complexes of graphite with metal chlorides have been widely investigated.   Only those metal chlorides containing multivalent metals in their highest oxidation states (Table 8.3) appear to be intercalated.[37] This suggests that the formation of these compounds depends on the transfer of electrons from the incompletely filled bands of graphite to the intercalated metallic cations.   Paramagnetism would then be expected to be a good criterion of the possibility of intercalation, and this is substantiated.[37]   Indeed, paramagnetic compounds other than halides are successfully intercalated (Table 8.3, last column).   The $CrO_2Cl_2$ and $CrO_2F_2$ complexes are stable to aqueous acids and alkalies.[38]   The $CrO_2Cl_2$ complex contains 43.0 to 36.3% of $CrO_2Cl_2$, depending upon the fineness of the graphite, and the interlayer spacing is expanded to about 9 A.   The $CrO_2Cl_2$ is released at 200° to 300°C with enormous exfoliation of the graphite.   There appears to be some possibility of the separation of $AlCl_3$ and $FeCl_3$ during the industrial chlorination of ferruginous aluminum ores by heating with suitable proportions of graphite.[39]   The $FeCl_3$-graphite complex containing 55% $FeCl_3$ has been examined by X-ray and electron diffraction and found to consist of about 17% free graphite and 83% of a $FeCl_3$-graphite compound.[40]   In the compound, single layers of $FeCl_3$ lie between successive parallel graphite layers.

3. *Graphite halides.*   In the electrolytic preparation of fluorine, in which carbon electrodes are used, it was observed that a swelling of the electrodes frequently occurred, with an attending large increase in the resistance of the cell.[41]   Investigations of these phenomena have demonstrated that graphite and "amorphous" carbon quietly take up fluorine at temperatures around 400° to 550°C to form a gray to white solid with the limiting composition $(CF)_x$.[29,42]   The presence of gaseous HF lowers the reaction temperature to 250°−360°C.[43]   Carbon monofluoride is insoluble in all solvents; aqueous acids and bases do not react with it; on heating it decomposes with a slight explosion liberating a large volume

[35] G. R. Hennig et al., *J. Chem. Phys.* 19, 922 (1951); 20, 1438 (1952); *Phys. Rev.* 95, 1088 (1954).

[36] W. Rüdorff, *Z. anorg. Chem.* 254, 319 (1947).

[37] R. C. Croft, *Nature* 177, 725 (1953).

[38] R. C. Croft and R. G. Thomas, *ibid.* 168, 32 (1951).

[39] R. C. Croft, *J. Appl. Chem.* 2, 557 (1952).

[40] J. M. Cowley and J. A. Ibers, *Acta Cryst.* 9, 421 (1956).

[41] See also Vol. III, *This Series.*

[42] O. Ruff and O. Bretschneider, *Z. anorg. allgem. Chem.* 217, 1 (1934).

[43] W. Rüdorff and G. Rüdorff, *Chem. Ber.* 80, 413 (1947).

of finely divided sootlike carbon and volatile carbon fluorides. Hydrogen at 400°C will not react with the fluorine of $(CF)_x$, but zinc dust and acetic acid regenerate the original graphite. The metallic luster is lost and the specific resistance is $10^5$ times that of graphite.

An early structure proposal with $F^-$ ions in six close-packed layers between the carbon sheets is highly improbable.[42] Another study finds the distance between carbon layers varying inversely with the fluorine content with a minimum of 6.6 A and a maximum of about 9 A. The hexagonal lattice of graphite is expanded in the plane of the layers to $a_0 = 2.56$ A.[44] This is compatible with a turbostratic piling of puckered tetrahedral carbon layers with F atoms attached to both sides of the layer by covalent links. A third study is in substantial agreement with this picture.[45]

Another graphite-fluorine compound results from the action of a gaseous fluorine-hydrogen fluoride mixture on graphite at room temperature.[46] The C:F ratio varies from 3.6:1 to 4:1, and the compound is designated tetracarbon monofluoride, $(C_4F)_x$. Occluded HF cannot be completely removed at room temperature by evacuation; boiling dilute acids and alkalies do not attack it. Its electrical resistance is about 100 times that of graphite. The X-ray pattern is distinctly different from that of $(CF)_x$ and shows the graphite layers unchanged except that the interplanar spacing is 5.34 to 5.50 A. The F atoms lie in layers between two C planes, probably at a distance of 1.4 A in a layer below and a layer above each C layer.

Graphite absorbs about 83.5% by weight of bromine when in contact with an atmosphere saturated with bromine vapor, but gives it up again completely on standing in air.[29,47] This uptake of bromine corresponds roughly to the formula $C_8Br$. The bromine-saturated graphites show diffraction patterns with a minimum identity period of 10.4 A, which is best explained by 7.05-A bromine layers separated by pairs of C layers. Graphite bromide is weakly diamagnetic and has a better electrical conductivity than graphite.[48] Exposure of graphite to fast neutrons sharply decreases the initial rate of bromine absorption. Heating, however, again restores the original rate of bromine uptake.[49]

4. *Graphite-potassium alloys.* Graphite is wetted and penetrated by molten potassium metal.[29] Here, again, the crystal form of the graphite

[44] W. Rüdorff and G. Rüdorff, *Z. anorg. Chem.* **253**, 281 (1945).
[45] D. E. Palin and K. D. Wadsworth, *Nature* **162**, 925 (1948).
[46] W. Rüdorff and G. Rüdorff, *Chem. Ber.* **80**, 417 (1947).
[47] W. Rudörff, *Z. anorg. allgem. Chem.* **245**, 383 (1940).
[48] F. R. M. McDonnell *et al.*, *J. Chem. Soc.* **1951**, 191.
[49] A. Novick and T. J. Neubert, *J. Appl. Phys.* **27**, 572 (1956).

is retained; the only change is swelling in the direction perpendicular to the graphite sheets.[50]  Two compounds, $C_8K$, copper red or bronze in color, and $C_{16}K$, steel blue in color, are formed with definite dissociation pressures of potassium.  Treatment with mercury readily removes the potassium from either compound and regenerates the graphite.  Rubidium and cesium, but not sodium, react with graphite in a similar manner.  In $C_8K$ all graphite sheets are interleaved with potassium atoms, whereas in $C_{16}K$ the metal atoms are inserted between alternate sheets.  The marked diamagnetism of graphite is completely destroyed in $C_8K$ which shows a temperature-independent paramagnetism of the same order as that of metallic calcium.  The conductivity of $C_8K$ is better than that of graphite.[48]

**Silicides.**  General methods for preparing the silicides are similar to those for the carbides:[51]

$$5Cu + Si \rightarrow Cu_5Si$$
$$4Mg + SiO_2 \rightarrow Mg_2Si + 2MgO$$

Some metallic silicates may be heated with carbon electrodes in an electric furnace reducing them to silicon and metal and metallic silicides.  Certain silicides may be obtained by a reaction similar to the Goldschmidt *thermite* reaction by heating a mixture of metallic oxide, silica, and aluminum powder.  Most of the known silicides of the metallic elements are listed in Table 8.4.

Some of the silicides are readily hydrolyzed by dilute acids, but the reaction products are more complex than in the case of the carbides.  $Mg_2Si$ is largely used to prepare silicon hydrides.  It would be expected to hydrolyze according to the simple equation

$$Mg_2Si + 4H_2O \rightarrow 2Mg(OH)_2 + SiH_4$$

but instead a mixture of very varied hydrogen compounds is obtained containing $SiH_4$ to $Si_6H_{14}$.  On digesting $CaSi_2$ with hydrochloric acid the compound siloxen, $Si_6O_3H_6$, is obtained (see Chapter 3).  Melting points have been reported for a series of silicides.[52]  Several silicides are superconducting (Table 8.4), the transition temperature for $V_3Si$ being 17.1°K, the highest known for any binary compound.[53]  A few data on

[50] A. Schleede and M. Wellmann, *Z. physik. Chem.* **B18**, 1 (1932).

[51] For a detailed treatment of the preparation and properties of the silicides, see Schwarzkopf and Kieffer, *op. cit.* ref. 16, pp. 319–350.

[52] L. Brewer *et al.*, *The Chemistry and Metallurgy of Miscellaneous Materials—Thermodynamics*, edited by L. L. Quill, McGraw-Hill Book Co., New York, 1950, pp. 40 ff.

[53] G. F. Hardy and J. K. Hulm, *Phys. Rev.* **93**, 1004 (1954).

TABLE 8.4.  KNOWN SILICIDES OF THE METALS

| | | | | | | |
|---|---|---|---|---|---|---|
| $Li_3Si$ | $B_3Si$ | $HfSi$ | $Cr_2Si$ | $MnSi$ | $Ni_2Si_3$ (?) | $NpSi_2$ |
| $NaSi_2$ | $B_6Si$ | $HfSi_3$ | $Cr_2Si_3$ | $Mn_3Si$ | | $PuSi_2$ |
| | | | $Cr_3Si$ | $MnSi_2$ | $RuSi$ | |
| $Cu_3Si$ | $YSi_2$ | $\alpha$-$ThSi_2$* | $Cr_3Si_2$ (?) | $Mn_5Si_3$ | $Ru_2Si_3$ | $NaAlSi_4$ |
| $Cu_5Si$ | $LaSi_2$ | $\beta$-$ThSi_2$* | | | $Ru_3Si_2$ | $Mg_6Si_7Cu_{16}$ |
| $Cu_{31}Si_8$ | $CeSi$ | | $MoSi_2$ | $ReSi_2$ | $RhSi$ | $Mn_3SiAl_9$ |
| | $CeSi_2$ | $VSi_2$ | $Mo_2Si$ | | $Rh_2Si_3$ | $ZrBeSi$ |
| $Mg_2Si$ | $PrSi_2$ | $V_2Si$ | $Mo_2Si_3$ | $FeSi$ | $Rh_3Si_2$ | |
| $Mg_5Si_3$ | $NdSi_2$ | $V_3Si$* | $Mo_3Si$* | $FeSi_2$ | $PdSi$ | |
| | $SmSi_2$ | $V_5Si_3$ | $Mo_5Si_3$ | $Fe_3Si_2$ | $Pd_2Si$ | |
| $CaSi$ | | | | | | |
| $CaSi_2$ | $CSi$ | $NbSi_2$ | $WSi_2$ | $CoSi$ | $OsSi_2$ | |
| $Ca_2Si$ | | $Nb_5Si_3$ | $W_2Si_3$ | $CoSi_2$ | $Os_2Si_3$ | |
| $Ca_3Si_2$ | $TiSi_2$ | | $W_3Si_2$* | $Co_2Si$ | $IrSi$ | |
| | $Ti_2Si$ | $TaSi_2$ | $W_5Si_3$ | $CoSi_3$ | $Ir_2Si_3$ | |
| $SrSi$ | $Ti_5Si_3$ | $Ta_2Si$ | | $Co_3Si_2$ | $Ir_3Si_2$ | |
| $SrSi_2$ | | $Ta_4Si$ | $USi$ | | $PtSi$ | |
| | $ZrSi_2$ | $Ta_5Si_3$ | $\alpha$-$USi_2$ | $NiSi$ | $Pt_2Si$ | |
| $BaSi$ | $Zr_2Si$ | | $\beta$-$USi_2$ | $Ni_2Si$ | | |
| $BaSi_2$ | $Zr_5Si_3$ | $CrSi$ | $U_3Si$ | $Ni_3Si$ | | |
| $BaSi_3$ | | $CrSi_2$ | $U_3Si_2$ | $Ni_3Si_2$ | | |

* These silicides are superconducting at some temperature above $1.20°K$.

high-melting silicide solid solutions are available.  Various two-component mixtures of the disilicides of Cr, Mo, W, Ti, and Ta have been investigated.[54]  The system $Ti_5Si_3$–$Zr_5Si_3$ is continuously soluble, but in $Ti_5Si_3$–$Mo_5Si_3$ and $Ti_5Si_3$–$W_5Si_3$ only partial replacement of Ti by Mo or W is permitted.[55]  Ternary silicides that have been recognized as compounds are listed in the last column of Table 8.4.  The so-called $\beta$(AlCrSi) phase of composition approximating $CrSi_2Al_4$ is not a true compound but a solid solution of aluminum in $CrSi_2$.[56]

The silicides form excellent crystals.  In general they have a metallic luster varying from silver white to lead gray.  When very rich in silicon they approach "metallic" silicon in color but are usually more gray.  Some of them tarnish somewhat in the air.  From Table 8.4 it is seen that definite types of compounds are formed, particularly the compositions MSi, $MSi_2$, and $M_2Si$, and that the usual valence rules are largely violated.  The silicon atom is too large to go into the interstices of the metal lattices; hence solid solutions containing silicon are substitutional in nature, and the silicides show a great variety of crystal structure types.  At least six different structures are found among the disilicides of the

[54] H. Nowotny et al., Monatsh. 83, 1243 (1952); R. Kieffer, F. Benesovsky, and H. Schroth, Z. Metallkunde 44, 437 (1953).

[55] H. Schachner, E. Cerwenka, and H. Nowotny, Monatsh. 85, 245 (1954).

[56] K. Robinson, Acta Cryst. 6, 667 (1953).

transition metals of the IV–VI groups. $TiSi_2$ has the C54 structure; $ZrSi_2$ the C49 structure; $VSi_2$, $NbSi_2$, $TaSi_2$, and $CrSi_2$ are C40; $MoSi_2$ and $WSi_2$ are C11b; $\alpha$-$ThSi_2$, $\alpha$-$USi_2$, $NpSi_2$, and $PuSi_2$ (also the rare-earth disilicides) are tetragonal with space group I4/$amd$; and $\beta$-$ThSi_2$ and $\beta$-$USi_2$ are hexagonal, C6/$mmm$. The three copper silicides $Cu_5Si$, $Cu_{31}Si_8$, and $Cu_3Si$ are, respectively, $\beta$, $\gamma$, and $\epsilon$ "electron compounds."[57] Several $M_3Si$ compounds, $Cr_3Si$, $V_3Si$, and $Mo_3Si$, crystallize with the $\beta$-tungsten structure, A15-type. The $M_5Si_3$ compounds are isomorphous and have hexagonal cells. The silicides $FeSi$, $CrSi$, $MnSi$, $CoSi$, and $NiSi$ are isomorphous and possess the cubic space group $T^4$–$P2_13$. They are especially interesting as examples of coordination number 7. In $FeSi$, for instance, each iron atom has seven silicon neighbors at distances 2.29 A (1), 2.34 A (3), and 2.52 A (3), and six iron atoms at a greater distance, 2.75 A. A complete discussion of the $FeSi$ structure has been given in terms of Pauling's resonating-valence-bond theory.[58]

Ferrosilicon is the silicide of greatest technical importance because of its use in the manufacture of steel. Depending upon its method of preparation, ferrosilicon with a silicon content up to 90% can be obtained. Thermal analysis has revealed with certainty only the compound $FeSi$ in ferrosilicon; alloys richer in iron are apparently mixed crystals of $FeSi$ richer in iron; alloys richer in silicon always contain microscopic crystals of free silicon. Ca-Si alloys of about 30 to 35% calcium (by weight) are also used as deoxidizers in the production of stainless steels.

**Borides.**   Metallic borides[59] are nearly as numerous as the silicides. In general, the same reactions used for the preparation of the carbides and silicides are available for boride synthesis. They may also be prepared by heating $B_2O_3$ with carbides and by electrolysis of fused-salt baths containing the metal oxide and boron oxide.[60]  Some borides may be produced by vapor-phase decomposition on incandescent tungsten filaments yielding fine crystalline deposits:[61]

$$HfCl_4 + 2BBr_3 + 5H_2 \rightarrow HfB_2 + 4HCl + 6HBr$$

Most of the known metallic borides are listed in Table 8.5.

[57] W. Hume-Rothery and G. V. Raynor, *The Structure of Metals and Alloys*, The Institute of Metals, London, 3rd Edition, 1954, pp. 194–210.

[58] L. Pauling and A. M. Soldate, *Acta Cryst.* 1, 212 (1948).

[59] Excellent reviews of the metallic borides have been given by Schwarzkopf and Kieffer, *op. cit.* ref. 16, pp. 19–24, 271–315; R. Kiessling, *Acta Chem. Scand.* 4, 209–227 (1950).

[60] L. Andrieux and G. Weiss, *Bull. soc. chim. France* 15, 598 (1948).

[61] K. Moers, *Z. anorg. allgem. Chem.* 198, 243 (1931); I. E. Campbell et al., *J. Electrochem. Soc.* 96, 318 (1949).

TABLE 8.5. KNOWN BORIDES OF THE METALS

| | | | |
|---|---|---|---|
| $Cu_3B_2$ | $Ti_2B$ | $CrB$ | $CoB$ |
| | $Ti_2B_5$ | $CrB_2$ | $CoB_2$ |
| $CaB_6$ | | $Cr_2B$ | $Co_2B$ |
| $BaB_6$ | $ZrB*(?)$ | $Cr_3B_2$ | |
| $SrB_6$ | $ZrB_2$ | $Cr_3B_4$ | $NiB$ |
| | $ZrB_{12}$ | | $NiB_2$ |
| $MgB_2$ | | $MoB$ | $Ni_2B$ |
| $MgB_4$ | $HfB$ | $MoB_2$ | |
| $Mg_3B_2$ | $HfB_2$ | $Mo_2B*$ | $RuB$ |
| | | $Mo_2B_5$ | $RuB_2$ |
| $AlB_2$ | $ThB$ | $Mo_3B_2$ | $Ru_2B$ |
| $AlB_{12}$ | $ThB_2$ | | $Ru_2B_3$ |
| | $ThB_4$ | $WB$ | |
| $YB_6$ | $ThB_6$ | $WB_2$ | $RhB$ |
| $YbB_6$ | | $W_2B*$ | $Rh_2B$ |
| $LaB_6$ | $VB$ | $W_2B_5$ | |
| $CeB_4$ | $VB_2$ | | $OsB$ |
| $CeB_6$ | $V_2B$ | $UB_2$ | |
| $NdB_6$ | | $UB_4$ | $IrB$ |
| $PrB_6$ | $NbB*$ | $UB_{12}$ | $IrB_2$ |
| $GdB_6$ | $NbB_2$ | | $Ir_3B_2$ |
| $ErB_6$ | $Nb_2B$ | $MnB$ | |
| | $Nb_3B$ | $MnB_2$ | $Mo_7Al_6B_7$ |
| $CB_4$ | $Nb_3B_4$ | $Mn_2B$ | $Mo_2CoB_2$ |
| | | $Mn_3B_4$ | $Mo_2NiB_2$ |
| $SiB_3$ | $TaB$ | | $Mo_2FeB_4$ |
| $SiB_6$ | $TaB_2$ | $FeB$ | $Mo_2CoB_4$ |
| | $Ta_2B*(?)$ | $Fe_2B$ | $Mo_2NiB_4$ |
| $TiB$ | $Ta_3B$ | | |
| $TiB_2$ | $Ta_3B_4$ | | |

* These borides are superconducting at some temperature above 1.20°K.

There is evidence that the boride formed on the reaction of magnesium and $B_2O_3$ is $MgB_2$ and not $Mg_3B_2$.[62] The latter is probably an unstable compound. Magnesium diboride is formed on heating the elements in an atmosphere of hydrogen. Magnesium diboride has the $AlB_2$ structure with a density of 2.633. The single-bond radius of boron in this compound is 0.77 A. Other borides with the $AlB_2$ structure are $TiB_2$, $VB_2$, $CrB_2$, $ZrB_2$, $NbB_2$, $TaB_2$, and $MoB_2$.

Borides are usually not hydrolyzed or attacked by hydrochloric acid, although $Mg_3B_2$ yields a mixture of boron hydrides on hydrolysis. The simplest hydride, $BH_3$, is not known; instead $B_2H_6$ is obtained along with the main product, tetraborane, $B_4H_{10}$. Aqua regia, $HNO_3$, and hot $H_2SO_4$, however, attack many borides and nearly all of them are decomposed by fused alkalies and peroxides. The poorer the compounds in

[62] M. E. Jones and R. E. Marsh, *J. Am. Chem. Soc.* **76**, 1434 (1954).

boron the more readily acids attack them; thus $Cr_3B_2$ is slightly attacked but CrB is not.    All borides of Ti, Zr, V, Nb, and Ta except the diborides, $MB_2$, are decomposed when heated with carbon.[63]    Similarly, the borides of Cr and W react to form nitrides when heated with dry $NH_3$.[64]    The thermally most stable borides of the transition metals of Group IV are the diborides, while the monoborides appear to be the most stable for Group VI elements.    The different boride phases of Group V transition metals appear about equally stable.    Highest melting of the transition metal bromides is $ZrB_2$, 3040°C.

All borides have a strong metallic luster.    Their formulas, such as $CaB_6$, $AlB_{12}$, and $CB_4$, are more unusual from the standpoint of ordinary valence rules than those of the carbides and silicides.    They are poorer conductors than the carbides and nitrides.    Like the carbides they are very hard and brittle.    $TiB_2$ scratches corundum and silicon carbide, and both it and $Cr_3B_2$ are rated +9 on the Mohs scale.

The borides are interstitial structures, and some of their most interesting aspects relate to their crystal structures.    There is a general tendency for the boron atoms to form chains, nets, or three-dimensional frameworks with increasing boron content.[59]    The radius of the boron atom in metal-boron or boron-boron contacts is about 0.86 to 0.88 A.    Several $M_2B$-borides have the $CuAl_2$-type (C16) structure with isolated boron atoms surrounded by eight metal neighbors at equal distances.    The mono-borides, MB, crystallize in three closely related structures: FeB-type, MoB-type, and CrB-type.    Each B atom is at the center of a trigonal prism of metal atoms, and forms a zigzag chain with other borons.    The

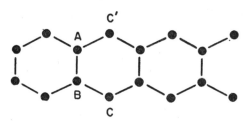

FIG. 8.6.    Double boron chains in the $M_3B_4$ borides.

$M_3B_4$-borides possess double chains (Fig. 8.6) which might be regarded as fragments of hexagonal boron nets.    Boron-boron distances in either half of the double chain, as at $BC$ or $AC'$, are the expected $2r_B$, but the distance $AB$ between adjacent boron atoms in different halves is only

[63] F. W. Glaser, *J. Metals* **4**, 391 (1952).
[64] R. Kiessling and Y. H. Liu, *ibid.* **3**, 639 (1951).

1.50 A and appears to be a regular covalent double bond. The next step leads to the borides of the $AlB_2$-type (C32) and the $M_2B_5$-borides with extended two-dimensional hexagonal nets of boron atoms. The nets are either plane $(H)$ or slightly puckered $(K)$, and each boron's neighbors are at the usual B–B distance. The metal atoms in these structures are in close-packed sheets $(A, B, C$ in the usual notation of hexagonal and cubic close-packing). The sequence of metal sheets and boron nets is then $AHAHAH$ for the $AlB_2$-type, $AHAKBHBKAHA$ for the $W_2B_5$-type, and $AHAKBHBKCHCKAHA$ for the $Mo_2B_5$-type. A great number of borides crystallize with the $CaB_6$ structure $(D2_1)$. In all of these, the metal atoms are arranged in a simple cubic lattice, and the borons form a three-dimensional framework with the metal atoms in the interstices. Borides of the $MB_{12}$-type are closely related to the $MB_6$-type.

**Nitrides.** Two groups of binary compounds of nitrogen with metals are known. One group is entirely saltlike, very explosive, and contains the group $N_3^-$. These are the salts of the very unstable hydrazoic acid, $HN_3$.[65] The salts in general are less explosive than the pure acid and vary somewhat in this property. The univalent heavy metal azides are very explosive, while others require strong percussion. Lead azide, $Pb(N_3)_2$, is used as a detonator for high explosives. The alkali-metal azides are not exploded on percussion, and can almost be melted before they explode. The azide ion, $N_3^-$, is linear and symmetrical, with each N–N distance equal to 1.15 A. Some of the known azides and other nitrides of the metals are listed in Table 8.6.

The other large class of nitrides is characterized by stability. Many of them are related to ammonia in which the hydrogen has been replaced by the metals acting with their normal valence ($Li_3N$, $Mg_3N_2$). Another group of them contains nitrogen and the metal combined atom for atom (TiN, CbN, TaN, VN) although the metal is not trivalent. In these and related solid solutions it is evident that geometry dictates the structure, which is a packing of the small nitrogen atoms in certain interstices of the metal lattices.[66]

Several methods of preparation are important. Some of the nitrides can be produced by heating the corresponding metal amide, analogous to the decomposition of a hydroxide to give the oxide:

$$3Ba(NH_2)_2 \rightarrow Ba_3N_2 + 4NH_3$$

[65] Hydrazoic acid and the azides are discussed in detail by H. H. Sisler in Vol. V, This Series.

[66] The nitrides of the transition elements of Groups IV–VI are treated in detail by: Schwarzkopf and Kieffer, *op. cit.* ref. 16, pp. 223–268. The nitrides of the metals of the first long period have been reviewed by: R. Juza, *Chemie* **58**, 25 (1945).

TABLE 8.6.  AZIDES AND NITRIDES OF THE METALS

| Azides | Nitrides | | | |
|---|---|---|---|---|
| $NH_4N_3$ | $Li_3N$ | AlN | VN* | $MnN_2$ |
| $NaN_3$ | $Na_3N$ | GaN | $V_3N$ | $Mn_2N$ |
| $KN_3$ | $K_3N$ (?) | $Ga_3N_4$ | NbN* | $Mn_3N_2$ |
| $RbN_3$ | $Rb_3N$ | InN | $Nb_2N$ | $Mn_4N$ |
| $CsN_3$ | $Cs_3N$ | | $Nb_4N_3$* | |
| | | ScN | TaN | $Re_2N$ (?) |
| $Ca(N_3)_2$ | $Be_3N_2$ | LaN | $Ta_2N$ | |
| $Sr(N_3)_2$ | $Mg_3N_2$ | GdN | $Ta_3N_5$ | $Fe_2N$ |
| $Ba(N_3)_2$ | $Ca_3N_2$ | PrN | | $Fe_3N$ |
| $Ra(N_3)_2$ | $Sr_3N_2$ | CeN | BiN | $Fe_4N$ |
| | $Ba_3N_2$ | NdN | | |
| $HgN_3$ | | | CrN | $Co_2N$ |
| $AgN_3$ | $Cu_3N$ | $Si_3N_4$ | $Cr_2N$ | $Co_3N$ |
| $CuN_3$ | $Ag_3N$ | $Ge_3N_2$ | $Cr_3N$ | $Ni_3N$ |
| $TlN_3$ | $Hg_3N_2$ | $Ge_3N_4$ | MoN* | |
| $Pb(N_3)_2$ | $Cd_3N_2$ | $Sn_3N_4$ (?) | $Mo_2N$* | NpN |
| $Fe(N_3)_2$ | $Zn_3N_2$ | | | PuN |
| $Cd(N_3)_2$ | | $TiN$* | WN | |
| | BN | $Ti_3N_4$ | $W_2N$ | LiMgN |
| | $BN_2$ | ZrN* | $W_2N_3$ | LiZnN |
| | | HfN | UN | $Li_3FeN_2$ |
| | | ThN | $UN_2$ | $Li_3AlN_2$ |
| | | $Th_3N_4$ | $U_2N_3$ | $Li_3GaN_2$ |
| | | | $U_3N_4$ | $Li_5SiN_3$ |
| | | | | $Li_5TiN_3$ |
| | | | | $Li_5GeN_3$ |

* These nitrides are superconducting at some temperature above 1.20°K.

Many of the nitrides may be synthesized directly from the metal and nitrogen:

$$3Mg + N_2 \rightarrow Mg_3N_2$$

Variations of this involve heating the metal or metal oxide with ammonia.   Nitrides may also be deposited on incandescent tungsten filaments from vapor mixtures of the respective metal halide, $N_2$, and $H_2$:

$$2TiCl_4 + N_2 + 4H_2 \rightarrow 2TiN + 8HCl$$

The most important reaction of the nitrides is their hydrolysis to yield ammonia:

$$Ca_3N_2 + 6H_2O \rightarrow 3Ca(OH)_2 + 2NH_3$$

Not all of them hydrolyze equally readily.   Some always have the odor of ammonia about them due to decomposition by atmospheric moisture. Both $Mn_3N_2$ and $W_2N_3$ are attacked very slowly, while CrN is not attacked even at 200°C. Acids generally attack them more easily than water, resulting in the formation of ammonium salts. Thermal decomposition into the metal and nitrogen is difficult, as in the case of most oxides; however, the noble metal nitrides decompose more easily just as with the oxides. TiN, ZrN, HfN, Th$_3$N$_4$, UN, and others are the most thermostable with a nitrogen partial pressure of 10$^{-3}$ atmospheres or less at 2500°K.[67] Many of the nitrides are difficult to reduce with hydrogen.

In physical properties the nitrides parallel the oxides to a considerable extent. Many have high melting points: Ta$_2$N, 3090°C; ZrN, 2980°C; TiN, 2930°C. Their colors vary: CrN, yellow; NbN, light gray; TaN, dark gray; VN, gray brown; HfN and ZrN, yellow brown; TiN, light brown to bronze brown. The metallic ones are conductors of electricity, being intermediate between the carbides and the borides in this respect. Several nitrides are superconducting (Table 8.6), NbN having the rather high transition temperature of 14.7°K. The free energies, heats of formation, and entropies of formation at room temperature have been determined for several nitrides.[67] Except for TaN, the mononitrides of the metals of groups IV and V have the NaCl structure (B1). Like the corresponding carbides, they are completely miscible with the exception of the systems ZrN–VN and HfN–VN.[66] Limited solid solubility has been reported for several M$_3$N pairs: (Li, Co)$_3$N to 17 atomic per cent Co; (Li, Ni)$_3$N to 21 atomic per cent Ni; and (Li, Cu)$_3$N to 10 atomic per cent Cu.[68]

Solid solutions of mononitrides in monocarbides are common when both have the NaCl structure. A famous example is the system TiN–TiC which leads to the formation of the so-called "blast-furnace cubes" (Hochofenwürfel), first described by Wöhler.[69] The 20 per cent TiC–80 per cent TiN composition is usually regarded as a solid solution,[70] but some have considered it a true carbonitride compound. Its significance in iron and steel metallurgy has been widely discussed.[71] Among the completely miscible carbide-nitride systems are TiC–VN, TiC–TiN, TiC–NbN, TiC–ZrN, NbC–VN, NbC–TiN, NbC–NbN, VC–VN, VC–TiN, VC–NbN, and UC–UN. Molybdenum,[72] cobalt,[73] manganese,[74]

[67] L. Brewer et al., loc. cit. ref. 50.
[68] W. Sachsze and R. Juza, *Z. anorg. Chem.* **259**, 278 (1949).
[69] F. Wöhler, *Liebigs Ann.* **73**, 34 (1850).
[70] V. M. Goldschmidt, *Nachr. Ges. Wiss., Göttingen* 390 (1927); J. R. Weeks, D. McLachlan, Jr., and J. R. Lewis, *J. Metals* **3**, *Trans.*, 393 (1951).
[71] Gmelin, *Handbuch d. Anorg. Chemie*, Syst. No. 41 (Ti), Verlag Chemie, Weinheim, 1951, pp. 276, 369–370.
[72] S. P. Ghosh, *J. Ind. Chem. Soc.* **30**, 98 (1953).
[73] J. Clarke and K. H. Jack, *Chemistry and Industry* 1951, 1004.
[74] K. H. Jack, *Proc. Roy. Soc. (London)* **195A**, 41 (1948).

and iron[74] also form carbonitrides.    The δ-iron nitride phase has a homo-
geneity range for carbon extending approximately to the composition
$Fe_8C_3N$, the phase remaining isomorphous with $Fe_2N$.    Carbonitrides
of the ε-phase range from composition $Fe_2X$ to $Fe_3X$ in which the maximum carbon content is not less than 16 atomic per cent.    The nitrides
and carbonitrides enter into the processes of tempering and case-harden-
ing of steel.[74]    The ternary nitrides listed in Table 8.6 appear to be
true compounds.[75]

Boron nitride, BN, has long been one of the most interesting nitrides
to the chemist.    It is actively oxidized in air at 800° to 900°C after 2
hours to $B_2O_3$.[76]    A redetermination of its crystal structure has disclosed
that its structure, long thought identical
with that of graphite, is slightly different.[77]
The difference between them lies in the nature of the layer packing.    The hexagonal
rings in BN are stacked directly on top of
one another (Fig. 8.7), whereas in graphite
(Fig. 8.4) the atoms of alternate layers lie
between the centers of the hexagonal rings
of adjacent layers.    The B–N bond has an
electrical dipole moment, and it is suggested
that the different packing in BN may result
from the interlayer interaction of these di-
poles.    The length of the coplanar B–N
bonds is 1.446 A, somewhat shorter than
the sum (1.58 A) of the single-bond covalent
radii.    Explanations of the short bond are
conflicting.    It has been explained as a
resonating single bond-double bond,[78] but
this is at variance with its electrical prop-

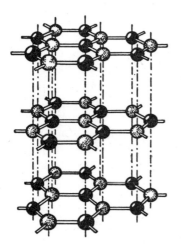

FIG. 8.7.   The structure of
boron nitride.   (Pease, *Acta
Cryst.* **5**, 356.)

erties; it is not, like graphite, a good conductor of electricity.    Others
have argued that its whiteness and low conductivity demand that the
bond be single, thus leaving its shortness unexplained.[79]    Thermodynamic
properties of BN are: Debye characteristic temperature $\theta_2 = 598°K$; at
298.16°K, $C_p = 4.78_3$ cal/mole deg and $S^0 = 3.67_3$ eu; heat of combustion

[75] R. Juza and F. Hund, *Z. anorg. Chem.* **257**, 1, 13 (1948); R. Juza, H. H. Weber,
and E. Meyer-Simon, *ibid.* **273**, 48 (1953).
[76] I. L. Zagyanskii and G. V. Samsonov, *J. Appl. Chem. U.S.S.R.* **25**, 629 (1952).
[77] R. S. Pease, *Acta Cryst.* **5**, 356 (1952).
[78] H. Levy and L. O. Brockway, *J. Am. Chem. Soc.* **59**, 2085 (1937).
[79] W. Hückel, *Anorganische Strukturchemie*, Enke, Stuttgart, 1948, p. 586.

is $90.2 \pm 0.5$ kcal/mole; heat of formation is exothermic $60.7 \pm 0.7$ kcal/mole.[80]

Cubic boron nitride, borazon, has been reported as being the hardest known substance.[81] Boron and nitrogen brought together at one million psi and 3000°F form the cubic nitride. The packing of the atoms is comparable to that in the diamond. Crystals thus far prepared have been white, yellow, red, brown gray, or black. In contrast to diamond, which ozidizes in air at 1600°F, the borazon can withstand temperatures up to 3500°F. This high temperature-resistance property presents great potentialities for the product in industrial tools.

**Phosphides, Arsenides, Antimonides, and Bismuthides.** Analogous to ammonia, the hydrogen of phosphine and arsine can be replaced by metals to yield phosphides and arsenides. $PH_3$ with potassium or sodium in liquid ammonia forms white needles of $KPH_2$ or $NaPH_2$. On warming, these compounds lose $PH_3$ and are converted to the normal phosphide:

$$3KPH_2 \rightarrow K_3P + 2PH_3$$

With arsine and metallic calcium, $Ca_3As_2$ can be prepared in a similar fashion.

The phosphides and arsenides which do not contain hydrogen are much more numerous (Table 8.7). Indeed, seven phosphides of tin are reported: $Sn_5P_2$, $Sn_2P$, $Sn_3P$, $SnP$, $SnP_2$, $Sn_4P_3$, and $SnP_3$. Six copper phosphides are listed: $Cu_3P$, $Cu_5P_2$, $Cu_2P$, $Cu_3P_2$, $CuP$, and $CuP_2$. Many phosphides, arsenides, antimonides, etc., are readily prepared by direct union of the corresponding element with the metals. The phosphorus is usually supplied in the vapor state, while arsenic, antimony, or bismuth is simply fused with the other metal in an atmosphere of hydrogen.[82] Phosphides can also be prepared by reducing phosphates with carbon in the electric furnace:

$$Ca_3(PO_4)_2 + 8C \rightarrow Ca_3P_2 + 8CO$$

Electrolytic synthesis of phosphides, arsenides, and similar compounds is well-known. A fused bath of phosphate (or arsenate) containing metallic oxides or halides is electrolyzed, whereupon metallic phosphides (or arsenides) are formed and easily isolated at the cathode.[83]

---

[80] A. S. Dworkin, D. J. Sasmor, and E. R. Van Artsdalen, *J. Chem. Phys.* **22**, 837 (1954).

[81] *Chem. and Eng. News* **36**, 28 (1957).

[82] M. I. Kochnev, *J. Applied Chem. U.S.S.R.* **23**, 595 (1950) (Engl. trans.).

[83] J. L. Andrieux, *Congr. chim. ind., Compt. rend. 18me congr., Nancy*, Sept.–Oct., 1938, pp. 124–127; M. Chene, *Ann. chim.* **15**, 187 (1941).

TABLE 8.7. FORMULAS AND STRUCTURES OF SOME PHOSPHIDES, ARSENIDES, ANTIMONIDES, AND BISMUTHIDES

| NaCl-type B1 | NiAs-type B8 | Zinc blende-type B3 | MnP-type B31 | Na₃As-type DO₁₈ | Cu₂Sb-type C38 |
|---|---|---|---|---|---|
| CeAs | CrAs (?) | AlAs | CoAs | Li₃As | Cr₂As |
| LaAs | FeAs (?) | AlP | CrAs | Na₃As | Fe₂As |
| NdAs | MnAs | AlSb | FeAs | K₃As | Mn₂As |
| PrAs | NiAs | GaAs | MnAs (?) | α-Li₃Sb | Cu₂Sb |
| SnAs | CoSb | InAs | CoP | Na₃Sb | Mn₂Sb |
| CeSb | CrSb | GaP | CrP | K₃Sb | |
| LaSb | FeSb | GaSb | FeP | Li₃P | |
| NdSb | MnSb | InP | MnP | Na₃P | **Fe₃P-type** |
| PdSb | NiSb | InSb | WP | Na₃Bi | |
| PrSb | PtSb | | RhSb | K₃Bi | Fe₃P |
| SnSb | VP | | | | Cr₃P |
| NdP | RhBi | | | | Mn₃P |
| α-ZrP | | **La₂O₃-type D52** | **Mn₂O₃-type D5₃** | **Zn₃P₂-type D5₉** | Mo₃P |
| UBi | | | | | Ni₃P |

| | | Mg₃Bi₂ | Bi₃P₂ | Zn₃P₂ | |
|---|---|---|---|---|---|
| **Pyrite-type C2** | **Marcasite-type C18** | Mg₃Sb₂ | Mg₃As₂ | Cd₃P₂ | **Fe₂P-type C22** |
| | | Zn₃Sb₂ | Mg₃P₂ | Zn₃As₂ | |
| | | | | Cd₃As₂ | |
| PtAs₂ | FeAs₂ | | | | Fe₂P |
| PdAs₂ | *NiAs₂ | | | | Mn₂P |
| AuSb₂ | CoAs₂ | | | | Ni₂P |
| PdSb₂ | CoSb₂ | | | | |
| PtSb₂ | FeSb₂ | | Miscellaneous structure types | | |
| PtP₂ | NiSb₂ | | | | |
| PtBi₂ | FeP₂ | Ag₃Sb | AsSb | Rh₂P | β-TaP |
| | | Ag₂Sb | TiP | KBi₂ | MoP |
| | | †NiAs₂ | β-ZrP | Au₂Bi | Th₃P₄ |
| | | β-Cu₁₂Sb₄ | Li₃Bi | Tl₇Sb₂ | CdSb |
| | | Cu₃Sb | β-Li₃Sb | α-NbP | ZnSb |
| | | Cu₂As | InBi | α-TaP | In₂Bi |
| | | Cu₃P | InP | β-NbP | Co₂P |
| | | | TlSb | | |
| | | | TlBi | | |

\* Rammelsbergite.

† Pararammelsbergite.

Metallic character is much more evident in most of these compounds than in the nitrides. The arsenides, antimonides, and bismuthides, indeed, frequently have the properties of intermetallic compounds, and properly deserve discussion with these compounds. The phosphides of the baser metals are resistant to heat. $Ca_3P_2$ is not reduced by hydrogen at 900°C and fuses with difficulty. Phosphides of the more noble metals are reversibly decomposed by heat. Thus, $AgP_2$ has an equilibrium vapor pressure of 94 mm at 605°C, and CuP has one of 214 mm at 570°C. The more metallic ones (the more noble metals) are little hydrolyzed, while the red to brown compounds of the baser metals hydrolyze readily:

$$Ca_3P_2 + 6H_2O \rightarrow 3Ca(OH)_2 + 2PH_3$$

Ordinary $Ca_3P_2$ during hydrolysis also yields a certain amount of the spontaneously flammable $P_2H_4$, which by its presence in the $PH_3$ gas causes the latter to take fire when in contact with the air. High purity $AlP_2$, however, forms pure $PH_3$.[84] Whether absolutely pure $Ca_3P_2$ would yield only $PH_3$ has not been established. Some of the arsenides and antimonides show their relationship to the phosphides by a similar hydrolysis to form $AsH_3$ and $SbH_3$.

A few of these compounds have unexpectedly high melting points compared with those of their constituents. Thus $Mg_3Sb_2$ melts at 1228°C, compared with magnesium at 651°C and antimony at 630.5°C. $Li_3Bi$ melts at 1145°C, lithium at 186°C, and bismuth at 271°C. Accompanying these high melting points are high heats of formation (e.g., 68 kcal for $Mg_3Sb_2$), so that combination of the constituent elements on melting may take place explosively. Data have been reported on the melting points and stabilities of a few phosphides.[85]

The phosphides, arsenides, antimonides, etc., crystallize in many structure types (Table 8.7). For MX compounds the frequently observed structures are NaCl-type, NiAs-type, zinc blende-type, and MnP-type. Metallic character, as evidenced by metallic luster, semiconduction, and magnetic properties, is highly common among the MX types as well as with the $MX_2$ compounds of pyrite and marcasite types. GaAs and InAs[86] have been obtained as $n$-type semiconductors, as has also $K_3Sb$.[87] InSb has been produced as an $n$-type conductor by substituting Group VI impurity elements for Sb and as a $p$-type conductor by replacing indium with small amounts of Group II elements.[88] The ferromagnetism of Mn–P alloys appears to be due to the compound MnP over the range 27 to 58 mole per cent P.[89] CrSb has been investigated for the relation between its antiferromagnetism and its crystal structure.[90] Diatomic $X_2$ groups occur in the pyrite- and marcasite-type $MX_2$ compounds.

[84] W. E. White and A. H. Bushey, *J. Am. Chem. Soc.* **66**, 1666 (1944).
[85] Brewer *et al.*, *loc. cit.* ref. 52.
[86] F. Gans, J. Lagrenaudie, and P. Seguin, *Compt. rend.* **237**, 310 (1953).
[87] R. Suhrmann and Cl. Kangro, *Naturwiss.* **40**, 137 (1953).
[88] H. J. Hrostowski, *Bell Labs. Record* **34**, 246 (1956).
[89] K. H. Sweeny and A. B. Scott, *J. Chem. Phys.* **22**, 917 (1954).
[90] B. T. M. Willis, *Acta Cryst.* **6**, 425 (1953).

The $M_3X_2$ compounds are especially interesting from their bond character. Those crystallizing with the $Mn_2O_3$-type or $La_2O_3$-type structures are ionic and contain $P^{-3}$, $As^{-3}$, etc., ions. $Mg_3P_2$ is transparent, and all the $Mg_3X_2$ compounds are saltlike. The $Zn_3P_2$-type compounds, however, although closely related to the $Mn_2O_3$-type phosphides and arsenides, have metallic conductivity and are opaque.

Several ternary compounds have been structurally characterized. LiMgP, LiZnP, and LiZnAs are reported to have the $CaF_2$-type structure, C1.[91] The compounds, $Li_3AlP_2$ and $Li_3AlAs_2$, are saltlike in character and are based on rhombically deformed superstructures of the $CaF_2$-type lattice.[92] CuMgAs, AgMgAs, and $MgNi_2Sb$ have also been investigated.

The metallic properties of the heavy-metal phosphides permit them to mix or fuse with other metals and alloys. This admixture of phosphide may strongly affect the properties of the metal or alloy. Thus, in phosphor bronze it is advantageous, but in iron or steel it is harmful, since it leads to cold-shortness.

**Hydrides.** The chemistry and applications of the hydrides are so extensive and important that a voluminous literature has appeared.[93] Indeed, hydrogen combines with nearly all the elements, resulting in products of three general classes: (1) covalent hydrides, (2) ionic hydrides, and (3) metallic hydrides (Table 8.8). The members of class (1) are largely molecular compounds and volatile in nature, those of class (2) are saltlike in character, and those of the third class are interstitial compounds or solid solutions with metallic binding. The *borderline hydrides* are relatively unstable compounds with properties rather intermediate between those of the covalent hydrides and those of the transition metal hydrides. Division between the other classes is not entirely sharp in all cases.

The ability of an element to form volatile hydrides appears to be a function of its electronegativity. It has been pointed out[94] that the electronegativity of those elements forming volatile covalent hydrides

[91] H. Nowotny and K. Bachmayer, *Monatsh.* **80**, 734 (1949); **81**, 488 (1950).

[92] R. Juza and W. Schulz, *Z. anorg. allgem. Chem.* **269**, 1–12 (1952).

[93] Among the many books devoted to the hydrides are: A. Stock, *Hydrides of Boron and Silicon*, Cornell University Press, Ithaca, New York, 1933; D. P. Smith, *Hydrogen in Metals*, University of Chicago Press, Chicago, Ill., 1948; D. T. Hurd, *Chemistry of the Hydrides*, John Wiley and Sons, Inc., New York, 1952; N. G. Gaylord, *Reduction with Complex Metal Hydrides*, Interscience Publishers, New York, 1956; *A Bibliography on the Hydrides of Metals and Metalloids*, Metal Hydrides Incorporated, Beverly, Mass., 1949, 161 pages.

[94] T. H. Liu, *J. Chinese Chem. Soc.* **9**, 119 (1942).

TABLE 8.8.   PERIODIC TABLE OF THE ELEMENTS SHOWING DISTRIBUTION OF HYDRIDE TYPES*

| GROUP | I | II | | | | | | VIIIB | | | | | III | IV | V | VI | VII | 0 |
|---|---|---|---|---|---|---|---|---|---|---|---|---|---|---|---|---|---|---|
| Period I | H | | | | | | | | | | | | | | | | | He |
| Period II | Li | Be | | | | | | | | | | | B | C | N | O | F | Ne |
| Period III | Na | Mg | | | | | | | | | | | Al | Si | P | S | Cl | A |
| SUBGROUP | IA | IIA | IIIB | IVB | VB | VIB | VIIB | Fe Co Ni | Ru Rh Pd | Os Ir Pt | IB | IIB | IIIA | IVA | VA | VIA | VIIA | 0 |
| Period IV | K | Ca | Sc | Ti | V | Cr | Mn | Fe | Co | Ni | Cu | Zn | Ga | Ge | As | Se | Br | Kr |
| Period V | Rb | Sr | Y | Zr | Nb | Mo | Tc | Ru | Rh | Pd | Ag | Cd | In | Sn | Sb | Te | I | Xe |
| Period VI | Cs | Ba | 57–71 | Hf | Ta | W | Re | Os | Ir | Pt | Au | Hg | Tl | Pb | Bi | Po | At | Rn |
| Period VII | Fr | Ra | 89–96 | | | | | | | | | | | | | | | |

Ionic hydrides

Transitional metal hydrides

Borderline hydrides

Covalent hydrides

Elements 57–71 (rare-earth metals) : La, Ce, Pr, Nd, Pm, Sm, Eu, Gd, Tb, Dy, Ho, Er, Tm, Yb, Lu
Elements 89–102 (actinide elements) : Ac, Th, Pa, U, Np, Pu, Am, Cm, Bk, Cf, En, Fm, Mv, No.

* Courtesy of Hurd, *Chemistry of the Hydrides*, and John Wiley and Sons, Inc., New York.

exceeds 1.6 on Pauling's electronegativity scale.[95]   These elements are chiefly the members of the *B* subgroups of the fourth, fifth, sixth, and seventh groups of the periodic table.   If the electronegativity of an element is 1.0 or less, it is expected to have a saltlike ionic hydride.   Thus, Li 1.0, Na 0.9, K and Rb 0.8, Cs 0.7, Ca and Sr 1.0, and Ba 0.9 form this type of hydride.   Lastly, if the electronegativity lies between 1.0 and 1.6, the hydride (as a true compound) is usually indefinite and/or unstable.   Some elements in this class are Be 1.5, Mg 1.2, Sc and Y 1.3, Ti and Zr 1.6.   They tend to form metallic interstitial type hydrides. Within any given group there is a progressive decrease in hydride stability with increase in atomic weight and electropositive nature.

With increasing electronegativity of the nonmetal component element there is a general increase in the number of its binary compounds with metals that yield volatile hydrides by hydrolysis.[96]   Weakly electronegative elements, such as boron and silicon, yield hydride-forming compounds with metals only when the metals are strongly electropositive. Reactive compounds are also formed by the union of strongly electronegative elements with the less strongly electropositive metals.   Thus, while very few metallic borides may be hydrolyzed to form boranes, virtually all fluorides yield HF on hydrolysis.   However, the phosphides, carbides, and nitrides of the less electropositive elements are hydrolyzable to form volatile hydrides.

Most of the elements forming covalent hydrides are nonmetallic but several have pronounced metallic properties.   Their volatile hydrides show physical properties primarily related to the respective molecular weights of the compounds.   The hydrides $H_2O$, $NH_3$, and HF, however, are abnormal exceptions because of strong hydrogen bonding in their condensed phases.   Within a related series of hydrides from the same group of the periodic table, $CH_4$, $SiH_4$, $GeH_4$, and $SnH_4$, for example, boiling points and melting points tend to increase regularly with molecular weight.   For a series of hydrides of elements lying in the same row of the periodic table, for instance, $GeH_4$, $AsH_3$, $SeH_2$, and HBr, other factors, such as polar nature and molecular size, may mask the regularity of the effect of molecular weight on some properties.   The covalent hydrides of C, B, Si, and N exist in polynuclear forms, those of carbon being especially numerous: $C_2H_6$, $C_6H_6$, $Si_2H_6$, $Si_3H_8$, $B_2H_6$, $N_2H_4$, etc.   Some of the most metallic of the elements in class (1) also seem capable of taking up hydrogen in a manner similar to those of class three.   Specific prop-

[95] L. Pauling, *Nature of the Chemical Bond*, Cornell University Press, Ithaca, N. Y., 2nd Edition, 1940, p. 58.
[96] D. T. Hurd, *J. Am. Chem. Soc.* 69, 1647 (1947).

erties of most of the covalent hydrides are discussed elsewhere in these volumes.

The ionic, saltlike hydrides include those of the alkali metals and the alkaline-earth metals except magnesium. They are readily prepared by heating the metal in hydrogen. LiH and NaH may be made by hydrogenating a suspension of finely divided metal in an inert medium such as kerosene or molten paraffin. A commercial synthesis of $CaH_2$ involves reduction of CaO with magnesium metal and hydrogen at a high temperature:[97]

$$CaO + Mg + H_2 \rightarrow CaH_2 + MgO$$

Beautiful crystalline compounds result, whose hydrogen is demonstrated by electrolysis to be present as the negative hydride ion, $H^-$.[98] The hydride ion behaves chemically and physically as if it were a halide ion, and X-rays reveal that the alkali-metal hydrides have the same crystal structure as sodium chloride. The saline hydrides have high melting points, high heats of formation (Table 8.9), and the exact stoichiometry

TABLE 8.9.  PHYSICAL PROPERTIES OF ALKALI-METAL AND
ALKALINE-EARTH METAL HYDRIDES

| Hydride | Melting Point °C | Heat of Formation kcal/mole | Density g/cc |
|---|---|---|---|
| LiH | ca. 680 | ca. 22 | 0.76–0.8 |
| NaH | decomposes | 13.8 | 1.306 |
| KH | decomposes | 14.45 | 1.43 |
| RbH | ... | 12 | 2.59 |
| CsH | ... | 19.9 | 3.42 |
| $CaH_2$ | >1000 | 46.6 | 1.9 |
| $SrH_2$ | ... | 42.2 | 3.72 |
| $BaH_2$ | ... | 40.96 | 4.21 |

associated with ionic compounds, or salts, in general. It is also observed that the saline hydrides are more dense than the pure metals, whereas the metallic hydrides are less dense. In the alkali-metal hydrides this difference in density amounts to 45 to 75%. The effective radius of the hydride ion has been estimated to range from about 1.26 A in LiH to 1.54 A in CsH,[99] which is large in comparison with the covalent radius of hydrogen, 0.30 A. $BeH_2$, although a nonvolatile white solid is not

[97] P. P. Alexander, U. S. 2,082,134 (1937).
[98] See Vol. VI, This Series.
[99] E. Zintl and A. Harder, Z. physik. Chem. B14, 265 (1931).

ionic like $CaH_2$. It appears to be a highly polymerized hydride molecule held together by hydrogen bridge bonding similar to that in the boron hydrides. On the other hand, the nature of the $MgH_2$ crystal has been completely characterized.[100]

The saline hydrides react with water yielding hydrogen and hydroxides:

$$NaH + H_2O \rightarrow NaOH + H_2$$

The reaction of NaH with water is much more violent than that of LiH, and the reaction of calcium hydride, $CaH_2$, is so readily controlled that it is sold under names such as *hydrolith* and *hydrogenite* for use as a source of hydrogen. These hydrides are extremely strong reducing agents, NaH being able to reduce carbon dioxide to carbon. Some of them burn in oxygen if heated. They are decomposed when very strongly heated. Their handling is hazardous, especially when finely powdered. CsH is reported as being spontaneously flammable in air. Powdered LiH is highly flammable and is very sensitive to moisture, and a lithium-hydride fire, once started, is very difficult to extinguish. The usual fire-extinguishing agents, water, carbon dioxide, and carbon tetrachloride, will be reduced by the burning hydride, and thus aggravate the problem. A laboratory fire of LiH is best extinguished by blanketing it with an inert gas, such as argon, or by otherwise excluding air.

The hydrides of the third class are much less easily characterized. It has been known for a long time that many metals adsorb or occlude relatively large quantities of hydrogen at room temperature or when heated.[101] Finely divided metals especially show this property. The capacity of metals to interact with hydrogen decreases progressively from left to right across the periodic table. The rare-earth and actinide metals, Group IIIB, possess the highest ability to adsorb hydrogen, and the Group VIIIB metals (except for palladium) are rather inert to hydrogen. Likewise, the heat of reaction of the transition elements with hydrogen decreases progressively from left to right across the periodic table. When the hydrogen is supplied at constant pressure the elements of Groups IIIB, IVB, and VB show a decrease in the hydrogen taken up with increase in temperature, and the reaction is exothermic. The elements of Groups VIB, VIIB, and VIIIB, on the other hand, show increased formation of the hydride with increase in temperature (Fig. 8.8), the reaction being endothermic. Tungsten adsorbs very little hydrogen when placed in the gas, and Cd, Tl, Zn, Pb, Bi, Sn, Sb, Au, Ag, and Rh are not able to

[100] F. H. Ellinger *et al.*, *J. Am. Chem. Soc.* **77**, 2647 (1955).

[101] C. J. Smithells, *Gases and Metals*, John Wiley and Sons, Inc., New York, 1937, pp. 159–170; Smith, *op. cit.* ref. 93.

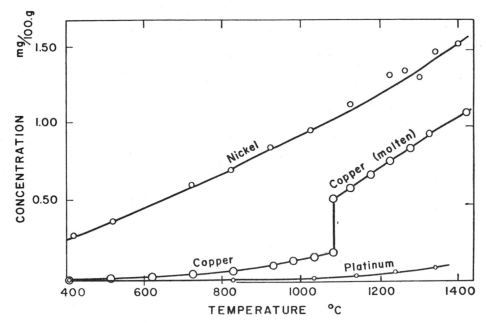

FIG. 8.8. Endothermic occluders of hydrogen. Solubility isobars at 1 atm. (Smith, *Hydrogen in Metals;* courtesy *University of Chicago Press.*)

take up any gas under these conditions. They can, however, take up the gas under certain conditions, for instance, during electrolysis. Electrolytic charging when the metal is used as a cathode permits the metal to take up more hydrogen than by any other method. A palladium cathode adsorbs 1000 times its volume of hydrogen. At the beginning of electrolysis with a palladium cathode no hydrogen is evolved because of its rapid adsorption by the metal. Then, after the current is shut off, a saturated palladium cathode evolves gas for a long time.

In contrast to the ionic hydrides, the transition metal lattice always expands during the adsorption or occlusion of hydrogen, so that the hydrides are less dense than the corresponding pure metals. This expansion is great enough in some instances to cause a rearrangement of the original metal structure into new structures or phases. Along with the hydride formation appears a partial loss of the metallic properties of the element. Tantalum wire or metal, for instance, when heated in hydrogen, loses its luster and ductility and is converted to a dark-gray, brittle solid. The electrical resistance of the hydrogen-charged metals is higher than for the pure metals, the effect being somewhat less for the endothermic occluders.   Supersaturation with hydrogen is thought to give rise to the phenomenon of overvoltage in electrolysis.   The hydrogen-charged metals are strong reducing agents.   The atomic hydrogen evolved will reduce mercury(II) to free mercury, and $Fe^{+3}$ to $Fe^{++}$.   The familiar hydrogenation phenomena in the presence of finely divided nickel must be closely related to the hydride formation and decomposition herein discussed.

Hydrogen diffuses into the transition metals primarily through *intergranular rifts* or minute cracks in the metal, from which it may enter the metal lattice.   The state of the hydrogen in the metal is not known, but it is probably not present in true chemical combination.   These systems seem in many cases to be solid solutions or interstitial compounds.   The hydrogen is present as atoms or ions, not as molecules.   In fact, it has been described as "metallic" hydrogen by some investigators.   If this is the case, the valence electrons of the hydrogen atoms become a part of the general resonating electron system of the metal and are relatively mobile.   Different metals take up hydrogen at different temperatures, and this has been thought to be the result of difference in the energy of activation of the dissociation, $H_2 \rightarrow 2H$, at the metal surface.   Palladium at room temperature forms $PdH_{0.8}$, thorium at 400°C gives $ThH_{3.07}$, zirconium cooled in hydrogen from 900°C to room temperature gives $ZrH_{1.92}$, while $TaH_{0.8}$ and $TiH_{1.75}$ are formed under the same conditions.

The compound $UH_3$ is not held together by the usual intermetallic bonds, but largely by hydrogen "bridge" bonds.[102]   Uranium atoms are bonded to neighboring uranium atoms through hydrogen "bridges," the U–H–U distance being 3.707 A.   These "half bonds" from hydrogen to its two uranium neighbors satisfactorily account for the high melting point, hardness, and brittleness of the compound.   It is somewhat metallic, its conductivity being of the same order of magnitude as that of uranium metal.   The bridge type of bonding may be present in $ThH_2$ and $ZrH_2$.[103]

$UH_3$ and $ThH_2$ are regarded as distinct compounds.   Many of the transition metal hydrides, however, are of rather indefinite composition (Table 8.10).   Fractional compositions indicated in Table 8.10 usually represent about the maximum hydrogen content that has been attained with the corresponding metal.   In many instances virtually all compositions from zero hydrogen content to those indicated may be obtained.

[102] R. E. Rundle, *J. Am. Chem. Soc.* **69**, 1719 (1947); L. Pauling and F. J. Ewing, *ibid.* **70**, 1660 (1948).
[103] R. E. Rundle *et al.*, *U. S. Atomic Energy Comm. Publ.* AECD-2120, 9 pp., 1948.

TABLE 8.10. FORMULAS OF SIMPLE TRANSITION METAL
HYDRIDES AND DEUTERIDES

| | | | |
|---|---|---|---|
| $LaH_{2.76}$ | $NbH_{0.86}$ | $UH_3$ | $EuD_{1.95}$ |
| $CeH_{2.69}$ | $TaH_{0.76}$ | $ThH_2$ | $YbD_{1.98}$ |
| $PrH_{2.84}$ | $TiH_{1.75}$ | $Pd_2H$ (?) | $HfD_{1.63}$ |
| $ThH_{3.62}$ | $ZrH_{1.92}$ | $CuH$ (?) | $HfD_{1.98}$ |
| $VH_{0.71}$ | $CrH_{1.7}$ | $CuH_2$ (?) | $TiD_{1.97}$ |
| $PdH_{0.8}$ | $HfH_{2.10}$ | $ZnH_2$ | $UD_3$ |
| | | $CdH_2$ | |

For the higher hydrogen contents there may be one or more solid solution and/or compound phases present, plus additional physically adsorbed hydrogen. The latter is particularly difficult to differentiate from the former two. The complexity of the problem is well illustrated by data for the Th–H system (Table 8.11).[104] Study of the cubic phase of this

TABLE 8.11. THE THORIUM-HYDROGEN SYSTEM

| Composition | Phases and Intensity |
|---|---|
| $ThH_{0.92}$ | Th (medium)—Tetragonal (medium) |
| $ThH_{1.24}$ | Th (weak)—Tetragonal (medium) |
| $ThH_{1.50}$ | Th (weak)—Tetragonal (strong) |
| $ThH_{1.78}$ | Tetragonal |
| $ThH_{1.98}$ | Tetragonal ($ThH_2$) |
| $ThH_{2.11}$ | Tetragonal (strong)—Cubic (very weak) |
| $ThH_{2.49}$ | Tetragonal (medium)—Cubic (medium) |
| $ThH_{2.96}$ | Tetragonal (weak)—Cubic (strong) |
| $ThH_{3.12}$ | Tetragonal (weak)—Cubic (strong) |
| $ThH_{3.53}$ | Cubic |
| $ThH_{3.62}$ | Cubic |

system has established that its ideal composition is $ThH_{3.75}$ (or $Th_4H_{15}$) and that very possibly its composition is sharply defined by the latter formula.[105]

The Pd–H system is one of the most widely studied hydrogen alloy systems. Palladium is one of the strongest adsorbers of hydrogen at room temperature, but at 200°C it holds almost none. Since the saltlike hydrides also dissociate at high temperatures, this suggests, if not a difference in the type of binding, certainly a difference in the firmness of binding. The best studies indicate the existence of two immiscible solid solutions in the Pd–H system.

The rare-earth hydrides resemble the saline hydrides in their high heats of formation ($LaH_{2.76}$ = 40.09 kcal, $CeH_{2.69}$ = 42.26 kcal). Otherwise they follow the pattern of the transition metal hydrides as to density and variable stoichiometry. $CeH_{2.69}$ is 17% less dense than the metal.

[104] R. E. Rundle, C. G. Shull, and E. O. Wollan, *Acta Cryst.* 5, 22 (1952).
[105] W. H. Zachariason, *Acta Cryst.* 6, 393 (1953).

Brief mention should be made of the borderline hydrides (Table 8.8). Copper, whose endothermic action with hydrogen was depicted in Fig. 8.8, appears to form both an unstable gaseous hydride and an unstable solid hydride.   When copper powder (or filings) is heated in hydrogen, a copper mirror is frequently observed to deposit on the walls of the tube. It is suggested that this deposition arises from the existence of a transient volatile hydride of copper.   A reddish-brown solid, believed by some to be a true hydride, $CuH$ or $CuH_2$, is precipitated when copper salts are treated with hypophosphites.[106]   Silver and gold may occlude small amounts of hydrogen under some conditions, but no definite compounds have been isolated or characterized.[107,108]   Mercury, when treated with atomic hydrogen, is reported to yield a solid hydride, $HgH$ or $HgH_2$, stable only below $-125°C$.[109]   Dimethyl zinc reacts metathetically with lithium aluminum hydride in an ether solution:[110]

$$Zn(CH_3)_2 + 2LiAlH_4 \rightarrow ZnH_2 + 2LiAlH_3CH_3$$

The white $ZnH_2$ is a nonvolatile solid which slowly decomposes at room temperature.   $CdH_2$, prepared in the same manner, is unstable at $0°C$. Red needles of $CuH$ stable to $60°C$ may be prepared in pyridine-ether solution by the reaction of $CuI$ and $LiAlH_4$.[111]

A number of complex ternary hydrides are known.   These are co-valent or saltlike compounds containing $BH_4^-$, $AlH_4^-$, $GaH_4^-$, and $InH_4^-$ anions.[111,112]   Borohydrides of Li, Na, Mg, Be, Zn, Zr, Hf, Th, U, Np, and Pu are stable solids, whereas $Al(BH_4)_3$ is an unstable covalent liquid.   Other complex hydrides are $LiAlH_4$, $AgAlH_4$, $Mg(AlH_4)_2$, $Ga(AlH_4)_3$, $LiGaH_4$, $LiInH_4$, and $In(AlH_4)_3$.

The outstanding chemical property of nearly all hydrides is their activity as reducing agents, which varies from mild to violent.[113]   $LiAlH_4$ is unique as a reducing agent in organic chemistry because of its tendency to avoid side reactions, cleavages, or condensations which $NaH$ and other ionic hydrides commonly cause.   Moreover, the reductions are generally almost quantitative, and the products are very pure.[114]   One of the most

[106] G. F. Hüttig and F. Brodkorb, *Z. anorg. allgem. Chem.* **153**, 235 (1926).

[107] E. Pietsch and F. Seuferling, *Naturwiss.* **19**, 573 (1931).

[108] E. Pietsch and E. Josephy, *ibid.* **19**, 737 (1931).

[109] K. H. Geib and P. Harteck, *Ber.* **B65**, 1550 (1932).

[110] G. D. Barbaras *et al.*, *J. Am. Chem. Soc.* **73**, 4585 (1951).

[111] E. Wiberg and W. Henle, *Z. Naturforsch.* **7b**, 250 (1952).

[112] Hurd, *op. cit.* ref. 93, pp. 156–171; E. Wiberg and M. Schmidt, *Z. Naturforsch.* **6b**, 172 (1951).

[113] *Chem. and Eng. News* **35**, 28 (1957).

[114] Gaylord, *op. cit.* ref. 93; also see a chapter by W. G. Brown in *Organic Reactions*, Vol. VI, John Wiley and Sons, Inc., New York, 1951.

powerful reducing agents is the pyrophoric $UH_3$, which is considered a dangerous material to handle. Sizable quantities of it react violently with $H_2O$, 30% $H_2O_2$, and the gaseous halogens at elevated temperatures.

Several deuterides of the transition metals have been studied (Table 8.10). Their preparation is similar to that of the hydrides. $EuD_{1.95}$ and $YbD_{1.98}$ are reported to be isostructural with the hydrides of the alkaline earth metals.[115] Neutron and X-ray diffraction studies disclose that $HfD_{1.63}$ and $TiD_{1.97}$ have face-centered cubic structures, and that $HfD_{1.98}$ is face-centered tetragonal.[116] $UD_3$ has a cubic cell very slightly smaller than that of $UH_3$, but the bridge bonds found in the hydride are not formed in $UD_3$.[117]

**Tungsten Bronzes.** In 1824 Wöhler reduced acid sodium tungstate with hydrogen at a red heat and produced a chemically inert material with a metallic bronze color. Since then various workers[118,119,120] by heating a mixture of $Na_2WO_4$, $WO_3$, and tungsten in an inert atmosphere, by electrolytic reduction of fused alkali tungstates, and by reducing $Na_2WO_4$ by hydrogen or molten zinc, iron, or tin, have obtained a series of products with metallic luster and varying in color from golden yellow through orange red to blue violet. These materials are known as tungsten bronzes and are represented by the general formula $Na_xWO_3$ in which $x$ varies between 0 and 1. The rest of the alkali metals form similar compounds,[121–124] and their hydrogen analogues[125] have likewise been prepared (Table 8.12). They are all intensely colored, extremely inert solids with high density and good electrical conductivity. Only hydrofluoric acid and in some cases hot aqua regia attack them. Because of their metallic luster they find important application as pigments in bronze paints.

The extreme inertness of these substances poses a problem in their analysis. One procedure attacks them by heating at 500°C in a stream of hydrogen chloride and oxygen, whereupon the sodium is left as a

[115] W. L. Korst and J. C. Warf, *Acta Cryst.* **9**, 452 (1956).
[116] S. S. Sidhu, L. Heaton, and D. D. Zauberis, *ibid.* **9**, 607 (1956).
[117] R. E. Rundle, *U. S. Atomic Energy Commission Publ.* AECD-3111, 12 pp. (1951).
[118] E. Engels, *Z. anorg. allgem. Chem.* **37**, 125 (1903); V. I. Spitzin, *ibid.* **148**, 69 (1925); V. I. Spitzin and L. Kaschtanoff, *ibid.* **157**, 141 (1926).
[119] E. O. Brimm *et al.*, *J. Am. Chem. Soc.* **73**, 5427 (1951).
[120] B. W. Brown and E. Banks, *ibid.* **76**, 963 (1954).
[121] M. E. Straumanis and S. S. Hsu, *J. Am. Chem. Soc.* **72**, 4027 (1950).
[122] M. E. Straumanis and G. F. Doctor, *ibid.* **73**, 3492 (1951).
[123] A. Magnéli and B. Blomberg, *Acta Chem. Scand.* **5**, 372 (1951).
[124] A. Magnéli, *ibid.* **7**, 315 (1953).
[125] O. Glemser and C. Naumann, *Z. anorg. allgem. Chem.* **265**, 288 (1951).

TABLE 8.12. TUNGSTEN BRONZES

| Bronze | $x$ Range | Typical Formulas | Color | Structure | Lattice Constants (in A) | References |
|---|---|---|---|---|---|---|
| $Li_xWO_3$ | 0.28–0.56 | $Li_{0.56}WO_3$ | Violet-blue | Cubic | $a = 3.7218$ | (1)(2) |
|  | <0.28 | $Li_{0.28}WO_3$ | Blue | Cubic | $a = 3.7366$ |  |
|  |  | ? | ... | Tetragonal (?) | $a = 5.14, c = 3.80$ |  |
| $Na_xWO_3$ | 0.3–1.0 | $NaWO_3$ | Bright yellow | Cubic | $a = 3.8662$ | (2)(3) |
|  |  | $Na_{0.82}WO_3$ | Red | Cubic | $a = 3.846$ |  |
|  |  | $Na_{0.56}WO_3$ | Violet | Cubic | $a = 3.829$ |  |
|  |  | $Na_{0.42}WO_3$ | Blue | Cubic | $a = 3.818$ |  |
|  | 0.28–0.38 | $Na_{0.28}WO_3$ | Blue | Tetragonal I | $a = 17.10, c = 7.496$ |  |
|  | <0.28 | $Na_{0.10}WO_3$ | Dark blue | Tetragonal II | $a = 5.25, c = 3.90$ |  |
| $K_xWO_3$ | 0.40–0.57 | $K_{0.57}WO_3$ | Red violet | Tetragonal | $a = 12.317, c = 3.841$ | (4)(2)(5) |
|  | <0.40 | $K_{0.27}WO_3$ | Dark blue | Hexagonal | $a = 7 40, c = 7.56$ |  |
| $Rb_xWO_3$ | <0.33 (?) | $Rb_{0.27}WO_3$ | Dark blue | Hexagonal | $a = 7.39, c = 7.54$ | (2)(5) |
| $Cs_xWO_3$ | <0.33 (?) | $Cs_{0.32}WO_3$ | Dark blue | Hexagonal | $a = 7.42, c = 7.63$ | (2)(5) |
| $H_xWO_3$ | 0.10–0.5 | $H_{0.5}WO_3$ | Blue | Cubic | $a = 3.76$ | (6) |
|  |  | $H_{0.33}WO_3$ | Blue | Tetragonal | $a = 3.75, c = 3.80$ |  |
|  |  | $H_{0.10}WO_3$ | Blue | Orthorhombic | $a = 7.25, b = 7.50, c = 3.84$ |  |

(1) M. E. Straumanis and S. S. Hsu, J. Am. Chem. Soc. 72, 4027 (1950).
(2) A. Magnéli and B. Blomberg, Acta Chem. Scand. 5, 372 (1951).
(3) M. E. Straumanis, J. Am. Chem. Soc. 71, 679 (1949).
(4) E. O. Brimm et al., ibid. 73, 5427 (1951).
(5) A. Magnéli, Acta Chem. Scand. 7, 315 (1953).
(6) O. Glemser and C. Naumann, Z. anorg. u. allgem. Chem. 265, 288 (1951).

residue of NaCl.  Another scheme decomposes them by heating with $(NH_4)_2S_2O_8$.[126]

The structure of the cubic tungsten bronzes as first revealed by X-ray diffraction studies[127] is one of the most interesting examples of the sub-traction type of Berthollide compound.  All cubic bronzes are based on the perovskite structure (Fig. 8.9).  Essentially pure $NaWO_3$ is attain-

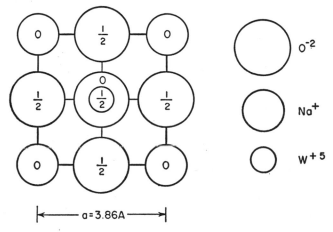

FIG. 8.9.  Projection on (100) of cubic, perovskite-type $NaWO_3$.

able,[128] and would contain tungsten in the W(V) state.  The actual bronzes, $Na_xWO_3$, may be considered as being derived from this compound by the removal of a portion of the sodium ions.  With the removal of the sodium ions a corresponding number of W(V) ions must be oxidized to the W(VI) state to maintain electrical neutrality of the total ionic charges.  The formula might be written $Na_xW_x{}^VW_{1-x}{}^{VI}O_3$.  The sodium ions are distributed statistically over the positions for such ions, and the W(V) and W(VI) ions become equivalent through the statistical distribu-tion of the extra valency electron by the process of resonance.  The mobility of this extra valency electron confers the metallic luster and metallic conductivity possessed by most of the tungsten bronzes.  The deep color is likewise associated with the presence in the same compound of the same element in two valency states.  The lattice constant of the cubic cell shrinks with loss of sodium, and loss of 60 to 70% of the sodium ions destroys the cubic arrangement in favor of a tetragonal packing.

[126] A. Magnéli, *Arkiv Kemi* **1**, 273 (1949).
[127] G. Hägg, *Nature* **135**, 874 (1935); *Z. physik. Chem.* **B29**, 192 (1935).
[128] M. E. Straumanis, *J. Am. Chem. Soc.* **71**, 679 (1949).

Removal of all of the sodium ions ($x = 0$) leads to the end member of the series, $WO_3$, tungstic oxide.   This removal is accompanied by further loss of symmetry, although the cell dimensions are not greatly changed. Tungstic oxide is monoclinic, or lower, in symmetry.

The sodium tungsten bronzes have had by far the most study.  Single crystals up to 12 mm on an edge have been grown by cathodic reduction of tungstate melts.[120]   Metals may be electrodeposited on such crystals.[129]   The diffusion of sodium in these bronzes has been investigated, and the diffusivity in $Na_{0.78}WO_3$ is represented by the equation, $D = D_0 \exp (-\Delta H/RT)$, where $D_0 = 0.87$  cm²/sec  and  $\Delta H = 51.8$ kcal/mole.[130]   $Na_{0.66}WO_3$ has a resistivity of $(1.9 \pm 0.2) \times 10^{-4}$ ohm-cm at 0°C, and the resistivity decreases linearly with decreasing temperature, 300° to 125°K.   The Hall coefficient varies less than 2% with temperature over the range 78° to 370°K, and is inversely proportional to the sodium concentration from $x = 0.58$ to $x = 0.9$.   Its value for $Na_{0.66}WO_3$ at 20°C in a constant magnetic field with 10 cycle ac is $(-5.1 \pm 0.2) \times 10^{-4}$ cm³/coulomb.[131]   Over its entire range the Hall coefficient corresponds to one free electron for each Na atom in the crystal.   $MoO_3$ is not dissolved by the sodium tungsten bronzes.[132]

Magnetic susceptibility measurements have been reported for Na, K,[133] and Li[134] tungsten bronzes:

$Na_{0.55}WO_3$ (21°C) $5.8 \times 10^{-6}$      $K_{0.53}WO_3$ (21°C) $194 \times 10^{-6}$

$Na_{0.96}WO_3$ (27°C) $15.3 \times 10^{-6}$      $Li_{0.36}WO_3$   $\cdots$   $10.0 \times 10^{-6}$

These very low observed susceptibilities are decidedly smaller than the susceptibilities calculated on the Straumanis model[121,128] of the bronzes which considers them to be solid solutions of $WO_3$ in the compound $MWO_3$.   There is satisfactory agreement, however, between experimental and calculated susceptibilities for a model[133,134] that considers the bronzes to be solid solutions of the alkali metal, Li, Na, K, etc., in $WO_3$. The former model considers the electron of the alkali metal atom to be strongly associated with the tungsten to give a W(V) ion, whereas in the latter model the alkali metal electron is part of the free electron gas that is weakly associated with the whole lattice.

[129] D. Stirpe, Rev. Sci. Instruments 24, 1071 (1953).

[130] J. F. Smith and G. C. Danielson, J. Chem. Phys. 22, 266 (1954).

[131] E. J. Huibregtse, D. B. Barker, and G. C. Danielson, Phys. Rev. 84, 142 (1951); W. R. Gardner and G. C. Danielson, ibid. 93, 46 (1954).

[132] M. E. Straumanis and K. K. Irani, J. Am. Chem. Soc. 74, 2114 (1952).

[133] F. Kupka and M. J. Sienko, J. Chem. Phys. 18, 1296 (1950).

[134] L. E. Conroy and M. J. Sienko, J. Am. Chem. Soc. 74, 3520 (1952).

# INDEX